New Horizons in
Platelet Activating Factor Research

New Horizons in
Platelet Activating Factor Research

Edited by

C.M. Winslow
and
M.L. Lee

Sandoz Research Institute

A Wiley Medical Publication

JOHN WILEY & SONS

Chichester • New York • Brisbane • Toronto • Singapore

Library of Congress Cataloging-in-Publication Data:

New horizons in platelet activating factor research.

   (A Wiley medical publication)
   1. Platelet activating factor—Physiological effect.
I. Winslow, C. M. II. Lee, M. L. (Mark L.)
III. Series.
QP752.P62N49   1987   612'.117   86–23427

ISBN 0 471 91237 9

British Library Cataloguing in Publication Data:

New horizons in platelet activating factor
   research.
   1. Blood platelets
   I. Winslow, C.M. II. Lee, M.L.
   599.01'13   QP97

ISBN 0 471 91237 9

Typeset by Woodfield Graphics, Arundel, West Sussex.

Printed and bound in Great Britain.

Contents

PATHOPHYSIOLOGY OF PLATELET ACTIVATING FACTOR

ROLE OF PLATELET ACTIVATING FACTOR IN HUMAN DISEASE

List of Contributors

Frank J. D'Aries, *Sandoz Research Institute, East Hanover, New Jersey, USA*

N. Akkerman, *University Hospital Utrecht, Catharijnesinge, Utrecht, The Netherlands*

Robert C. Anderson, *Sandoz Research Institute, East Hanover, New Jersey, USA*

B. Arnoux, *Yale University School of Medicine, New Haven, Connecticut, USA*

Josepha L. Arroyave, *Northwestern University Medical School, Chicago, Illinois, USA*

Lena Beijer, *University of Gottenburg, Sweden*

J. Benveniste, *Immunopharmacologie de l'Allergie et de l'Inflammation, INSERM U-200 Clamart, France*

Merle L. Blank, *Oak Ridge Associated Universities, Oak Ridge, Tennessee, USA*

P. Braquet, *IHB-IPSEN, Le Plessis Robinson, France*

Tommy A. Brock, *Brigham and Women's Hospital and Harvard Medical School, Boston, Massachusetts, USA*

F. Bussolino, *University of New York, Buffalo, New York, USA and Laboratorio di Immunopatologia, Cattedra de Nefrologia, Clinica Medica I, Torino, Italy*

Dennis B. Buxton, *University of Texas Health Science Center, San Antonio, Texas, USA*

P.R. Caldwell, *University of New York, Buffalo, New York, USA*

Giovani Camussi, *University of New York, Buffalo, New York, USA and Laboratorio di Immunopatologia, Cattedra de Nefrologia, Clinica Medica I, Torino, Italy*

J. Casals-Stenzel, *Boehringer Ingelheim KG, Ingelheim am Rhein, FRG*

Vincent Castranova, *National Institute for Occupational Safety and Health, Morgantown, West Virginia, USA*

Shih-Wen Chang, *University of Colorado School of Medicine, National Jewish Hospital and Research Center for Immunology and Respiratory Medicine, Denver, Colorado, USA*

M. Chignard, *Immunopharmacologie de l'Allergie et de l'Inflammation, INSERM U-200 Clamart, France*

Andrea K. DeLillo, *Sandoz Research Institute, East Hanover, New Jersey, USA*

Edward M. Driscoll, *The University of Michigan Medical School, Ann Arbor, Michigan, USA*

Y. H. Ehrlich, *College of Medicine, University of Vermont, Burlington, Vermont, USA*

Christian O. Feddersen, *University of Colorado School of Medicine, National Jewish Hospital and Research Center for Immunology and Respiratory Medicine, Denver, Colorado, USA*

Diane Felsen, *The James Buchanan Brady Foundation and Cornell University Medical College, New York, USA*

Sagrario Fernandez-Gallardo, *Servicio de Nefrologia, Fundacion Jimenez Diaz, Universidad Autonoma de Madrid, Spain*

Rory A. Fisher, *University of Texas Health Science Center, San Antonio, Texas, USA*

Veronica Fitzgerald, *Oak Ridge Associated Universities, Oak Ridge, Tennessee, USA*

Marie L. Foegh, *Georgetown University Medical Center, Washington DC, USA*

Robert M. Freund, *The James Buchanan Brady Foundation and Cornell University Medical College, New York, USA*

Glenn E. Frisch, *Sandoz Research Institute, East Hanover, New Jersey, USA*

M. Frolich-Lafrance, *Kaiser Regional Research Laboratory, Los Angeles, California, USA*

Arturo Genovese, *Cornell University Medical College, New York, USA*

C.N. Gillis, *Yale University School of Medicine, New Haven, Connecticut, USA*

Michael A. Gimbrone, Jr, *Brigham and Women's Hospital and Harvard Medical School, Boston, Massachusetts, USA*

Julian Gomez-Cambronero, *Servicio de Nefrologia, Fundacion Jimenez Diaz, Universidad Autonoma de Madrid, Spain*

F. Gonzalez-Crussi, *Northwestern University Medical School, Chicago, Illinois, USA*

I.S. Grewal, *Kaiser Regional Research Laboratory, Los Angeles, California, USA*

Kathy K. Griendling, *Brigham and Women's Hospital and Harvard Medical School, Boston, Massachusetts, USA*

Donald J. Hanahan, *University of Texas Health Science Center, San Antonio, Texas, USA*

Dean A. Handley, *Sandoz Research Institute, East Hanover, New Jersey, USA*

D.H. Hardwick, *College of Medicine, University of Vermont, Burlington, Vermont, USA*

Kathleen E. Harris, *Northwestern University Medical School, Chicago, Illinois, USA*

P.G. Hellewell, *MRC Clinical Research Centre, Harrow, Middlesex*

Peter M. Henson, *University of Colorado School of Medicine, National Jewish Hospital and Research Center for Immunology and Respiratory Medicine, Denver, Colorado, USA*

Ceredwyn E. Hill, *University of Texas Health Science Center, San Antonio, Texas, USA*

Dennis R. Hoffman, *University of Texas Health Science Center, Dallas, Texas, USA*

Johnathon Homeister, *The University of Michigan Medical School, Ann Arbor, Michigan, USA*

William J. Houlihan, *Sandoz Research Institute, East Hanover, New Jersey, USA*

Wei Hsueh, *Northwestern University Medical School, Chicago, Illinois, USA*

San-Bao Hwang, *Merck Sharp & Dohme Research Laboratories, Rahway, New Jersey, USA*

O. Wayne Isom, *Cornell University Medical College, New York, USA*

Charles V. Jackson, *The University of Michigan Medical School, Ann Arbor, Michigan, USA*

John M. Johnston, *University of Texas Health Science Center, Dallas, Texas, USA*

Bijan S. Khirabadi, *Georgetown University Medical Center, Washington DC, USA*

R.J. King, *University of Texas Health Science Center, San Antonio, Texas, USA*

Ed Kloprogge, *University Hospital Utrecht, Catharijnesinge, Utrecht, The Netherlands*

E. Kornecki, *College of Medicine, University of Vermont, Burlington, Vermont, USA*

R. Korth, *Immunopharmacologie de l'Allergie et de l'Inflammation, INSERM U-200, Clarmart, France*

Karl H. Krieger, *Cornell University Medical College, New York, USA*

R. Kumar, *University of Texas Health Science Center, San Antonio, Texas, USA*

P.M. Lad, *Kaiser Regional Research Laboratory, Los Angeles, California, USA*

My-Hanh Lam, *Merck Sharp & Dohme Research Laboratories, Rahway, New Jersey, USA*

D.B. Learn, *Kaiser Regional Research Laboratory, Los Angeles, California, USA*

Mark L. Lee, *Sandoz Research Institute, East Hanover, New Jersey, USA*

Ten-ching Lee, *Oak Ridge Associated Universities, Oak Ridge, Tennessee, USA*

R.H. Lenox, *College of Medicine, University of Vermont, Burlington, Vermont, USA*

Roberto Levi, *Cornell University Medical College, New York, USA*

Benedict R. Lucchesi, *The University of Michigan Medical School, Ann Arbor, Michigan, USA*

Janet C. Ludwig, *University of Texas Health Science Center, San Antonio, Texas, USA*

Linda M. McManus, *University of Texas Health Science Center, San Antonio, Texas, USA*

Boyd Malone, *Oak Ridge Associated Universities, Oak Ridge, Tennessee, USA*

John Morley, *Pharmaceutical Division, Sandoz Research Ltd, Basel, Switzerland*

Yasuhito Nakagawa, *Teikyo University, Kanagawa 199–01, Japan*

Maria Luisa Nieto, *Servicio de Nefrologia, Fundacion Jimenez Diaz, Universidad Autonoma de Madrid, Spain*

Santosh Nigam, *Klinikum Steglitz Free University, Berlin, FRG*

Ewa Ninio, *Immunopharmacologie de l'Allergie et de l'Inflammation, INSERM U-200 Clamart, France*

Jun Nishihira, *Bowman-Gray School of Medicine Wake Forest University, Winston-Salem, North Carolina, USA*

X. Norel, *Immunopharmacologie de l'Allergie et de l'Inflammation, INSERM U-200 Clamart, France*

D. Nunez, *Immunopharmacologie de l'Allergie et de l'Inflammation, INSERM U-200 Clamart, France*

Joseph T. O'Flaherty, *Bowman-Gray School of Medicine Wake Forest University, Winston-Salem, North Carolina, USA*

C.V. Olson, *Kaiser Regional Research Laboratory, Los Angeles, California, USA*

Merle S. Olson, *University of Texas Health Science Center, San Antonio, Texas, USA*

C.P. Page, *Pharmaceutical Division, Sandoz Research Ltd, Basel, Switzerland*

Roy Patterson, *Northwestern University Medical School, Chicago, Illinois, USA*

R. Neal Pinckard, *University of Texas Health Science Center, San Antonio, Texas, USA*

Peter W. Ramwell, *Georgetown University Medical Center, Washington DC, USA*

Donna A. Robertson, *Cornell University Medical College, New York, USA*

John R. Rowles, *Georgetown University Medical Center, Washington DC, USA*

Ragnar Rylander, *University of Gottenburg, Sweden*

Mariano Sanchez Crespo, *Servicio de Nefrologia, Fundacion Jimenez Diaz, Universidad Autonoma de Madrid, Spain*

S. Sanjar, *Pharmaceutical Division, Sandoz Research Ltd, Basel, Switzerland*

Robert N. Saunders, *Sandoz Research Institute, East Hanover, New Jersey, USA*

S. J. Scott, *University of Texas Health Science Center, San Antonio, Texas, USA*

T.Y. Shen, *Merck Sharp & Dohme Research Laboratories, Rahway, New Jersey, USA*

T.A. Sherwood, *Medical University of South Carolina, Charleston, South Carolina, USA*

Shivendra D. Shukla, *University of Texas Health Science Center, San Antonio, Texas, USA*

Sandor Sipka, *University Medical School, Debrecen, Hungary*

P.A. Smiley, *Kaiser Regional Research Laboratory, Los Angeles, California, USA*

Lewis J. Smith, *Northwestern University Medical School, Chicago, Illinois, USA*

Fred Snyder, *Oak Ridge Associated Universities, Oak Ridge, Tennessee, USA*

Norma P. Stimler-Gerard, *Beth Israel Hospital and the Thorndike Laboratory of Harvard Medical School, Boston, USA*

Takayuki Sugiura, *Teikyo University, Kanagawa 199−01, Japan*

C. Tetta, *University of New York, Buffalo, New York, USA and Laboratorio di Immunopatologia, Cattedra de Nefrologia, Clinica Medica I, Torino, Italy*

Frank H. Valone, *University of California and the Veterans Administration Medical Center, San Francisco, California, USA*

Knox Van Dyke, *West Virginia University, Morgantown, West Virginia, USA*

Ronald G. Van Valen, *Sandoz Research Institute, East Hanover, New Jersey, USA*

B. Boris Vargaftig, *Institut Pasteur, INSERM 285, Paris, France*

E. Darracott Vaughan, Jr, *The James Buchanan Brady Foundation and Cornell University Medical College, New York, USA*

Susan Velasco, *Servicio de Nefrologia, Fundacion Jimenez Diaz, Universidad Autonoma de Madrid, Spain*

G. Virella, *Medical University of South Carolina, Charleston, South Carolina, USA*

Norbert F. Voelkel, *University of Colorado School of Medicine, National Jewish Hospital and Research Center for Immunology and Respiratory Medicine, Denver, Colorado, USA*

Keizo Waku, *Teikyo University, Kanagawa 199–01, Japan*

Steven M. Weisman, *The James Buchanan Brady Foundation and Cornell University Medical College, New York, USA*

Jan Willem, *University Hospital Utrecht, Catharijnesinge, Utrecht, The Netherlands*

T.J. Williams, *MRC Clinical Research Centre, Harrow, Middlesex*

C. M. Winslow, *Sandoz Research Institute, East Hanover, New Jersey, USA*

Sam J. Yee, *Cornell University Medical College, New York, USA*

Introduction

New Horizons in Platelet Activating Factor Research
Edited by C. M. Winslow and M. L. Lee
© 1987 John Wiley & Sons Ltd.

1

Extracellular and Intracellular Activities of Platelet Activating Factor

Peter M. Henson

INTRODUCTION

From its initial description as a mediator of allergic reactions (Henson, 1969, 1970a; Benveniste *et al.*, 1972), platelet activating factor (PAF) has come to be recognized as a potential participant in an extremely wide variety of cell—cell interactions encompassing areas which extend far beyond those initiated by reactions of antigen with IgE antibody. The term 'mediator' might be defined as a molecule released from one cell (or from an extracellular substrate) which acts on another cell via the action of specific receptors, and is intermediate in life span in tissues (and therefore distance of action), between neurotransmitters and hormones. As such PAF would seem to be the archetypal mediator—but of which specific reactions *in vivo*, still remains to be determined. This uncertainty is because, while the molecule has been shown to have so many actions *in vitro*, or when deliberately administered *in vivo*, it is still not clear in which natural pathogenic or physiologic processes it actively takes a part. In this brief discussion, the potential role of PAF as an extracellular mediator will be considered, as well as its possible additional contribution to non-mediator processes within the cell of origin.

PAF AS MEDIATOR

From the aforementioned definition, four properties of PAF would be required to class it as a mediator:

1. Release from the cells of origin.
2. Biologic effects on target cells.
3. Interaction of PAF with specific receptors on, or in, these target cells.
4. The presence of efficient inhibitory or inactivating mechanisms in plasma and tissue to limit the extent of action.

These four issues are discussed in greater detail by investigators later in this volume and so will be summarized only briefly herein.

1. *Release from cells*. To date, most of the studies of PAF (from 1969 on, Henson, 1969) have emphasized the release of PAF from cells into the medium. In most cases this has been because only the extracellular medium was assayed after cell stimulation. By contrast, as will be discussed below, recent investigations have provided evidence that much of the PAF that is synthesized is, in fact, retained intracellularly. Nevertheless, the extreme potency of PAF as a mediator, places emphasis on the need for only minute amounts of PAF to be released in order to produce significant biologic effects. The following calculation exemplifies this point. Phagocytosis of opsonized yeast cell walls by neutrophils is a potent stimulus for PAF production: 10 ng of PAF are readily produced by 1×10^6 cells, of which 0.3 ng may be released (Lynch and Henson, 1986). Since platelets or neutrophils themselves respond to 10^{-10} M PAF, as few as 1×10^5 stimulated neutrophils /ml^{-1} would be plenty to provide enough PAF to provide a significant stimulus to target cells. This is consistent with earlier reported experiments in which one neutrophil per 10 000 platelets exhibited an effect on the platelet release action (Henson, 1970b).

   PAF is produced by, (and probably released from), a wide variety of cells (see Benveniste, 1985; Snyder, 1985; Lynch *et al.*, 1984 and this volume) including basophils, eosinophils, neutrophils, mononuclear phagocytes, platelets, epithelial and endothelial cells and neuronal tissue (Clay and Baker, 1985). Perhaps it is pertinent to question what cell types do not synthesize those molecules. At this point, our knowledge of the extent of cellular synthesis of PAF-like materials is limited by knowing the appropriate stimuli for each cell type and possibly by the platelet bioassay which is usually used as the detection system (see below).

2. *Effects on target cells*. As detailed extensively (Benveniste, 1985; Snyder, 1985; Lynch *et al.* 1984 and elsewhere in this volume), PAF stimulates many different target cells. In each case, however, the response is that for which the responding cell is preprogrammed and is not unique to PAF as a stimulus. The clear implication is that PAF acts through specific receptors and that these represent only one of a number of types of receptors on the target cell which can lead to engagement of common intracellular response pathways.

3. *PAF receptors*. Clear demonstration of receptors for an hydrophobic phospholipid like PAF is difficult. Nevertheless, a number of lines of evidence support the concept of specific receptors, and perhaps that they may be of more than one type. These include:

   (a) The low concentrations required for target cell stimulation.
   (b) The structure—function specificity of the molecules.
   (c) Stimulus-specific desensitization or down regulation of cellular responses.
   (d) Monoclonal antibodies against platelets which specifically inhibit PAF-induced stimulation (Lynch *et al.*, 1982).

(e) Reports of high affinity, saturable binding of PAF (Valone, 1984; Winslow *et al.*, 1986; Hwang *et al.*, 1986).
(f) The increasing number of relatively specific antagonists which are becoming available.

While none of these studies have definitively proved the presence and nature of the receptor, nevertheless, the combined evidence is overwhelmingly in favor of PAF acting (at least on platelets and neutrophils) through such structures.

Interestingly, recent experiments have suggested that neutrophil responses to low concentrations of PAF (induction of adhesion and morphologic polarization by $10^{-8}-10^{-10}$M PAF) were not blocked by antagonists of PAF action on platelets (Voelkel *et al.*, 1986). By contrast, a series of alcohols, including ethanol, were effective inhibitors of the neutrophil stimulation by PAF, while having no effect on activation by formyl methionyl leucyl phenylalanine. The alcohols were ineffective when PAF effects on platelets were examined (P.M. Henson, unpublished). These data suggest the possibility of more than one receptor for PAF. A similar suggestion based on inhibitor data was made by Lambrecht and Parnham (1986). Studies of potentially different 'receptors' for PAF will likely prove to be important in the future. Additionally, it seems reasonable to question whether those molecular species of PAF which have proven to be most active against platelets will turn out to be the optimal species for stimulation of other cells and systems.

4. *Inactivation of PAF.* Plasma and tissue acetylhydrolase(s) have been well described (Farr *et al.*, 1983). Their action would certainly seem to serve the function of limiting the time and extent of PAF action *in vivo*. Nevertheless, as pointed out to me by Keith Clay and Robert Murphy, if the K_m of these enzymes is much above the concentration required for cellular stimulation, the molecule may persist long enough to initiate significant *in vivo* effects. Additional modes of inactivation likely involve non-specific binding to cellular membranes (Shaw and Henson, 1980) and/or uptake into, and metabolism by, blood and tissue cells (Chilton *et al.*, 1983; Haroldsen et al., 1985).

INTRACELLULAR PAF

In complete contrast to the data showing extracellular release of PAF and the implications of this for PAF as a mediator, a number of reports have started to appear emphasizing that the majority of PAF that is synthesized, is retained in an intracellular location. This is evident in neutrophils (Lynch and Henson, 1985; Ludwig *et al.*, 1984, 1985), mononuclear phagocytes (Lynch and Henson, 1985; Benveniste *et al.*, 1982), mast cells (L. Lichtenstein and R.N. Pinckard, personal communication and endothelial cells (Lynch and Henson, 1985; Prescott *et al.*, 1984) and may be applicable to most cell types that synthesize PAF. Early reports of this cell-associated PAF suggested that release occurred first, and was then followed by reuptake. However, this appears not to be the case and experiments with extracellular traps for released PAF support the concept that only a small fraction of the synthesized PAF is actually released to the outside (Lynch and Henson, 1985). In neutrophils this proportion varied with the stimulus but was never greater than 30 percent of the total, and following phagocytosis was usually less than 5 percent (Lynch and Henson, 1985), in endothelial cells it appeared to be even lower (Prescott *et al.*, 1984).

These observations raise the important possibility that PAF plays an intracellular role in the physiology or pathology of the cells that synthesize it. Since intracellular concentrations can get quite high (up to 10^{-5} M), physical effects of the molecule would have to be considered. Additionally, these data emphasize the importance of gaining an understanding of how the PAF is released from cells if this represents but a small, although critically important, component of the process.

Accordingly, a brief discussion of two broad possibilities (out of many) for intracellular activities of PAF might be considered.

PAF and alkyl acylglycerophosphocholine cycle.

Data presented elsewhere in this volume has led to the concept of an alkylacylGPC pathway in cells (Chilton *et al.*, 1983; Chilton and Murphy, 1986; Figure 1). In this, it is suggested that phopholipases A_2 act to produce lyso-PAF from alkyl acylGPC (predominantly alkyl arachidonyl GPC) which is then acetylated by the activatable acetyl transferase. In reverse, PAF is converted back to lyso-PAF by a relatively specific acetylhydrolase, and is then reacylated, probably by a transacylase reaction (Chilton and Murphy, 1986; Kramer *et al.*, 1984) which utilizes different fatty acids depending on the state of stimulation of the cell (Chilton *et al.*, 1983).

The participation of PAF in such a cycle could explain, by itself, the intracellular concentrations of the molecule. Thus, if the acetyl hydrolase represents a rate-limiting step after cell stimulation, a build-up of PAF would be seen. This is consistent with the data presented by Ninio (Chapter 3), suggesting that variation in PAF production within different populations of mononuclear phagocytes may be due in part to intracellular amounts of acetylhydrolase.

Physical effects of PAF on membranes

The relatively high amounts of PAF that are produced intracellularly also suggest that the molecule might have a direct effect on the membranes of the cell that produces it (independant of receptors). Initial experiments to pursue this possibility have been reported (Harris *et al.*, 1985), and indicate that PAF rather specifically increases the fluidity of artificial dipalmitoyl phosphatidylcholine membranes and inhibits the calcium-induced phase separation of phosphatidylserine—phosphatidylethanolamine membrane preparations. These alterations were not seen with lyso-PC and were less evident with lyso-PAF than with PAF itself. Effects were seen with concentrations from one to ten moles percent of added PAF.

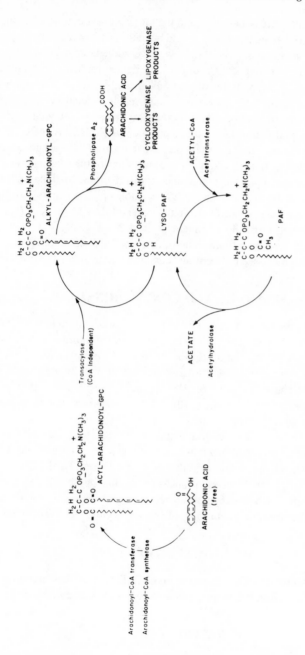

Figure 1.　A proposed scheme for the alkylacylglygerophosophocholine cycle. *Reproduced from Chilton and Murphy (1986) by permission of the American Society of Biological Chemists*

If these actions of PAF are to be relevant to the intracellular circumstance, the local concentrations of PAF that are generated should be in the same range as those required to alter the artificial membranes. Accordingly, we have studied intracellular distribution of PAF synthesized during phagocytosis of particles by neutrophils. We hypothesized that local stimulation by the particles of portions of the plasma membrane destined for internalization to form the phagosome, would result in local synthesis of PAF at that site. This concept was based on earlier experiments showing such local stimulation of neutrophil membranes during phagocytosis (Henson, 1971). If valid, higher concentrations of PAF would be expected in the phagosomes (or phagolysosomes) after particle uptake than in other areas of the plasma membrane. Subcellular fractionation of phagocytosing neutrophils demonstrated that indeed this was the case. The specific activity (moles PAF to moles phospholipid phosphorus) was highest in the phagolysosome fraction and reached 0.64 M percent (Riches *et al.*, 1985). This was felt to be close enough to the 1 M percent that was shown to have effects in the artificial membrane system, that a physical effect of PAF (or lyso-PAF) on cellular membranes seems likely, and certainly worthy of further investigation.

SUMMARY AND CONCLUSIONS

PAF is synthesized in response to stimuli by a wide variety of cells and, when released into the extracellular environment, acts in turn to stimulate multiple cell responses. This action of PAF as a 'mediator' results in many different cellular responses, including secretion, aggregation, adhesion, contraction or dilation, depending on the cell types involved. These functions of PAF apparently result from its interaction with specific receptors on the responding cells and these may be of more than one type.

By contrast, synthesis of PAF in many types of cells apparently results in only a fraction of that PAF being released to the outside. This raised the question of how the molecule is secreted and additionally whether it may have an intracellular function over and above its extracellular activity as a mediator. Participation in an alkylacetylglycerophosphocholine cycle is one such possible intracellular role for PAF. However, the molecule also has membrane-active properties which might indicate its participation in membrane alterations during endocytosis and exocytosis.

ACKNOWLEDGMENT

Supported by NIH Grant HL33755. From the Frank L. Bryant, Jr. Research Laboratory for the Mechanisms of Lung Disease, Department of Pediatrics.

REFERENCES

Benveniste, J. (1985). 'PAF-acether (Platelet-Activating Factor)', *Adv. Prostaglandin Thromboxane Leukotriene Res.*, **13**, 11.

Benveniste, J., Henson, P.M., and Cochrane, C.G. (1972). 'Leukocyte-dependent histamine release from rabbit platelets: The role of IgE, basophils and a platelet activating factor', *J. Exp. Med.*, **136**, 1356–1376.

Benveniste, J., Roubin, R., Chignard, M., Jouvin-Marche, E., and LeCouedic, P. (1982). 'Release of platelet-activating factor (PAF-acether) and 2-lysoPAF-acether from three cell types', *Agents Actions*, 12, 711–713.

Chilton, F.H., and Murphy, R.C. (1986). 'Remodeling of arachidonate-containing phosphoglycerides within the human neutrophil', *J. Biol. Chem.*, **261**, 7771–7777.

Chilton, F.H., O'Flaherty, J.T., Ellis, J.M., Swendsen, C.L., and Wykle, R.L. (1983). 'Metabolic fate of platelet-activating factor in neutrophils', *J. Biol. Chem.*, **258**, 6357–6361.

Chilton, F.H., O'Flaherty, J.T., Ellis, J.M., Swendsen, C.L., and Wykle, R.L. (1983). 'Selective acylation of lyso platelet-activating factor by arachidonate in human neutrophils', *J. Biol. Chem.*, **258**, 7268–7271.

Clay, K.F., and Baker, R.C. (1985). 'Determination of platelet activating factor in mouse brain tissue', *Proc. 33rd Annual Conference on Mass Spectrometry and Allied Topics*, **1985**, 700–701, Abstract.

Farr, R.S., Wardlow, M.L., Cox, C.P., Meng, K.E., and Greene, D.R. (1983). 'Human serum acid-labile factor is an acylhydrolase that inactivates platelet-activating factor', *Fed. Proc.*, **42**, 3120–3122.

Haroldsen, P.E., Voelkel, N.F., and Murphy, R.C. (1985). 'Metabolism of PAF in the isolated perfused rat lung', *Pharmacologist*, **27**, 175A.

Harris, R.A., Clay, K., Murphy, R., and Henson, P. (1985). 'Effects of PAF and related lipids on membrane physical properties', *Fed. Proc.*, **44**, 858.

Henson, P.M. (1969). 'Role of complement and leukocytes in immunologic release of vasoactive amines from platelets', *Fed. Proc.*, **28**, 1721–1728.

Henson, P.M. (1970a). 'Release of vasoactive amines from rabbit platelets induced by sensitized mononuclear leukocytes and antigen', *J. Exp. Med.*, **131**, 287–306.

Henson, P.M. (1970b). 'Mechanisms of release of constitutents from rabbit platelets by antigen-antibody complexes and complement. II. Interaction of platelets with neurophils', *J. Immunol.*, **105**, 490–501.

Henson, P.M. (1971). 'The immunologic release of constituents from neutrophil leukocytes. II. Mechanisms of release during phagocytosis, and adherence to nonphagocytosable surfaces', *J. Immunol.*, **107**, 1547–1557.

Hwang, S., Lam, M., and Pong, S. (1986). 'Ionic and GTP regulation of binding of platelet-activating factor to receptors and platelet-activating factor-induced activation of GTPase in rabbit platelet membranes', *J. Biol. Chem.*, **261(2)**, 532–537.

Kramer, R.M., Patton, G.M., Pritzker, C.R., and Deykin, D. (1984). 'Metabolism of platelet-activating factor in human platelets. Transacylase-mediated synthesis of 1-O-alkyl-2-arachidonoyl-sn-glycero-3-phosphocholine', *J. Biol. Chem.*, **259**, 13 316–13 320.

Lambrecht, G., and Parnham, M.J. (1986). 'Kadsurenone distinguishes between different platelet activating factor receptor subtypes on macrophages and polymorphonuclear leukocytes', *Br. J. Pharmac.*, **87**, 287–289.

Ludwig, J.C., Hoppens, C.L., McManus, L.M., Mott, G.E., and Pinckard, R.N. (1985). 'Modulation of platelet-activating factor (PAF) synthesis and release from human polymorphonuclear leukocytes (PMN): Role of extracellular albumin', *Arch. Biochem. Biophys.*, **241**, 337–347.

Ludwig, J.C., McManus, L.M., Clark, P.D., Hanahan, D.J., and Pinckard, R.N. (1984). 'Modulation of platelet-activating factor (PAF) synthesis and release from human polymorphonuclear leukocytes (PMN): Role of extracellular albumin', *Arch. Biochem. Biophys.*, **241**, 337–347.

Lynch, J.M., and Henson, P.M. (1985). 'The intracellular retention of newly synthesised platelet activating factor', *Fed. Proc.*, **44**, 1272.

Lynch, J.M., Spears, P., and Henson, P.M. (1982). 'The specific inhibition of platelet activating factor (PAF) stimulation of rabbit platelets by a monoclonal antiplatelet antibody', *Fed. Proc.*, **41**, 528.·

Lynch, J.M., Worthen, G.S., and Henson, P.M. (1984). 'Platelet Activating Factor'. In E. Buckle and H. Smith (eds.) *The Development of Anti-Asthmatic Drugs*, Butterworth & Co., London, pp. 73–88.

Prescott, S.M., Zimmerman, G.A., and McIntyre, T.M. (1984). 'Human endothelial cells in culture produce platelet-activating factor (1-alkyl-2-acetyl-sn-glycero-3-phosphocholine) when stimulated with thrombin', *Proc. Natl. Acad. Sci. USA.*, **81**, 3534–3538.

Riches, D.W.H., Young, S.K., Seccombe, J.F., Lynch, J.M., and Henson, P.M. (1985).'The subcellular distribution of platelet-activating factor (PAF) in phagocytosing human neutrophils', *Fed. Proc.*, **44**, 737.

Shaw, J.O., and Henson, P.M. (1980). 'The binding of rabbit basophil-derived platelet activating factor to rabbit platelets', *Am. J. Pathol.*, **98**, 791–810.

Snyder, F. (1985). 'Chemical and biochemical aspects of platelet activating factor: A novel class of acetylated ether-linked choline-phospholipids', *Med. Res. Rev.*, **5**, 107–140.

Valone, F.H. (1984). 'Isolation of a platelet membrane protein which binds the platelet-activating factor 1-0-hexadecyl-2-acetyl-*sn*-glycero-3-phosphorylcholine', *Immunology*, **52**, 169–174.

Voelkel, N.F., Chang, S., Worthen, G.S., McMurtry, I.F., and Henson, P.M. (1986). 'PAF antagonists: Different effects on platelets, neutrophils, guinea pig ileum and PAF-induced vasodilation in isolated rat lung', (submitted).

Biosynthesis and Metabolism of Platelet Activating Factor

New Horizons in Platelet Activating Factor Research
Edited by C. M. Winslow and M. L. Lee
© 1987 John Wiley & Sons Ltd.

2

The Significance of Dual Pathways for the Biosynthesis of Platelet Activating Factor: 1-alkyl-2-lyso-*sn*-glycero-3-phosphate as a Branchpoint

Fred Snyder

INTRODUCTION

The initial enzymatic studies from our laboratory demonstrated that two different enzyme systems, acetyl-CoA:1-alkyl-2-lyso-Gro-3-PCho acetyltransferase (Wykle *et al.*, 1980) and CDP-choline:1-alkyl-2acetyl-Gro-DTT-insensitive cholinephosphotransferase (Renooij and Snyder, 1981) can catalyze the reactions that form PAF. Enzyme activities and characteristics of the reactions that produce the substrate (1-alkyl-2-lyso-Gro-3-PCho) for the acetyltransferase has been documented from much earlier studies that originally established the metabolic pathways for ether-linked phospholipids (Hajra, 1985; Snyder *et al.*, 1985b). In contrast, the source of the substrate (1-alkyl-2-acetyl-Gro) for the DTT-insensitive cholinephosphotransferase was unknown until recently (Malone *et al.*, 1986; Lee *et al.*, 1986; Snyder *et al.*, 1985a,c, 1986a). Therefore, since the discovery of PAF, it is not surprising that the 1-alkyl-2-lyso-Gro-3-PCho acetyltransferase route was thought to be the only relevant pathway for the biosynthesis of PAF.

However, the significance of the DTT-insensitive cholinephosphotransferase pathway took on more meaning when our laboratory obtained experimental evidence that clearly demonstrates 1-alkyl-2-acetyl-Gro can be enzymatically synthesized *de novo* from 1-alkyl-2-lyso-Gro-3-P by microsomal enzymes from rat spleens (Malone *et al.*, 1986; Lee *et al.*, 1986; Snyder *et al.*, 1985a,c, 1986a) and other tissues. Moreover, the activity of the enzyme involved in this final step for PAF biosynthesis is considerably higher in most cells and tissues than the activity of 1-alkyl-2-lyso-Gro-3-PCho acetyltransferase, the alternative route for PAF biosynthesis (see 'Biosynthesis of PAF via the DTT-insensitive cholinephosphotransferase pathway' below). Thus, 1-alkyl-2-lyso-Gro-3-P appears to be an important branch point in the ether lipid biosynthetic pathway since this intermediate can serve as an acceptor molecule of acyl groups transferred by either a specific short chain acetyltransferase or long chain acyltransferases.

This report summarizes evidence for the existence of the enzymatic steps in both pathways of PAF biosynthesis (Figure 1) and describes pertinent properties of the enzymes involved. In conclusion, the relevance of dual pathways for PAF biosynthesis is discussed in terms of their possible physiological and pathological importance.

1-ALKYL-2-LYSO-*sn*-GLYCERO-3-P: THE BRANCHPOINT FOR ALTERNATE ROUTES OF PAF BIOSYNTHESIS

Formation of the ether lipid precursors required for the production of PAF by either biosynthetic pathway starts with the formation of the alkyl ether bond through the conversion of acyl-DHAP and long chain fatty alcohols to alkyl-DHAP in a reaction catalyzed by alkyl-DHAP synthase (Hajra, 1985; Snyder *et al.*, 1985b).

$$\text{acyldihydroxyacetone-P} + \text{ROH} \rightarrow \text{alkyldihydroxyacetone-P} + \text{RCOOH}$$

A ping-pong mechanism has been proposed for this reaction in experiments conducted with a 1000-fold purified preparation of alkyl-DHAP synthase by our laboratory (Brown and Snyder, 1982, 1983; Brown *et al.*, 1985). The product, alkyl-DHAP (the first intermediate that can be isolated in the formation of the ether bond), is then reduced to 1-alkyl-2-lyso-Gro-3-P by an NADPH-dependent oxidoreductase (EC 1-1.1.100).

$$\text{alkyldihydroxyacetone-P} + \text{NADPH} + \text{H}^+ \rightarrow \text{1-alkyl-2-lyso-}sn\text{-Gro-3-P} + \text{NADP}^+$$

This oxidoreductase has been extensively investigated in a variety of cells (Hajra, 1985; Snyder *et al.*, 1985b).

The 1-alkyl-2-lyso-Gro-3-P produced by this step can either serve as a substrate for an acyl-CoA (long chain) acyltransferase or an acetyl-CoA acetyltranferase to form the *sn*-2 acyl or *sn*-2 acetyl alkyl analogs of phosphatidic acid, respectively.

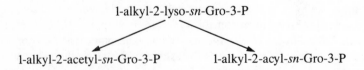

These acetylation and acylation reactions and the subsequent steps in the biosynthesis of PAF from either 1-alkyl-2-acetyl-Gro-3-P or 1-alkyl-2-acyl-Gro-3-P are described in the following two sections.

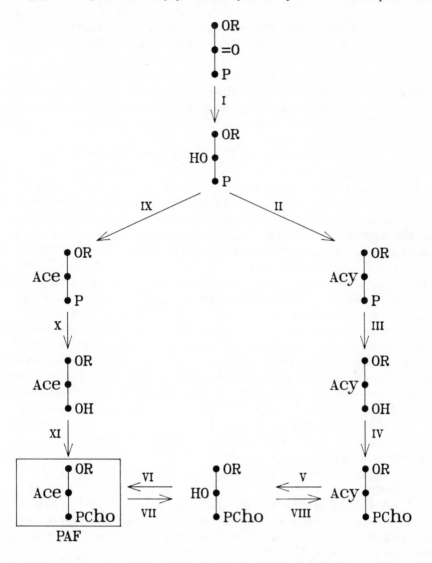

Figure 1. Dual pathways for the biosynthesis of PAF. The individual reaction steps are catalyzed by the following enzymes: I—NADPH:alkyldihydroxyacetone-P oxidoreductase (EC 1.1.1.1000); II—acyl-CoA:1-alkyl-2-lyso-*sn*-Gro-3-P acyltransferase (EC 2.3.1.63); III—1-alkyl-2-acyl-*sn*-glycero-P phosphohydrolase; IV—1-alkyl-2-acyl-*sn*-Gro:CDP-choline cholinephosphotransferase (EC 2.7.8.2); V—phospholipase A_2; VI—acetyl-CoA:alkyl-2-lyso-*sn*-Gro-3-PCho acetyltransferase (EC 2.3.1.67); VII—1-alkyl-2-acetyl-*sn*-Gro-3-PCho acetylhydrolase (EC 3.1.1.48); VIII—donor phospholipid (20:4):1-alkyl-2-lyso-*sn*-Gro-3-PCho transacylase; IX—acetyl-CoA:1-alkyl-2-lyso-*sn*-Gro-3-P acetyltransferase; X—1-alkyl-2-acetyl-*sn*-Gro-3-P phosphohydrolase; and XI—CDP-choline:1-alkyl-2-acetyl-*sn*-Gro cholinephosphotransferase (EC 2.7.8.16). Symbols used in this illustration represent Alk for alkyl, Acy for acyl, and Ace for acetyl.

BIOSYNTHESIS OF PAF VIA THE DTT-INSENSITIVE
CHOLINEPHOSPHOTRANSFERASE PATHWAY

The transfer of acetate from acetyl-CoA to 1-alkyl-2-lyso-Gro-3-P by an acetyltransferase has only recently been characterized in rat spleen microsomes (Malone *et al.*, 1986; Lee *et al.*, 1986; Snyder *et al.*, 1985a,c, 1986a). A subsequent dephosphorylation step, catalyzed by a phosphohydrolase, forms the alkylacetylglycerols.

$$1\text{-alkyl-2-acetyl-}sn\text{-Gro-3-P} \rightarrow 1\text{-alkyl-2-acetyl-}sn\text{-Gro} + P_i$$

Properties of the acetyl-CoA:1-alkyl-2-lyso-Gro-3-P acetyltransferase were characterized under conditions that minimized phosphohydrolase activity. Inhibition of the phosphohydrolase activity was accomplished by the addition of sodium vanadate and sodium fluoride to the incubation mixtures and by conducting the assays at a reduced temperature (23 °C). Under these conditions the K_m for acetyl-CoA was 226μM and the optimum concentration of 1-alkyl-2-lyso-Gro-3-P was 16$-$25 μM. The pH optimum for the acetyltransferase and phosphohydrolase in this pathway was 8.4 and 7.0, respectively. Both enzymes are of microsomal origin, based on the distribution of subcellular membrane markers.

Differences between the acetyl-CoA:1-alkyl-2-lyso-Gro-3-P acetyltransferase and the acetyl-CoA:1-alkyl-2-lyso-Gro-3-PCho acetyltransferase (see following section) in their pH optima and their sensitivities to elevated preincubation temperatures indicate the two acetyltransferases are distinctly different enzymes. This is further substantiated by the fact that the addition of 12.5 μM or 25 μM 1-alkyl-2-lyso-Gro-3-PCho to assays of the acetyl-CoA:1-alkyl-2-lyso-Gro-3-P acetyltransferase had no effect on the rate of the reaction. It is also noteworthy that 1-alkyl-2-acetyl-Gro-3-P phosphohydrolase does not appear to be the same as phosphatidate phosphohydrolase, since the addition of phosphatidic acid to the incubations didn't influence the hydrolysis of the phosphate moiety of 1-alkyl-2-acetyl-Gro-3-P by the phosphohydrolase (Malone *et al.*, 1986).

The alkylacetylglycerols formed from 1-alkyl-2-lyso-Gro-3-P serve as the substrate for the microsomal DTT-insensitive cholinephosphotransferase that catalyzes the final step in the biosynthesis of PAF (Renooij and Snyder, 1981; Snyder *et al.*, 1986a,b; Woodard *et al.*, 1984, 1985).

$$1\text{-alkyl-2-acetyl-}sn\text{-Gro} + \text{CDP-choline} \rightarrow \text{PAF} + \text{CMP}$$

Although it is unknown whether the cholinephosphotransferase activities responsible for the synthesis of lecithin (or its alkyl ether analog) and PAF are catalyzed by the same enzyme, it is clear that the synthetic activities for the short chain and long chain esters at the *sn*-2 position of the alkylglycerophosphocholines can be differentiated by the addition of DTT to the incubations. Whereas the cholinephosphotransferase activity that forms lecithin from diacylglycerols is blocked in the presence of 5$-$10 mM

DTT, the cholinephosphotransferase activity that produces PAF is insensitive to DTT, and in fact a slight stimulation is observed in the presence of DTT. Thus, DTT has been an extremely useful tool in assessing the activity of the specific cholinephosphotransferase activity in PAF biosynthesis. Of interest is that reduced glutathione, cysteine, or 2-mercaptoethanol (up to 5 mM) cannot be substituted for DTT (F. Snyder, unpublished data).

Optimal pHs for the cholinephostransferase activities that synthesize PAF versus lecithin are 8.0 and 8.5, respectively. The K_m for CDP-choline with both phosphotransferase activities were virtually identical (K_m = 36−37 μM). However, optimum concentrations for the lipid substrates were 100 μM for 1,2-dioleoyl-Gro and 200 μM for 1-alkyl-2-acetyl-Gro. Both cholinephosphotransferase activities required Mg^{2+} (10 mM), whereas Ca^{2+} was a potent inhibitor. Ethanol, which is used to solubilize the lipid substrates utilized by the cholinephosphotransferases, stimulates the reaction rate; a 2.5 percent level of ethanol is optimal. Addition of detergents can also influence both cholinephosphotransferase activities; however, their effects are not the same for the synthesis of PAF and lecithin. Also, at low concentrations of deoxycholate (up to 0.01 mM) there is no observable effect on the DTT-insensitive cholinephosphotransferase, but at 1 mM, the activity of the PAF-synthesizing enzyme was reduced by about 50 percent, and at 2 mM was completely inhibited.

The DTT-insensitive cholinephosphotransferase appears to be specific for alkylradylglycerols that possess short chain acyl moieties t the sn-2 position. Only neutral lipid substrates that can form PAF or biologically active analogs of PAF are utilized by the DTT-insensitive cholinephosphotransferase, i.e. alkylradylglycerols with methoxy, acetamide or oleoyl groups at the second position, are not substrates for the DTT-insensitive cholinephosphotransferase.

Table 1. Distribution of Enzyme Activities in PAF Biosynthesis for Several Rat Tissues

	Spleen	Liver	Lung	Kidney	
				Cortex	Medulla
	(nM min^{-1} mg^{-1}protein)				
[1] 1-Alkyl-2-lyso-Gro-3-P acetyltransferase	1.44	0.28	0.53	0.55	0.99
[2] 1-Alkyl-2-acetyl-*sn*-Gro cholinephosphotransferase	31.9	12.4	16.7	8.8	16.5
[3] 1-Alkyl-2-lyso-Gro-3-PCho acetyltransferase	8.9	0.2	4.0	0.2	2.0

[1] Data from Lee *et al.*, 1986
[2] Data from Renooij and Snyder, 1981
[3] Data from Wykle *et al.*, 1980

Specific activities of the acetyl-CoA:1-alkyl-2-lyso-Gro-3-P acetyltransferase, acetyl-CoA:1-alkyl-2-lyso-Gro-3-PCho acetyltransferase, and the DTT-insensitive cholinephosphotransferase for various rat tissues are given in Table 1. These data indicate that the complete enzymatic system for the synthesis of PAF via the choline-phosphotransferase route is present in most cells. Also it should be noted that the activities of the DTT-insensitive cholinephosphotransferase in unstimulated cells (Table 1) are much higher than those of the acetyltransferase activities that form 1-alkyl-2-acetyl-Gro-3-P or 1-alkyl-2-acetyl-Gro-3-PCho.

BIOSYNTHESIS OF PAF VIA THE PAF CYCLE

1-Alkyl-2-Acyl-Gro-3-PCho, the starting point (or end point depending on the directional flow) of the PAF cycle (Figures 1 and 2), is derived from 1-alkyl-2-lyso-Gro. The general steps in this sequence of reactions are similar to those already discussed above in that they involve an acyltransferase, phosphohydrolase and a cholinephosphotransferase.

1-alkyl-2-lyso-sn-Gro-3-P + acyl-CoA → 1-alkyl-2-acyl-sn-Gro-3-P + CoASH

1-alkyl-2-acyl-sn-Gro-3-P → 1-alkyl-2-acyl-sn-Gro + P_i

1-alkyl-2-acyl-sn-Gro + CDP-choline → 1-alkyl-2-acyl-sn-Gro-3-PCho + CMP

However, these reactions differ from those involving the alkylacetylglycerols, in that a long chain acyl moiety instead of acetate is transferred to the sn-2 position of the glycerolipid and the cholinephosphotransferase activity that catalyzes the final reaction step is strongly inhibited by DTT.

The acylation of 1-alkyl-2-lyso-Gro-3-P by an acyl-CoA acyltransferase is a well known reaction (Wykle and Snyder, 1970), which is analogous to the acyltransferase activity originally described many years ago by Hill and Lands (1968) for 1-acyl-2-lyso-Gro-3-P. Studies of kinetic properties, tissue distribution, and substrate competition indicate the acylation of the alkyl and acyl analogs are catalyzed by two different enzymes (Fleming and Hajra, 1977). Activity of this acyltransferase is highest in microsomes and is present in most mammalian tissues.

Dephosphorylation of 1-alkyl-2-acyl-Gro-3-P to the corresponding 1-alkyl-2-acyl-Gro is catalyzed by a phosphohydrolase, which appears to differ from 1-alkyl-2-acetyl-Gro-3-P phosphohydrolase (Malone et al., 1986) and those that hydrolyze the phosphate moiety of 1-alkyl-2-lyso-Gro-3-P and alkyl-DHAP. The activity of the 1-alkyl-2-acyl-Gro-3-P phosphohydrolase is modulated by Mg^{2+} ions and is maximally inhibited by NaF at a concentration of 40 mM or higher (Chae et al., 1973). Unfortunately, the properties of the phosphohydrolases involved in the metabolism of ether lipids have not been well characterized. In brain, there appears to be two pH optima (5.2−5.6 and 7.5−7.8) for the phosphohydrolase activity with 1-alkyl-2-acyl-Gro-3-P, 1-alkyl-2-lyso-Gro-3-P, or alkyl-DHAP as the substrates (El-Bassiouni et al., 1975). A phosphohydrolase, with a pH optimum of 6−7 is also located in lysosomes of rat liver that

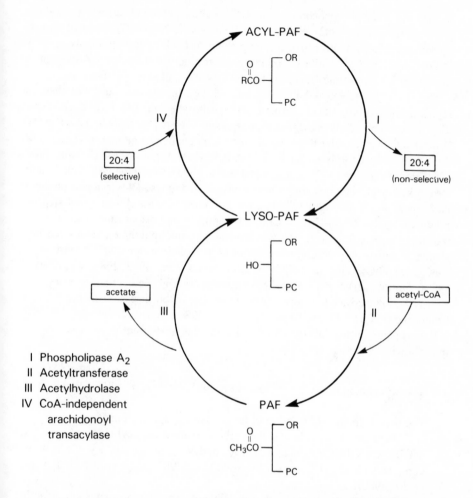

Figure 2. The PAF activation–inactivation cycle shuttles arachidonic acid and acetate into and out of alkylglycerolphosphocholines. The enzymes responsible are: I—phospholipase A$_2$, II—acetyltransferase, III—acetylhydrolase, and IV—arachidonoyltransacylase

can utilize 1-alkyl-2-acyl-Gro-3-P as a substrate (Stoffel and Heimann, 1974).

Alkylacylglycerols produced by the phosphohydrolase are substrates for the choline-phosphotransferase that forms 1-alkyl-2-acyl-Gro-3-PCho. This type of microsomal enzyme was first described by Kennedy and Weiss (1956)in their landmark discovery of the cytidine cofactors and enzymes responsible for the biosynthesis of the diacyl glycerophospholipids. In 1970, our laboratory demonstrated alkylacylglycerols could also be utilized by this cholinephosphotransferase to form the alkyl analog of phosphatidylcholine (Snyder *et al.*, 1970). A single enzyme appears to be responsible for the transfer of the phosphocholine from CDP-choline to both the diacyl- or alkylacyl-glycerols (Lee *et al.*, 1982a; Radominska-Pyrek *et al.*, 1976, 1977). Only the choline-phosphotransferase that utilizes the long chain diradylglycerols is highly sensitive to DTT, whereas Ca^{2+} inhibits cholinephosphotransferase activities regardless of the diradylglycerol substrate (i.e. diacyl-, alkylacyl-, or alkylacetyl-glycerols).

The 1-alkyl-2-acyl-Gro-3-PCho produced by the cholinephosphotransferase represents the stored precursor form of PAF in cells where the PAF cycle exists (Figure 2). The reservoir of alkylacylglycerophosphocholines is also maintained when PAF is inactivated since under these conditions a long chain acyl moiety (predominantly 20:4) is transferred to lyso-PAF by a CoA-independent transacylase (Kramer *et al.*, 1984; Robinson *et al.*, 1985; Sugiura and Waku, 1985). When the PAF cycle is activated, alkylacylglycerophosphocholines are converted to lyso-PAF by a phospholipase A_2 (Albert and Snyder, 1983). Although the phospholipase A_2-catalyzed step that produces 1-alkyl-2-lyso-Gro-3-PCho is still poorly understood, the final step—the transfer of acetate from acetyl-CoA to the lyso phospholipid intermediate—has been studied extensively by several laboratories (Albert and Snyder, 1983; Alonso *et al.*, 1982; Lee, 1985; Lee *et al.*, 1982a,b, 1984; Ninio *et al.*, 1982, 1983; Wykle *et al.*, 1980). Optimal pH for the acetyltransferase is 6.8 and the enzyme appears to be activated and inactivated via a phosphorylation-phosphohydrolase sequence (Gomez-Cambronero *et al.*, 1985b; Lenihan and Lee, 1984).

Experiments on the substrate specificity for this acetyltransferase have revealed the following features:

1. The acyl analog is also a substrate (Lee, 1985; Ninio *et al.*, 1983; Wykle *et al.*, 1980).
2. *sn*-1 Alkyl chains—18:0 > 16:0, and unsaturated > saturated.
3. *sn*-2 Acyl moiety—the longer the carbon chain of the acyl-CoA substrate, the smaller the values for the apparent K_m and V_{max}; long chain acyl-CoAs do not compete with acetyl-CoA as a substrate (Lee, 1985; Ninio *et al.*, 1982; Wykle *et al.*, 1980).
4. *sn*-3 Base groups—choline > dimethylethanolamine > monomethylethanolamine > ethanolamine, (Lee, 1985) and
5. The unnatural lyso-phospholipid analog (3-alkyl-2-lyso-Gro-1-PCho) is not a substrate (Wykle *et al.*, 1980).

Although EGTA or EDTA inhibit the acetyltransferase, a divalent cation, e.g. Ca^{2+} does not appear to be required (Wykle *et al.*, 1980); however, some controversy currently exists about the role of calcium in the expression of 1-alkyl-2-lyso-Gro-3-PCho acetyltransferase activity (Gomez-Cambronero *et al.*, 1985a; Wykle *et al.*, 1980), but the experimental conditions differed.

Specific activities of the acetyl-CoA:1-alkyl-2-lyso-Gro-3-PCho acetyltransferase for a variety of rat tissues that our laboratory has published using identical assay conditions are shown in Table 1. Specific activities of acetyl-CoA:1-alkyl-2-lyso-Gro-3-PCho acetyltransferase are significantly lower than those of the DTT-insensitive cholinephosphotransferase in unstimulated cells. A number of studies have shown that 1-alkyl-2-lyso-Gro-3-PCho acetyltransferase activity is greatly increased by a variety of agents that stimulate the cellular production of PAF (Albert and Snyder, 1983; Alonso *et al.*, 1982; Lee *et al.*, 1982b, 1984; Ninio *et al.*, 1982, 1983). In contrast, the activity of the DTT-cholinephosphotransferase in human polymorphonuclear leukocytes and rabbit platelets is unaffected by zymosan (Alonso *et al.*, 1982) or thrombin (Snyder *et al.*, 1986a).

SIGNIFICANCE OF DUAL PATHWAYS FOR THE PRODUCTION OF PAF

Why do two completely different pathways exist for the biosynthesis of PAF? At the present time we do not have sufficient information to fully answer this question, but it is clear that the various enzymes involved in the two metabolic routes have a distinctly different set of properties. Also it is evident that the 1-alkyl-2-lyso-Gro-3-PCho acetyltransferase is readily activated by all agents known to stimulate cells to produce PAF, whereas the DTT-insensitive cholinephosphotransferase does not appear to be similarly affected. Moreover, the specific activities of the two enzymes responsible for catalyzing the final step of PAF synthesis are significantly different under conditions of non-stimulation; the DTT-insensitive cholinephosphotransferase is generally much higher than the 1-alkyl-2-lyso-Gro-3-PCho acetyltransferase in most resting cells. The latter is also reflected in studies with intact platelets (Blank *et al.*, 1984) and HL-60 cells (Record and Snyder, 1986), since incubation of these cells with labeled alkylacetylglycerols leads to the rapid formation of significant quantities of labeled PAF. However, human endothelial cells apparently possess little if any DTT-insensitive cholinephosphotransferase activity since when they were incubated with [^{3}H] alkylacetylglycerols (Blank *et al.*, 1986), labeled alkylglycerols were detected, but insignificant radioactivity was found in the phospholipid fraction.

Conclusions reached from the observations summarized in this report have led to the following hypothesis. The DTT-insensitive cholinephosphotransferase pathway is required to maintain physiological levels of PAF for healthy normal cell function, whereas the 1-alkyl-2-lyso-Gro-3-PCho acetyltransferase biosynthetic route is only activated in hypersensitivity reactions or under conditions where PAF release is coupled to a stimulatory-dependent response. A potential role of the DTT-insensitive cholinephosphotransferase as a regulatory enzyme in maintaining normal blood pressure via the hypotensive activity of PAF also needs to be considered. The possible significance of PAF in blood pressure regulation is based on the fact that the DTT-insensitive cholinephosphotransferase in kidney tissue is very high, whereas the 1-alkyl-2-lyso-Gro-3-PCho acetyltransferase is extremely low (Renooij and Snyder, 1981; Snyder *et al.*, 1986a; Wykle *et al.*, 1980). These findings are especially interesting in view of the reports summarized by Muirhead (1980) regarding the antihypertensive neutral renal lipid (ANRL) and an antihypertensive polar renal lipid (APRL) that his group has isolated from rat and rabbit kidneys. It is quite likely that ANRL is a conglomerate of alkylacetylglycerols and that the active principle of APRL is PAF; if this is the case, the DTT-insensitive cholinephosphotransferase would explain the hypotensive actions of the ANRL.

Obviously, more extensive experiments at the cellular and enzymatic level are needed to assess the quantitative contributions of the dual pathways for PAF biosynthesis in cell types of different origin. Likewise, it is necessary to establish the physiological relevance of endogenous levels of PAF in cells and in the vascular compartment, in order to learn whether it plays an essential role in blood pressure regulation as has been implicated for ANRL and APRL. Nevertheless, regardless of their ultimate significance, neither pathway of biosynthesis can be ignored in studies of PAF production or the regulatory controls involved.

ACKNOWLEDGMENTS

This work was supported by the Office of Energy Research, US Department of Energy (Contract No. DE-AC05-760R00033), the National Heart, Lung, and Blood Institute (Grant HL-27109-05; Grant HL-35495-01), and the American Cancer Society (Grant BC-70P).

The submitted manuscript has been authored by a contractor of the US Government under contract number DE-AC05-760R00033. Accordingly, the US Government retains a non-exclusive, royalty-free license to publish or reproduce the published form of this contribution, or allow others to do so, for US Government purposes.

REFERENCES

Albert, D.H., and Snyder, F. (1983). 'Biosynthesis of 1-alkyl-2-acetyl-*sn*-glycero-3-phosphocholine (platelet-activating factor) from 1-alkyl-2-acyl-*sn*-glycero-3-phosphocholine by rat alveolar macrophages. Phospholipase A_2 and acetyltransferase activities during phagocytosis and ionophore stimulation', *J. Biol. Chem.*, **258**, 97−102.

Alonso, F., Garcia Gil, M., Sanchez-Crespo, M., and Mato, J.M. (1982). 'Activation of 1-alkyl-2-lyso-glycero-3-phosphocholine. Acetyl-CoA transferase during phagocytosis in human polymorphonuclear leukocytes', *J. Biol. Chem.*, **257**, 3376−3378.

Blank, M.L., Lee, T-c., Cress, E.A., Malone, B., Fitzgerald, V., and Snyder, F. (1984). 'Conversion of 1-alkyl-2-acetyl-*sn*-glycerols to platelet activating factor and related phospholipids by rabbit platelets', *Biochem. Biophys. Res. Commun.*, **124** 156−163.

Brown, A.J., Glish, G.L., McBay, E.H., and Snyder, F. (1985). 'Alkyldihydroxyacetonephosphate synthase mechanism: ^{18}O Studies of fatty acid release from acyldihydroxyacetone phosphate', *Biochemistry*, **24**, 8012−8016.

Brown, A.J., and Snyder, F. (1982). 'Alkyldihydroxyacetone-P synthase: solubilization, partial purification, new assay method, and evidence for a ping-pong mechanism', *J. Biol. Chem.*, **257**, 8835−8839.

Brown, A.J., and Snyder, F. (1983). 'The mechanism of alkyldihydroxyacetone-P synthase.

Formation of [^{3}H]H$_2$O from acyl[1-R-^{3}H]dihydroxyacetone-P by purified alkyldihydroxy-acetone-P synthase in the absence of acylhydrolase activity', *J. Biol. Chem.*, **258**, 4134−4189.

Chae, K., Piantadosi, C., and Snyder, F. (1973). 'Reductase, phosphatase, and kinase activities in the metabolism of alkyldihydroxyacetone phosphate and alkyldihydroxyaceton', *J. Biol. Chem.*, **248**, 6718−6723.

El-Bassiouni, E.A., Piantasdosi, C., and Snyder, F. (1975). 'Metabolism of alkyldihydroxy-acetone phosphate in rat brain', *Biochim. Biophys. Acta*, **388**, 5−11.

Fleming, P.J., and Hajra, A.K. (1977). '1-Alkyl-*sn*-glycero-3-phosphate: acyl-CoA acyltransferase in rat brain microsomes', *J. Biol. Chem.*, **252**, 1663−1672.

Gomez-Cambronero, J., Nieto, M.L., Mato, J.M., and Sanchez Crespo. M. (1985a). 'Modula-tion of lyso-platelet activating factor:acetyl-CoA acetyltransferase from rat splenic microsomes. The role of calcium ions', *Biochim. Biophys. Acta*, **845**, 511−515.

Gomez-Cambronero, J., Velasco, S., Mato, J.M., and Sanchez Crespo. M. (1985b). 'Modulation of lyso-platelet activating factor:acetyl-CoA acetyltransferase from rat splenic microsomes. The role of cyclic AMP-dependent protein kinase', *Biochim. Biophys. Acta*, **845**, 516−519.

Hajra, A.K. (1985). 'Biosynthesis of *O*-alkylglycerol ether lipids', In H.K. Mangold and F. Paltauf (eds.) *Ether Lipids, Biochemical and Biomedical Aspects*. Academic Press, New York, pp. 85−106.

Hill, E.E., and Lands, W.E.M. (1968). 'Incorporation of long-chain and polyunsaturated acids into phosphatidate and phosphatidylcholine', *Biochim. Biophys. Acta*, **152**, 645−648.

Kennedy, E.P., and Weiss, S.B. (1956). 'The function of cytidine coenzymes in the biosynthesis of phospholipides', *J. Biol. Chem.*, **222**, 193−214.

Kramer, R.M., Patton, G.M., Pritzker, C.R., and Deykin, D. (1984). 'Metabolism of platelet-activating factor in human platelets. Transacylase-mediated synthesis of 1-*O*-alkyl-2-arachi-donoyl-*sn*-glycero-3-phosphocholine', *J. Biol. Chem.*, **259**, 13 316−13 320.

Lee, T-c. (1985). 'Biosynthesis of platelet activating factor: substrate specificity of 1-alkyl-2-lyso-*sn*-glycero-3-phosphocholine:acetyl-CoA acetyltransferase in rat spleen microsomes', *J. Biol. Chem.*, **260**, 10 952−10 955.

Lee, T-c., Blank, M.L., Fitzgerald, V., and Snyder, F. (1982a). 'Formation of alkylacyl- and diacylglycerophosphocholines via diradylglycerol cholinephosphotransferase in rat liver', *Biochim. Biophys. Acta*, **713**, 479−483.

Lee, T-c., Malone, B., and Snyder, F. (1986). 'A new *de novo* pathway for the formation of 1-alkyl-2-acetyl-*sn*-glycerols, a precursor of platelet activating factor. Biochemical characteriz-ation of 1-alkyl-2-lyso-*sn*-glycero-3-P:acetyl-CoA acetyltransferase', *J. Biol. Chem.*, **261**, 5373−5377.

Lee, T-c., Lenihan, D.J., Malone, B., Roddy, L.L., and Wasserman, S.I. (1984). 'Increased biosynthesis of platelet activating factor in activated human eosinophils', *J. Biol. Chem.*, **259**, 5526−5530.

Lee, T-c., Malone, B., Wasserman, S.I., Fitzgerald, V., and Snyder, F. (1982b). 'Activities of enzymes that metabolize platelet-activating factor (1-alkyl-2-acetyl-*sn*-glycero-3-phospho-choline) in neutrophils and eosinophils from humans and the effect of a calcium ionophore', *Biochem. Biophys. Res. Commun.*, **105**, 1303−1308.

Lenihan, D.J., and Lee, T-c. (1984). 'Regulation of platelet activating factor synthesis: modulation of 1-alkyl-2-lyso-*sn*-glycero-3-phosphocholine:acetyl-CoA acetyltransferase by phosphoryla-tion and dephosphorylation in rat spleen microsomes', *Biochem. Biophys. Res. Commun.*, **120**, 834−839.

Malone, B., Lee, T-c., and Snyder, F. (1986). '*De novo* biosynthesis of alkylacetylglycerols, a precursor of platelet activating factor (PAF)', *Fed. Proc.*, **45**, 1529.

Muirhead, E.E. (1980). 'Antihypertensive functions of the kidney: Arthur C. Corcoran Memorial Lecture', *Hypertension*, **2**, 444−464.

Ninio, E., Mencia-Huerta, J.M., Heymans, F., and Benveniste, J. (1982). 'Biosynthesis of platelet-activating factor. I. Evidence for an acetyl-transferase activity in murine macrophages', *Biochim. Biophys. Acta*, **710**, 23−31.

Ninio, E., Mencia-Huerta, J.M., and Benveniste, J. (1983). 'Biosynthesis of platelet-activating factor (PAF-acether) V. Enhancement of acetyltransferase activity in murine peritoneal cells by calcium ionophore A23187', *Biochim. Biophys. Acta*, **751**, 298−304.

Radominska-Pyrek, A., Strosznajder, J., Dabrowiecki, Z., Chojnacki, T., and Horrocks, L.A. (1976). 'Effects of free fatty acids on the enzymic synthesis of diacyl and ether types of choline and ethanolamine phosphoglycerides', *J. Lipid Res.*, **17**, 657−662.

Radominska-Pyrek, A., Strosznajder, J., Dabrowiecki, Z., Goracci, G., Chojnacki, T., and Horrocks, L.A. (1977). 'Enzymic synthesis of ether types of choline and ethanolamine phosphoglycerides by microsomal fractions from rat brain and liver', *J. Lipid Res.*, **18**, 53−58.

Record, M., and Snyder, F. (1986). 'Biosynthesis of platelet activating factor (PAF) via alternate pathways: subcellular distribution of products in HL-60 cells', *Fed. Proc.*, **45**, 1529.

Renooij, W., and Snyder, F. (1981). 'Biosynthesis of 1-alkyl-2-acetyl-*sn*-glycero-3-phosphocholine (platelet activating factor and a hypotensive lipid) by cholinephosphotransferase', *Biochim. Biophys. Acta*, **563**, 545−556.

Robinson, M., Blank, M.L., and Snyder, F. (1985). 'Acylation of lysophospholipids by rabbit alveolar macrophages. Specificities of CoA-dependent and CoA-independent reactions', *J. Biol. Chem.*, **260**, 7889−7895.

Snyder, F., Blank, M.L., Johnson, D., Lee, T-c., Malone, B., Robinson, M., and Woodard, D. (1986a). 'Alkylacetylglycerols versus lyso-PAF as precursors in PAF biosynthesis and the role of arachidonic acid', *Pharmacol. Res. Commun.*, (in press).

Snyder, F., Blank, M.L., and Malone, B. (1970). 'Requirements of cytidine derivatives in the biosynthesis of *O*-alkyl phospholipids', *J. Biol. Chem.*, **245**, 4016−4018.

Snyder, F., Blank, M., Lee, T-c., Robinson, M., and Woodard, D. (1986b). 'Measurement of key enzyme activities involved in the metabolism of platelet activating factor (PAF)', *Methods Enzymol.*, (in press).

Snyder, F., Lee, T-c., Blank, M., Malone, B., Woodard, D., and Robinson, M. (1985a). 'Platelet activating factor (PAF): Alternate pathways of biosynthesis, the mechanism of inactivation, and the reacylation of lyso-PAF with arachidonate', *Adv. Prostaglandin Thromboxane Leukotriene Res.*, **15**, 693−696.

Snyder, F., Lee, T-c., and Wykle, R.L. (1985b). 'Ether-linked glycerolipids and their bioactive species: enzymes and metabolic regulation'. In A.N. Martonosi (ed.) *The Enzymes of Biological Membranes*. Plenum Publishing Co., New York, Vol. 2, pp. 1−58.

Snyder, F., Woodard, D., Malone, B., and Lee, T-c. (1985c). 'The enzymatic synthesis of alkylacetylglycerols and their subsequent conversion to platelet activating factor',. In *Abstracts, 13th International Congress of Biochemistry, Amsterdam, 1985*, Elsevier Science Publishers, Amsterdam, The Netherlands, p. 565, Abstract TH-479.

Stoffel, W., and Heimann, G. (1974). 'The action of lysosomal lipolytic enzymes on alkyl ether-containing phospholipids', *Hoppe Seylers Z. Physiol. Chem.*, **355**, 651−659.

Sugiura, T., and Waku, K. (1985). 'CoA-Independent transfer of arachidonic acid from 1,2-diacyl-*sn*-glycero-3-phosphocholine to 1-*O*-alkyl-*sn*-glycero-3-phosphocholine (lyso platelet-activating factor) by macrophage microsomes', *Biochem. Biophys. Res. Commun.*, **127**, 384−390.

Woodard, D.S., Lee, T-c., and Snyder, F. (1984). 'Biosynthesis of platelet activating factor via two enzymatic pathways in rat kidney', *Fed. Proc.*, **43**, 1655 (Abstract 1339).

Woodard, D.S., Lee, T-c., and Snyder, F. (1985). 'Platelet activating factor (PAF) biosynthesis via a specific cholinephosphotransferase in rat kidney medulla microsomes', *Fed. Proc.*, **44**, 1607 (Abstract 7000).

Wykle, R.L., and Snyder, F. (1970). 'Biosynthesis of an *O*-alkyl analogue of phosphatidic acid and *O*-alkylglycerols via *O*-alkyl ketone intermediates by microsomal enzymes of Ehrlich ascites tumour', *J. Biol. Chem.*, **245**, 3047−3058.

Wykle, R.L., Malone, B., and Snyder, F. (1980). 'Enzymatic synthesis of 1-alkyl-2-acetyl-*sn*-glycero-3-phosphocholine, a hypotensive and platelet-aggregating lipid', *J. Biol. Chem.*, **255**, 10 256–10 260.

New Horizons in Platelet Activating Factor Research
Edited by C. M. Winslow and M. L. Lee
© 1987 John Wiley & Sons Ltd.

3

Regulation of Platelet Activating Factor-Acether Biosynthesis in Various Cell Types

Ewa Ninio

Some years ago nobody thought that a phospholipid could be a potent mediator of inflammation, allergy and platelet aggregation. This is the case of PAF-acether (Benveniste *et al.*, 1972) a peculiar molecule possessing an ether bond on the first position of glycerol, a short chain of two carbons at the second and a polar phosphocholine group at the third position. As soon as this structure was attributed to PAF-acether independently by two groups (Benveniste *et al.*, 1979; Demopoulos *et al.*, 1979), the research concerning the biosynthesis of this mediator started in several laboratories. The concept of the initial action of a phospholipase A_2 on ether-linked phosphatidylcholine came from the following observations. Hog leukocytes incubated overnight at alkaline pH formed large amounts of the lyso analog of PAF-acether (1-*O*-alkyl-*sn*-glycero-3-phosphocholine) (Polonsky *et al.*, 1980). This compound could be transformed into PAF-acether by a simple chemical acetylation (Polonsky *et al.*, 1980). Later, several cell types including murine macrophages (Roubin *et al.*,1982), human leukocytes (Jouvin-Marche *et al.*, 1984) or platelets (Benveniste *et al.*, 1982) were recognized to form lyso PAF-acether during stimulation with their specific secretagogs. The inhibition of phospholipase A_2 activity in macrophages and platelets by EDTA, bromophenacyl bromide (BPB), 874 CB (Clin Midy) or mepacrine lead to subsequent lack of PAF-acether formation during cell stimulation (Mencia-Huerta *et al.*, 1981; Benveniste *et al.*, 1982). In the case of murine peritoneal macrophages it was shown (Mencia-Huerta *et al.*, 1981) that 10 min pretreatment of cells with BPB (0.1mM) inhibited PAF-acether formation upon stimulation with zymosan, and that addition of lyso PAF-acether and acetyl-CoA to such cell populations induced the synthesis of PAF-acether, even in the absence of stimulus (Table 1). This experiment suggested that PAF-acether was synthetized in a two step process involving:

1. Activation of a phospholipase A_2 that generates lyso PAF-acether.
2. This is subsequently acetylated by an acetyltransferase.

New Horizons in Platelet Activating Factor Research

Table 1.   PAF-acether release from rat adherent cells

| | PAF-acether | | |
Activator	Untreated cells	BPB-treated cells	Number of experiments
Zymosan	17.1 ± 4.1	0 ± 0	12
Acetyl CoA + Lyso PAF-acether	70.8 ± 8.7	61.6 ± 6.3	6
Acetyl-CoA	0 ± 0	0 ± 0	6
Lyso PAF-acether	0 ± 0	0 ± 0	6

Rat adherent peritoneal cells (1 × 10^6 cells ml^{-1}) were treated or not for 10 min with bromphenacyl bromide (BPB, 100µM). Zymosan (1 mg ml^{-1}), acetyl-CoA (100 µM) or lyso PAF-acether (0.2 µM) were added either alone or in combination for an additional 60 min period at 37 °C. The quantity of PAF-acether released by the cells was assessed using platelet aggregation (Benveniste et al., 1972, Cazenave et al., 1979) and the results are means ± 1 S.D. of the indicated number of experiments. (Reproduced from Mencia-Huerta, 1981, by permission of Birkhaüser Verlag, Basel, Switzerland).

Several pieces of evidence supported the implication of an enzymatic acetylation step in PAF-acether biosynthesis. An acetyltransferase (EC:2.3.1.67) capable of forming PAF-acether from synthetic lyso PAF-acether and acetyl-CoA was described in microsomes derived from several rat tissues (Wykle et al., 1980) and from murine macrophages (Ninio et al., 1982). The exposure of platelets to ionophore A 23187 in the presence of [³H]acetate leaded to the obtention of radiolabeled PAF-acether (Chap et al., 1981). Finally, rat peritoneal adherent cells stimulated with zymosan in the presence of [³H]acetyl-CoA generated [³H]PAF-acether (Mencia-Huerta et al., 1982) and similar results were obtained later using rabbit neutrophils (Mueller et al., 1983).

The question of the regulation of PAF-acether biosynthesis was soon raised since this mediator is synthetized only during cell stimulation of defined cell types. The most important observation linked to PAF-acether formation was the activation of the acetyltransferase upon cell stimulation. Activation of several cell types results in a very early several-fold increase in acetyltransferase level prior to PAF-acether synthesis. This phenomenon was observed in human neutrophils stimulated with opsonized zymosan (Alonso et al., 1982) or ionophore A 23187 (Jouvin-Marche et al., 1984), murine peritoneal and alveolar macrophages (Ninio et al., 1983; Albert and Snyder, 1983) human and rabbit platelets stimulated with thrombin (Coëffier et al., 1986) and human eosinophils stimulated with ionophore A23187 or specific secretagogs (Lee et al., 1982, 1984).

Recently, we confirmed a role for acetyltransferase and its activation in PAF-acether formation in the bone marrow-derived mast cell (BMMC) i.e. a model of immediate hypersensitivity (Ninio et al., 1986). BMMC passively sensitized with an optimal dose of dinitrophenyl (DNP)-specific monoclonal IgE, washed and challenged with DNP coupled to bovine serum albumin, released PAF-acether and expressed higher level of acetyltransferase than unstimulated cells (Figure 1). The activity of acetyltransferase doubled already within 30 s upon antigen challenge and in keeping with the results previously obtained (Mencia-Huerta *et al.*, 1983), the formation of PAF-acether was maximal by 2–3 min. The time-course of acetyltransferase stimulation preceded the formation and the release of PAF-acether by BMMC. Using these cells we also showed that the antigen-induced, IgE-dependent PAF-acether formation and activation of acetyltransferase were inhibited by the calcium channel blocker, Diltiazem (0.5 mM, 10 min at 37 °C).

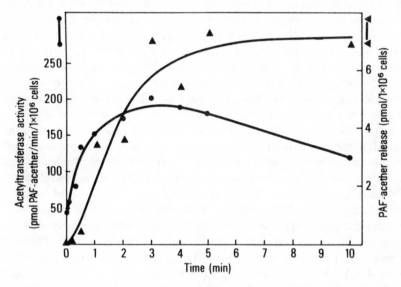

Figure 1. Time course of PAF-acether release (▲ ▲) and increase in acetyltransferase activity (● ●) in BMMC (1 × 10⁶ in 0.5 ml) passively sensitized with monoclonal IgE and challenged with 40 ng ml⁻¹ of antigen (DNP-BSA) at 37 °C. The quantity of PAF-acether was assessed by platelet aggregation as described by Benveniste, 1972; Cazenave, 1979 and the acetyltransferase activity as in Ninio, 1983. Results are means of duplicate determinations and are representative of six experiments

Recently, Benhamou *et al.*, (1986) demonstrated that treatment with dexamethasone (1 μM, 24 h) of BMMC inhibited the immunologic release of PAF-acether and the preformed granule marker β-hexosaminidase in a dose-and time-dependent fashion. In contrast, no inhibition of mediator release was observed when the dexamethasone-treated cells were stimulated with the ionophore A 23178 (1 μM). Dexamethasone treatment induced a dose-and time-dependent inhibition of ¹²⁵I-IgE binding to the cells. Scatchard analysis of ¹²⁵I-IgE binding on dexamethasone-treated BMMC revealed a 56 percent decrease in the IgE Fc receptor number without alteration of the K_d. Cytofluorometer analysis demonstrated that every cell in the dexamethasone-treated cell population exhibited a decreased IgE binding. The antigen-induced increase in acetyltransferase activity, used as an index of cellular activation, was inhibited by 37 percent in dexamethasone-treated cells as compared to untreated ones. These results suggest that dexamethasone inhibits the immunologic release of PAF-acether by decreasing the number of IgE Fc receptors available for sensitization. Thus, the modulation of IgE Fc receptor number could play a role in the anti-inflammatory properties of glucocorticosteroids.

In macrophages and BMMC the activation of acetyltransferase is Ca^{2+}-dependent and the K_m for acetyl-CoA is not affected upon cell stimulation. This suggested that an increase in the number of active enzyme molecules rather than a change in the kinetics parameters is responsible for the enhanced acetyltransferase activity (Ninio et al., 1983, 1986). We have suggested that some post-translational event could be involved in the acetyltransferase activation (Ninio et al., 1983). Recently, this hypothesis was supported by Lenihan and Lee (1984) who showed that a phosphorylation–dephosphorylation process might control the level of acetyltransferase in rat spleen microsomes. However, this model does not reflect the physiological or pathological synthesis of PAF-acether, so we made an attempt to determine whether such a phosphorylation–dephosphorylation mechanism was operational in antigen-stimulated BMMC. Indeed, we showed that the activity of the enzyme present in lysate from unstimulated cells doubled after preincubation with ATP and Mg^{2+} whereas adenylylimidodiphosphate, a non-phosphorylating analog of ATP, was without effect (Table 2) (Ninio et al., 1986). In contrast, ATP and Mg^{2+} were ineffective on lysates from antigen challenged cells, that exhibited already high level of acetyltransferase activity, suggesting that phosphorylation of the enzyme already took place at the time of cell stimulation. Thus we report on both the activation of a key enzyme for PAF-acether synthesis and on the mechanism of this activation in an antigen-stimulated pure mast cell population. A link between bridging of IgE receptors and an enzyme activity critical to the formation of a lipid mediator is thereby evidenced.

Table 2.   Variations in the acetyltransferase activity at 26 °C under conditions which favour phosphorylations.

Agent	Time	
	0	15 min
None	78	56 (72%)
ATP (5 mM)	112	138 (177%)
Adenylylimidodiphosphate (5 mM)	87	66 (85%)

Cell lysates obtained from unstimulated BMMC were preincubated at 26 °C with or without the defined agents. The acetyltransferase activity (Ninio et al., 1983) was measured thereafter in the presence of 40 μM lyso PAF-acether and 200 μM [^{3}H]acetyl-CoA (0.5 μCi 100 nmol^{-1}). Results in pM PAF-acether min^{-1} 1 $\times$ 10^6 cells^{-1} are means of duplicate determinations and are respresentative of three experiments. Parentheses indicate the percentage of acetyltransferase activity at 15 min as compared to time 0 without agent.

Thus, the acetyltransferase stimulation appears to be a key event in PAF-acether synthesis in several cell types. In addition the lack of PAF-acether formation could be related to the absence or a very low level of acetyltransferase activity in thioglycollate elicited mouse macrophages (Roubin *et al.*, 1982), human lymphocytes (Jouvin-Marche *et al.*, 1984) and rat kidney tubular cells (Pirotzky, 1984). However, rat kidney medullary cells, although they exhibit very low level of acetyltransferase are capable to form PAF-acether upon ionophore A 23187 stimulation (Pirotzky *et al.*, 1984). The involvement of an alternative route for PAF-acether biosynthesis via the CDP-choline cholinephosphotransferase (Renooij and Snyder, 1981) was envisioned. In addition (Woodard *et al.*, 1984) have shown that the activity of the latter enzyme was ten times higher in the medullary part of the rat kidney than in the cortex, suggesting that the CDP-choline cholinephosphotransferase is the major pathway of PAF-acether synthesis in medullary cells.

FORMATION OF PAF-ACETHER (♦) AND 2-LYSO PAF-ACETHER (●)
BY Io-STIMULATED HUMAN CELLS

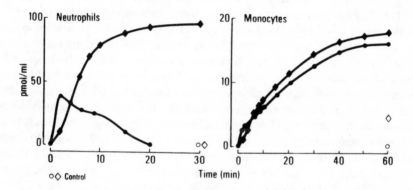

Figure 2.   PAF-acether (♦) and lyso-PAF-acether (●) formation by 1×10^6 neutrophils (A) and 1×10^6 monocytes (B) incubated in 1 ml HEPES buffer in the presence of ionophore A 23187 (2 μg ml⁻¹). PAF-acether (◊) and lyso-PAF-acether (○) produced by unstimulated cells. Representative of four experiments. *Reproduced from Jouvin-Marche et. al., 1984 by permission of the* Journal of Immunology

Generation and/or disponibility of lyso PAF-acether may control in part the level of PAF-acether production. In human neutrophils the generation of lyso PAF-acether formation precede PAF-acether formation and subsequently decayed (Figure 2) (Jouvin-Marche *et al.*, 1984). Addition of exogenous lyso PAF-acether to stimulated neutrophils doubled the amount of PAF-acether formed (Jouvin-Marche *et al.*, 1984). Interesting was also the lack of effect of acetyl-CoA alone on PAF-acether biosynthesis in this cell type. From these experimental data a cooperation between platelets, which generate large amounts of lyso PAF-acether, and neutrophils which are able to transform it into PAF-acether was postulated by Coëffier *et al.*, (1984). Indeed, when mixing neutrophils stimulated with opsonized zymosan together with platelets stimulated with thrombin, PAF-acether formation doubled with respect to the mere summation. Two explanations are possible:

1. Lyso PAF-acether released by platelets is transformed into PAF-acether by neutrophils.
2. Stimulated platelets produce a mediator capable of stimulating one of the biosynthetic steps of PAF-acether formation i.e. phospholipase A_2 or acetyltransferase.

In favour of the second hypothesis is the recent report by Billah *et al.*, (1985) on the modulatory effects of 5-lipoxygenase products on the expression of neutrophil phospholipase A_2.

Another aspect of PAF-acether regulation was studied in activated mouse macrophages (Roubin *et al.*, 1986). These cells obtained from mice injected with bacteria or immunostimulants derived from bacteria, synthesized in response to a zymosan challenge two to three times less PAF-acether than resident macrophages, although the level of phospholipid precursors for PAF-acether synthesis and acetyltransferase were similar in both populations. The biosynthesis of PAF-acether could be restored in activated macrophages by addition of acetyl-CoA, probably by preventing the reacylation of lyso PAF-acether into alkylacylglycerophosphocholine. The accumulation of lyso PAF-acether results probably from a very rapid hydrolysis of PAF-acether by an acetylhydrolase described first by Blank *et al.*, (1981). However, up to now there is no direct evidence showing the increase in such hydrolytic activity in activated macrophages.

The catabolic route for PAF-acether can be summarized as follows: acetylhydrolase cleaves the acetyl moiety of PAF-acether leading to the formation of lyso PAF-acether which is in turn reacylated into alkylacylglycerophosphocholine. In rabbit platelets (Malone *et al.*, 1985) and human neutrophils (Chilton *et al.*, 1983) the reacylation reaction of lyso PAF-acether is very efficient. By contrast, rat alveolar macrophages (Robinson *et al.*, 1985) and capillary endothelial cells (Tan and Snyder, 1985) appear to posses a low acyltransferase activity since a considerable amount of lyso PAF-acether is not metabolized.

Presently we know that different stimulants trigger more or less release of PAF-acether from cells into culture medium (Roubin *et al.*, 1982) and that the intracellular PAF-acether is not randomly distributed. In human neutrophils stimulated by the ionophore A 23187 or opsonized zymosan, PAF-acether was found in granules or in phagosomes, respectively (Riches *et al.*, 1985). The acetyltransferase in ionophore A 23187-stimulated and unstimulated human neutrophils is located in the internal membranes (Ribbes *et al.*, 1985). These results imply the presence of the PAF-acether transport system within the cell. The regulation of which could control the release of the mediator.

The regulation of PAF-acether biosynthesis occurs at several levels, the most important being certainly the activation of acetyltransferase. However, it is possible to imagine that a given cell type is able to use the alternative pathway through CDP-choline: cholinephosphotransferase under certain circumstances. From the point of view of pharmacological control of PAF-acether formation it is tempting to inhibit the activation of acetyltransferase, the most crucial enzyme in the biosynthesis of PAF-acether in majority of cells. This enzyme being specific towards lyso PAF-acether, suppressing its activity should not disturb very much the function of a whole cell. The same reasoning is not valid in the case of phospholipase A_2.

REFERENCES

Albert, D.H., and Snyder, F. (1983). 'Biosynthesis of 1-alkyl-2-acetyl-*sn*-glycero-3-phospho-choline (platelet-activating factor) from 1-alkyl-2-acyl-*sn*-glycero-3-phosphocholine by rat alveolar macrophages', *J. Biol. Chem.*, **258**, 97.

Alonso, F., Gil, M.G., Sanchez Crespo, M., and Mato, J.M. (1982). 'Activation of 1-alkyl-2-lyso-glycero-3-phosphorylcholine: acetyl-CoA transferase during phagocytosis in human poly-morphonuclear leukocytes', *J. Biol. Chem.*, **257**, 3376.

Benhamou, M., Ninio, E., Salem, P., Hiéblot, C., Bessou, G., Pitton, C., Liu, T-c., and Mencia-Huerta, J.M. (1986). 'Decrease in IgE Fc receptor expression on mouse bone marrow-derived mast cells and inhibition of paf-acether formation and β-hexosaminidase release by dexamethasone', *J. Immunol.*, **136**, 135–1392.

Benveniste, J., Chignard, M., Le Couedic, J.P., and Vargaftig, B.B. (1982). 'Biosynthesis of platelet-activating factor (PAF-acether). II. Involvement of phospholipase A_2 in the forma-tion of PAF-acether and lyso PAF-acether from rabbit platelets', *Thromb. Res.*, **25**, 375.

Benveniste, J., Henson, P.M., and Cochrane, C.G. (1972). 'Leukocyte-dependent histamine release from rabbit platelets. The role of IgE, basophils and a platelet-activating factor', *J. Exp. Med.*, **136**, 1356.

Benveniste, J., Tencé, M., Varenne, P., Bidault, J., Boullet, C., and Polonsky, J. (1979). 'Semi-synthèse et structure proposée du facteur activant les plaquettes (PAF): PAF-acéther, un alkyl éther analogue de la lysophosphatidylcholine', *C.R. Acad. Sc. Paris*, **289D**, 1037.

Billah, M.M., Bryant, R.W., and Siegel, M. (1985). 'Lipoxygenase products of arachidonic acid modulate biosynthesis of platelet-activating factor (1-*O*-alkyl-2-acetyl-*sn*-glycero-3-phosphocholine) by human neutrophils via phospholipase A_2', *J. Biol. Chem.*, **260**, 6899.

Blank, M.L., Lee, T-c., Fitzgerald, V., and Snyder, F. (1981). 'A specific acetylhydrolase for 1-alkyl-2-acetyl-*sn*-glycero-3-phosphocholine a hypotensive and platelet-activating lipid', *J. Biol. Chem.*, **256**, 175.

Casenave, J.P., Benveniste, J., and Mustard, J.F. (1979). 'Aggregation of rabbit platelets by platelet-activating factor is independent of the release reaction and the arachidonate pathway and inhibited by membrane-active drugs', *Lab. Invest.*, **41**, 275.

Chap, H., Mauco, G., Simon, M.F., Benveniste, J., and Douste-Blazy, L. (1981). 'Biosynthetic labelling of platelet-activating factor (PAF-acether) from radioactive acetate by stimulated platelets', *Nature*, **289**, 312.

Chilton, F.H., O'Flaherty, J.T., Ellis, J.M., Swendsen, C.L., and Wykle, R.L. (1983). 'Metabolic fate of platelet-activating factor in neutrophils', *J. Biol. Chem.*, **258**, 6357.

Coëffier, E., Chignard, M., Delautier, D., and Benveniste, J. (1984). 'Cooperation between platelets (P) and neutrophils (N) for paf-acether formation', *Fed. Proc.*, **43**, 781 (Abs).

Coëffier, E., Ninio, E., Le Couedic, J.P., and Chignard, M. (1986). 'Transient activation of the acetyltransferase necessary for paf-acether biosynthesis in thrombin-activated platelets', *Brit. J. Haematol.*, **62**, in press.

Demopoulos, C.A., Pinckard, R.N., and Hanahan, D.J. (1979). 'Platelet-activating factor.

Evidence for 1-*O*-alkyl-2-acetyl-*sn*-glyceryl-3-phosphorylcholine as the active component (a new class of lipid chemical mediators)', *J. Biol. Chem.*, **254**, 9355.

Jouvin-Marche, E., Ninio, E., Beaurain, G., Tencé, M., Niaudet, P., and Benveniste, J. (1984). 'Biosynthesis of paf-acether (platelet-activating factor). VII. Precursors of paf-acether and acetyltransferase activity in human leukocytes', *J. Immunol.*, **133**, 892.

Lee, T-c., Lenihan, D.J., Malone, B., Roddy, L.L., and Wasserman, S.I. (1984). 'Increased biosynthesis of platelet-activating factor in activated human eosinophils', *J. Biol. Chem.*, **259**, 5526.

Lee, T-c., Malone, B., Wasserman, S.I., Fitzgerald, V., and Snyder, F. (1982). 'Activities of enzymes that metabolize platelet-activating-factor (1-*O*-alkyl-2-acetyl-*sn*-glycero-3-phosphocholine) in neutrophils and eosinophils from human and the effect of a calcium ionophore', *Biochem. Biophys. Res. Comm.*, **105**, 3303.

Lenihan, D.J., and Lee, T-c. (1984). 'Regulation of platelet-activating factor synthesis: modulation of 1-*O*-alkyl-2-acetyl-*sn*-glycero-3-phosphocholine:acetyl-CoA acetyltransferase by phosphorylation and dephosphorylation in rat spleen microsomes', *Biochem. Biophys. Res. Commun.*, **120**, 834.

Malone, B., Lee, T-c., and Snyder, F. (1985). 'Inactivation of platelet-activating factor (PAF) by rabbit platelets: Lyso-PAF as a key intermediate with phosphatidylcholine as the source of arachidonic acid in its conversion to a tetraenoic acylated product', *J. Biol. Chem.*, **260**, 1531.

Mencia-Huerta, J.M., Lewis, R.A., Razin, E., and Austen, K.F. (1983). 'Antigen-initiated release of platelet-activating factor (paf-acether) from mouse bone marrow-derived mast cells sensitized with monoclonal IgE', *J. Immunol.*, **131**, 2958.

Mencia-Huerta, J.M., Ninio, E., Roubin, R., and Benveniste, J. (1981). 'Is platelet-activating factor (PAF-acether) synthesis by murine peritoneal cells (PC) a two-step process?', *Agents and Actions*, **11**, 556.

Mencia-Huerta, J.M., Roubin, R., Morgat, J., and Benveniste, J. (1982). 'Biosynthesis of platelet-activating factor (PAF-acether). III. Formation of PAF-acether from synthetic substrates by stimulated murine macrophages', *J. Immunol.*, **129**, 804.

Mueller, H.W., O'Flaherty, T.J., and Wykle, R.L. (1983). 'Biosynthesis of platelet-activating factor in rabbit polymorphonuclear neutrophils', *J. Biol. Chem.*, **258**, 6211.

Ninio, E., Mencia-Huerta, J.M., and Benveniste, J. (1983). 'Biosynthesis of platelet-activating factor (PAF-acether) V. Enhancement of acetyltransferase activity in murine peritoneal cells by calcium ionophore A 23187', *Biochim. Biophys. Acta*, **751**, 298.

Ninio, E., Mencia-Huerta, J.M., Heymans, F., and Benveniste, J. (1982). 'Biosynthesis of platelet-activating factor (PAF-acether). I. Evidence for an acetyltransferase activity in murine macrophages', *Biochim. Biophys. Acta*, **710**, 23.

Ninio, E., (1986) submitted for publication.

Pirotzky, E., Ninio, E., Bidault, J., Pfister, A., and Benveniste, J. (1982). 'Biosynthesis of Paf-acether. VI. Precursor of Paf-acether and acetyltransferase activity in isolated rat kidney cells', *Lab. Invest.*, **51**, 567.

Polonsky, J., Tencé, M., Varenne, P., Das, B.C., Lunel, J., and Benveniste, J. (1980). 'Release of 1-*O*-alkyl-2-acetyl-*sn*-glycero-3-phosphocholine, O-deacetyl platelet-activating factor, from leukocytes: chemical ionization mass spectrometry of phospholipids', *Proc. Natl. Acad. Sci. USA*, **77**, 7019.

Renooij, W., and Snyder, F. (1981). 'Biosynthesis of 1-*O*-alkyl-2-acetyl-*sn*-glycero-3-phosphocholine (platelet activating factor and a hypotensive lipid) by choline-phosphotransferase in various rat tissues', *Biochim. Biophys. Acta*, **663**, 545.

Ribbes, G., Ninio, E., Fontan, P., Record, M., Chap, H., Benveniste, J., and Douste-Blazy, L. (1985). 'Evidence that biosynthesis of platelet-activating factor (paf-acether) by human neutrophils occurs in an intracellular membrane', *FEBS Lett.*, **191**, 195.

Riches, D.W.H., Young, S.K., Seccombe, J.F., Lynch, J.M., and Henson, P.M. (1985). 'The subcellular distribution of platelet-activating factor (PAF) in phagocytosing human neutrophils', *Fed. Proc.*, **44**, 737.

Robinson, M., Blank, M.L., and Snyder, F. (1985). 'Acylation of lysophospholipids by rabbit alveolar macrophages. Specificities of CoA-dependent and CoA-independent reactions', *J. Immunol.*, **260**, 7889.

Roubin, R., Dulioust, A., Haye-Legrand, I., Ninio, E., and Benveniste, J. (1986). 'Biosynthesis of paf-acether. VIII. Impairment of paf-acether production in activated macrophages does not depend upon acetyl-transferase activity', *J. Immunol.*, **136**, 1796–1802.

Roubin, R., Mencia-Huerta, J.M., Landes, A., and Benvenisted, J. (1982). 'Biosynthesis of platelet-activating factor (PAF-acether). IV. Impairment of acetyltransferase activity in thioglycollate-elicited mouse macrophages', *J. Immunol.*, **129**, 809.

Tan, E.L., and Snyder, F. (1985). 'Metabolism of platelet-activating factor (1-*O*-alkyl-2-acetyl-*sn*-glycero-3-phosphocholine) by capillary endohelial cells isolated from rat epididymal adipose tissue', *Thromb. Res.*, **38**, 713.

Woodard, D.S., Lee, T-c., and Snyder, F. (1984). 'Biosynthesis of platelet-activating factor via two enzymatic pathways in rat kidney tissue', *Fed. Proc.*, **43**, 1655.

Wykle, R.L., Malone, B., and Snyder, F. (1980). 'Enzymatic synthesis of 1-*O*-alkyl-2-acetyl-*sn*-glycero-3-phosphocholine, a hypotensive and platelet-aggregating lipid', *J. Biol. Chem.*, **255**, 10 256.

New Horizons in Platelet Activating Factor Research
Edited by C. M. Winslow and M. L. Lee
© 1987 John Wiley & Sons Ltd.

4

Biosynthesis of Intermediate in the Platelet Activating Factor Metabolic Pathway: Characterization of 1-alkyl-2-acetyl-*sn*-glycerol Kinase in Rabbit Platelets

Ten-ching Lee, Merle L. Blank, Veronica Fitzgerald, Boyd Malone and Fred Snyder

Diradylglycerols consist of a number of lipid mediators. For example, diradylglycerols participate in the phosphorylation of specific cellular proteins by protein kinase C (Takai *et al.*, 1982). 1-Acyl-2-acetyl-*sn*-glycerols (acylacetyl-G) potentiate neutrophil activation by other mediators such as platelet activating factor, leukotriene B_4, formulated oligopeptide, $C5_a$, and 5-hydroxyeicosatetraenoate (O'Flaherty *et al.*, 1984, 1985; McCall *et al.*, 1985). 1-Alkyl-2-acetyl-*sn*-glycerols (alkylacetyl-G) elicit a hypotensive response (Blank *et al.*,, 1984a) and stimulate the differentiation of HL-60 promyelocytic leukemia cells to macrophage-like cells (McNamara *et al.*, 1984). Diacylglycerol kinase, which resides in both membranes and cytosols, catalyzes the conversion of diacylglycerols to phosphatidic acid, and is widely distributed in animal tissues (Bell and Coleman, 1980; see Kanoh *et al.*, 1983 for reference). *In situ* conversion of both oleoylacetyl-G to oleoylacetyl-GP in human platelets (Kaibuchi *et al.*, 1983) and alkylacetyl-G to alkylacetyl-GP in rabbit platelets (Blank *et al.*, 1984b) have been reported. Also, diacyl-GP (see Berridge, 1984 for review) and alkylacetyl-GP (Bussolino *et al.*, 1984) could function as a calcium ionophore.

The enzymes responsible for the synthesis of acylacetyl-GP and alkylacetyl-GP from their respective diradyl-G substrates have not been characterized; moreover, the control mechanism of the kinase action and the physiological function of these enzymes are not known. In this investigation, we demonstrate the presence of an alkylacetyl-G kinase in rabbit platelets and compare its substrate requirements and pH optimum with enzymes that use oleoylacetyl-G or diacylglycerol as substrates.

ORAU 8597.7a

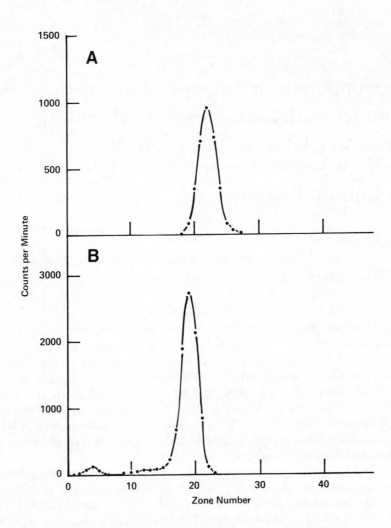

Figure 1.   Thin-layer chromatographic identification of alkylacetyl-GP.
A. [³H]alkylacetyl-GP was isolated from the incubation mixture as described in
the text and re-chromatographed in the solvent system of chloroform:methanol:ace-
tic acid:saline (50:25:8:6:,v/v). The radiolabeled peak co-migrated with an authentic standard of alkylacetyl-GP.
B. Diazomethane derivative of [³H]alkylacetyl-GP was prepared as described in
the text and developed in the thin-layer chromatography solvent system of chloroform: conc. NH₄OH (l00:1, v/v); the R_f value for methylated]³H]alkylacetyl-
GP corresponds to the synthetic standard

PRODUCT INDENTIFICATION

The standard assays contained 5 mM $CaCl_2$, 2-5 mM ATP, 5mM $MgCl_2$, 50 mM NaF, 10 mM sodium phosphate, pH 7.2, 150 μM [^{3}H]alkylacetyl-G (1 × 10^5 dpm) in 1 percent ethanol (also 1-[^{3}H]oleoyl-2-acetyl-G, 1-stearoyl-2-[^{3}H]arachidonoyl-G, or 1-palmitoyl-2-[^{3}H]arachidonoyl-G, when specified), and appropriate amounts of rabbit platelet homogenates or soluble fractions were incubated in a final volume of 0.25 ml. Reactions were carried out at 37 °C for 5–10 min and terminated by lipid extraction with a modified method of Bligh and Dyer (1959) in that 10 percent concentrated HCl was included in the methanol. Initial thin-layer chromatography analyses of the total labeled products were carried out with appropriate standards on silica gel G layers developed in a solvent system of chloroform:methanol:concentrated NH_4OH (65:35:8, v/v) and radioassayed by zonal scanning (Snyder and Kimble, 1965). The labeled component corresponding to authentic alkylacetyl-GP was isolated by preparative thin-layer chromatography in the solvent system described above and re-chromatographed in chloroform:methanol:acetic acid:saline (50:25:8:6, v/v). Figure 1A demonstrates that the purified labeled product co-migrates as a single peak with standard alkylacetyl-GP in this acidic solvent system. Further identification of the reaction product as alkylacetyl-GP was achieved when the isolated radiolabeled compound was reacted with diazomethane (Renkonen, 1968); the diazomethane derivative had the same R_f value as that of the methylated alkylacetyl-GP standard in the thin-layer chromatography solvent system of chloroform:concentrated NH_4OH (100:1, v/v) (Figure 1B).

SUBCELLULAR DISTRIBUTION

The subcellular distribution of alkylacetyl-G kinase in rabbit platelets was determined. Some 81 percent of the kinase in the homogenate was found in the 100,000 × g supernatant. Similarly, most (97.6 percent) of the cytosolic marker enzyme, lactate dehydrogenase, was recovered in the soluble fraction. These data reveal that alkylacetyl-G kinase is a cytosolic enzyme.

EFFECT OF ETHANOL ATP AND Mg^{2+} CONCENTRATION ON THE ACTIVITIES OF DIRADYLGLYCEROL KINASES

Alkylacetyl-G kinase required 1 percent ethanol (Figure 2) and 2-10 mM ATP-Mg^{2+} (Figure 3) for maximal activity. Similar findings were observed when diacylglycerols and oleoylacetyl-G (Figure 2 and data not shown) were the substrates.

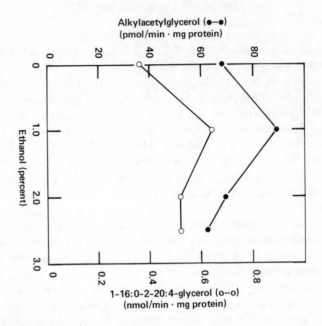

Figure 2.   Effect of ethanol concentration on the activities of diradylglycerol kinases

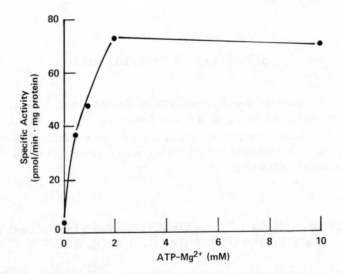

Figure 3.   Effect of ATP-Mg^{2+} concentration on the activity of alkylacetyl-G kinase

pH OPTIMA AND SUBSTRATE REQUIREMENTS

A broad pH optimum between 7.0 and 7.5 was noted for the alkylacetyl-G kinase, with maximal activity at pH 7.2 (Figure 4). Both diacylglycerol kinase (Figure 4) and oleoylacetyl-G kinase (data not shown) also had the highest activity around pH 7.2.

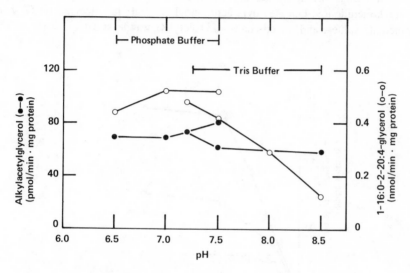

Figure 4. Effect of pH on cytosolic diradylglycerol kinase activities

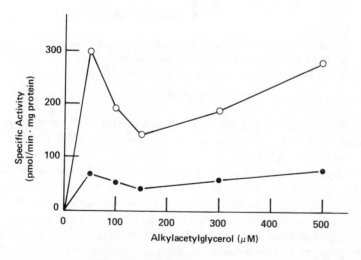

Figure 5. Effect of substrate concentration on the activity of alkylacetyl-G kinase. ○-○, hexadecylacetyl-G; and ●-●, mixed-chain alkylacetyl-G

Figure 5 shows the effect of alkylacetyl-G concentration on the activity of alkylacetyl-G kinase. Even though hexadecylacetyl-G yielded a higher specific activity than that of the mixed-chain alkylacetyl-G, both substrates displayed abnormal hyperbolic kinetics. On the other hand, when either oleoylacetyl-G or diacylglycerols were used as substrates, typical saturation kinetics were obtained (Figure 6). With oleoylacetyl-G as the substrate, the enzyme activity was the highest, whereas palmitoylarachidonoyl-G, stearoylarachidonoyl-G and hexadecylacetyl-G had intermediate values, and mixed-chain alkylacetyl-G was least active.

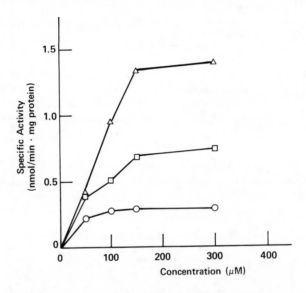

Figure 6.   Effect of substrate concentration on the activities of diradylglycerol kinase. $\triangle$-$\triangle$, aleoylacetyl-G, $\square$-$\square$, palmitoylarachidonoyl-G and $\bigcirc$-$\bigcirc$, stearoylarachidonoyl-G

CONCLUSION

Our experiments clearly show that alkylacetyl-G is converted to alkylacetyl-GP in the presence of ATP and Mg^{2+} using a cell free system of rabbit platelets as illustrated by the scheme below.

The enzyme requires 1 percent ethanol to suspend the substrate for maximal activity and has a pH optimum of 7.2. Subcellular distribution of the enzyme parallels that of the cytosolic marker enzyme, lactate dehydogenase. Under similar assay conditions, the rates of phosphorylation of alkylacetyl-G, oleoylacetyl-G, or diacylglycerols by the cytosols of rabbit platelets are different. However, these three different kinases have similar properties with respect to ethanol requirements, Mg^{2+} $-$ATP dependencies and pH optima. Whether a single enzyme catalyzes the conversion of the various substrates to phospholipids must await the purification of the protein.

$$\begin{array}{c}
\text{H}_2\text{COR} \\
| \\
\text{O} \quad | \\
\| \\
\text{H}_3\text{CCOCH} + \text{ATP} + \text{Mg}^{2+} \\
| \\
| \\
\text{H}_2\text{COH}
\end{array}
\qquad \rightarrow \qquad
\begin{array}{c}
\text{H}_2\text{COR} \\
| \\
\text{O} \quad | \\
\| \\
\text{H}_3\text{CCOCH} \\
| \\
| \quad \text{O} \\
\| \\
\text{H}_2\text{C-O-P-OH} \\
| \\
\text{OH}
\end{array}$$

ACKNOWLEDGMENTS

This work was supported by the Office of Energy Research, US Department of Energy (Contract No. DE-AC05-760R00033), the National Heart, Lung, and Blood Institute (Grant HL-27109-05; Grant HL-35495-01) and the American Cancer Society (Grant BC-70P).

The submitted manuscript has been authored by a contractor of the US Government under contract number DE-AC05-760R00033. Accordingly, the US Government retains a non-exclusive, royalty-free license to publish or reproduce the published form of this contribution, or allow others to do so, for US Government purposes.

REFERENCES

Bell, R.M., and Coleman, R.A., (1980). 'Enzymes of glycerolipid synthesis in eukaryotes', *Annu. Rev. Biochem.*, **49**, 459–487.

Berridge, M.J., (1984). 'Inositol triphosphate and diacylglycerol as second messengers', *Biochem. J.*, **220**, 345–360.

Blank, M.L., Cress, E.A., and Snyder, F., (1984a). 'A new class of antihypertensive neutral lipids: 1-alkyl-2-acetyl-*sn*-glycerols', *Biochem. Biophys. Res. Commun.*, **118**, 334–350.

Blank, M.L., Lee, T-c., Cress, E.A., Malone, B., Fitzgerald, V., and Snyder, F., (1984b). 'Conversion of 1-alkyl-2-acetyl-*sn*-glycerols to platelet activating factor and related phospholipids by rabbit platelets', *Biochem. Biophys. Res. Commun.*, **124**, 156–163.

Bligh, E.G., and Dyer, W.J. (1959). 'A rapid method of total lipid extraction and purification', *Can. J. Biochem. Physiol.*, **37**, 911–917.

Bussolino, F., Camussi, G., and Arese, P., (1984). 'Platelet-activating factor phosphatidate, but not platelet activating factor, is a powerful calcium ionophore in the human red cell', *Cell Calcium*, **5**, 463–473.

Kaibuchi, K., Takai, Y., Sawamura, M., Hoshijima, M., Fugikura, T., and Nishizuka, Y., (1983). 'Synergistic functions of protein phosphorylation and calcium mobilization in platelet activation', *J. Biol. Chem.*, **258**, 6701–6704.

Kanoh, H., Kondoh, H., and Ono, T., (1983). 'Diacylglycerol kinase from pig brain: purification and phospholipid dependencies', *J. Biol. Chem.*, **258**, 1767–1774.

McCall, C., Schmitt, J., Cousart, S., O'Flaherty, J.O., Bass, D., and Wykle, R.L., (1985). 'Stimulation of hexose transport by human polymorphonuclear leukocytes: a possible role for protein kinase C', *Biochem. Biophys. Res. Commun.*, **126**, 450−456.

McNamara, M.J.C., Schmitt, J.D., Wykle, R.L., and Daniel, L.W., (1984). '1-*O*-Hexadecyl-2-acetyl-*sn*-glycerol stimulates differentiation of HL-60 human promyelocytic leukemia cells to macrophage-like cells', *Biochem. Biophys. Res. Commun.*, **122**, 824−830.

O'Flaherty, J.T., Schmitt, J.D., McCall, C.E., and Wykle, R.L., (1984). 'Diacylglycerols enhance human neutrophil degranulation responses: relevancy to a multiple mediator hypothesis of cell function', *Biochem. Biophys. Res. Commun.*, **123**, 64−70.

O'Flaherty, J.T., Schmitt, J.D., Wykle, R.L., (1985). 'Interactions of arachidonate metabolism and protein kinase C in mediating neutrophil function', *Biochem. Biophys. Res. Commun.*, **127**, 916−923.

Renkonen, O. (1968). 'Chromatographic separation of plasmalogenic, alkyl-acyl, and diacyl forms of ethanolamine glycerolphosphatides', *J. Lipid Res.*, **9**, 34−39.

Snyder, F., and Kimble, J., (1965). 'An automatic zonal scraper and sample collector for radioassay of thin-layer chromatograms', *Anal. Biochem.*, **11**, 510−518.

Takai, Y., Minakuchi, R., Kikkawa, U., Sano, K., Kaibuchi, K., Yu, B., Matsubara, T., and Nishizuka, Y., (1982). 'Membrane phospholipid turnover, receptor function and protein phosphorylation', *Brain Res.*, **56**, 287−301.

New Horizons in Platelet Activating Factor Research
Edited by C. M. Winslow and M. L. Lee
© 1987 John Wiley & Sons Ltd.

5

Metabolism of 1-*O*-alkyl-2-arachidonoyl-*sn*-glycero-3-phosphocholine, A Putative Source of Potent Lipid Mediators in Macrophages

Takayuki Sugiura, Yasuhito Nakagawa and Keizo Waku

Macrophages are known to contain large amounts of ether phospholipids such as 1-*O*-alkyl-2-acyl-*sn*-glycero-3-phosphocholine (alkylacyl-GPC) and 1-*O*-alkenyl-2-acyl-*sn*-glycero-3-phosphoethanolamine (alkenylacyl-GPE) (Sugiura *et al.*, 1982, 1983; Albert and Snyder, 1983). These ether phospholipids include a much higher proportion of polyunsaturated fatty acids such as 20:4 (arachidonic acid) than the corresponding diacyl analogs (Sugiura *et al.*, 1983). This observation suggests that ether phospholipids act as storage for polyunsaturated fatty acids. Furthermore, alkylacyl-GPC has been considered as the stored precursor of alkylacetyl-GPC, platelet activating factor (PAF) (Albert and Snyder, 1983). However, thus far only little is known about the metabolism of alkylacyl-GPC. Here we demonstrate the formation of polyunsaturated fatty acid-containing alkylacyl-GPC via a transacylation reaction in macrophages.

MATERIALS AND METHODS

Macrophages were prepared from the pulmonary lavage of rabbits injected intravenously with 1.0 ml of Freund's complete adjuvant (Sugiura and Waku, 1985). The incubation was carried out in 20 mM HEPES-MEM (10^6 cells ml^{-1}) in the presence of ^{3}H-20:4 (0.2 μCi ml^{-1}) or [^{3}H]lyso-PAF (0.02 μCi ml^{-1}) at 37 °C. The chase experiment was performed after washing the cells three times with 0.2 percent BSA-containing 20 mM HEPES-MEM (Sugiura *et al.*, 1984).

Macrophage microsomes were prepared as described previously (Sugiura and Waku, 1985; Sugiura *et al.*, 1985). The transfer rates of radiolabeled-fatty acid between phospholipids are estimated as described earlier (Sugiura and Waku, 1985). Briefly, ^{14}C-labeled fatty acid-containing phospholipids (20000 dpm, 55−60 mCi mM[-1]), lysophospholipids (20 μM) and macrophage microsomes (200 μg) were incubated in 5 mM-EGTA-containing 0.1 M Tris-HCl buffer (pH 7.4) at 37 °C for 60 min. The incubation was terminated by adding chloroform:methanol (1:2). After the extraction of total lipids, individual phospholipids were separated by two-dimensional TLC. Alkenylacyl, alkylacyl and diacyl lipid classes were resolved as 1,2-diradyl-3-acetyl-glycerols by TLC as described previously (Sugiura *et al.*, 1983). The transfer rates were calculated from the radioactivity both in each lipid fraction and that in the substrate phospholipid fraction (Sugiura and Waku, 1985; Sugiura *et al.*, 1985).

The acylation pattern of radiolabeled lysophospholipids was also examined by incubating labeled-lysophospholipids (40000 dpm, 20 μM) with macrophage microsomes (200 μg) at 37 °C in the same buffer as described above. After the termination of the incubation, lipids were extracted and then separated using TLC developed with chroloform:methanol:water (65:25:4). In order to determine the distribution of the radioactivity in individual molecular species, phospholipids were converted to 1,2-diradyl-3-acetylglycerol derivatives (Sugiura *et al.*, 1983) and then resolved by 20 percent AgNO$_3$-containing TLC using the solvents, chroloform:methanol (44:0.3 and 44:0.15) according to the number of double bonds in the molecule. After the extraction of lipids from the plate, the radioactivity was estimated with a liquid scintillation counter.

RESULTS AND DISCUSSION

After 7.5 min incubation of macrophages with [3]H-20:4, 53 percent of the radioactivity in the cellular phospholipid fractions was found in the diacyl-GPC. The radioactivity in diacyl-GPC, however, decreased with time during the following chase incubation. On the contrary, the radioactivity of the alkylacyl-GPC and alkenylacyl-GPE fractions increased. The changes in the radioactivity in other lipid fractions were rather small. This observation strongly suggests that [14]C-20:4 was mobilized from diacyl-GPC to alkylacyl-GPC and alkenylacyl-GPE fractions. The mobilization of 20:4 from diacyl-GPC to ether-containing phospholipid fractions may lead to the accumulation or retention of 20:4 in the latter phospholipid fractions. We also found such a mobilization for 22:6 (Sugiura *et al.*, 1985) but not for 18:2 (Sugiura *et al.*, 1984).

In order to find the mechanism of the transfer of 20:4 from diacyl-GPC to ether lipid fractions, we next examined the enzyme activity. We found that 1-[^{3}H]alkyl-GPC([^{3}H]lyso-PAF) was rapidly acylated by the macrophage microsomes themselves. The addition of other factors was not necessary in the acylation. This result suggests that the acylation was due to a transacylation of 1-[^{3}H]alkyl-GPC with fatty acids derived from membrane lipids. We then investigate the molecular species of the acylated products of 1-[^{3}H]alkyl-GPC, i.e. 1-[^{3}H]alkyl-2-acyl-GPC. The radioactivity was mainly distributed in the tetraenoic species, indicating that 1-[^{3}H]-alkyl-GPC was predominantly acylated with 20:4 (Figure 1b). Considerable portions of radioactivities were also found in pentaenoic species, though the radioactivities in saturate, monoenoic and dienoic species were rather small. These results indicate that polyunsaturated fatty acids were preferentially transferred to 1-[^{3}H]alkyl-GPC from membrane lipids.

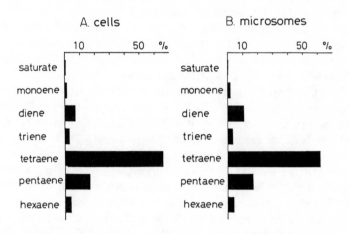

Figure 1. The acylation profiles of 1-[^{3}H]alkyl-GPC by intact macrophages (A) and macrophage microsomes (B). 1-[^{3}H]alkyl-2-acyl-GPC formed from 1-[^{3}H]alkyl-GPC was converted to 1-[^{3}H]alkyl-2-acyl-3-acetylglycerol and then separated into each molecular species according to the number of double bonds by AgNO$_3$-TLC as described in the text. The values express the distribution of the radioactivities

Interestingly, the acylation profile of 1-[^{3}H]alkyl-GPC using intact macrophages was very similar to that using macrophage microsomes. 1-[^{3}H]alkyl-GPC was rapidly acylated by intact macrophages. The radioactivity was also mainly found in tetraenoic species of 1-[^{3}H]alkylacyl-GPC formed in intact cells (Figure 1a). Only small radioactivities were found in saturate monoenoic and dienoic species. The above observation suggests that the acylation of 1-[^{3}H]alkyl-GPC in cells was mainly due to transacylation with polyunsaturated fatty acids, as observed in the case of microsomes.

We then checked the transfer of fatty acid between phospholipids, using the radiolabeled fatty acid-containing phospholipids as the acyl donor. We found that ^{14}C-20:4 was actually transferred from exogenously added diacyl-GPC to 1-alkyl-GPC. The optimal pH was 7.0-8.0. When a high concentration of 1-alkyl-GPC ($>80 \mu$M) was used, the transfer rates were rather reduced. This may be due to the detergent effect of 1-alkyl-GPC. In fact, detergents such as Triton X-100 (0.02 percent) and cholate

(0.2 percent) supressed the transfer rates. The transfer of ^{14}C-20:4 was also inhibited by SH-reagents such as p-chloromercuribenzensulfonic acid (5×10^{-5} M) and N-ethylmaleimide (10^{-3} M). Fatty acid once liberated from phospholipids could be reincorporated into the phospholipid fraction. However, we observed that the presence of CoA, ATP and Mg^{2+} was absolutely required for the esterification of free ^{3}H-20:4 to 1-alkyl-GPC in these experimental conditions. Furthermore, the addition of unlabeled 20:4 had only a small effects on transfers up to 20 μM. The addition of CoA caused only a small acceleration (about 20 percent). These results suggest that the transfer is a CoA-independent direct transfer.

The donor selectivity in the fatty acid transfer between ^{14}C-labeled fatty acid-containing diacyl phospholipids and 1-alkyl-GPC was next examined. We found that the transfer of fatty acid from the second position of 1-acyl-2-[^{14}C]16:0-GPC, 1-acyl-2-[^{14}C]18:0-GPC, 1-acyl-2-[^{14}C]18:1-GPC and 1-acyl-2-[^{14}C]18:2-GPC to 1-alkyl-GPC was very small compared to that from 1-acyl-2-[^{14}C]20:4-GPC. As distinct from these C$_{16}$ and C$_{18}$ fatty acids, [^{14}C]20:3 was transferred from diacyl-GPC to 1-alkyl-GPC to some extent (about 25 percent of the case for 20:4). Furthermore, it should be noted that ^{14}C-22:6 was transferred well from diacyl-GPC to 1-alkyl-GPC. The transfer rates of 22:6 was comparable to that of 20:4. It can be considered, therefore, that the transfer is a C$_{20}$ and C$_{22}$ polyunsaturated fatty acids-selective reaction. We further confirmed the similar selectivity, even if equal amounts of ^{14}C-16:0-, ^{14}C-18:1-, ^{14}C-18:2- and ^{14}C-20:4- containing diacyl-GPC were once mixed in the organic solvent and then used as the donors. On the other hand, considerable amounts of ^{14}C-20:4 were transferred from diacyl-GPE to 1-alkyl-GPC. However, the transfer rate was lower than in the case of diacyl-GPC as the acyl donor. No significant transfer of ^{14}C-20:4 occurred from diacyl-GPC to 1-alkyl-GPC. These observations indicate that there exists a distinct donor selectivity in the fatty acid transfer between phospholipids. In addition, these results are in general agreement with the mobilization of 20:4 22:6 from diacyl-GPC to ether phospholipid fractions observed in intact cells and the transacylation of 1-[^{3}H]alkyl-GPC with polyunsaturated fatty acids from membrane lipids as described above and elsewhere (Sugiura and Waku, 1985; Sugiura et al., 1985).

Then we investigated the transfer of ^{14}C-20:4 from diacyl-GPC to various lysophospholipids. We used 1-alkenyl-GPC, 1-alkyl-GPC, 1-alkenyl-GPE, 1-alkyl-GPE, 1-acyl-GPE, 1-acyl-GPS, and 1-acyl-GPI as the acceptor. We found that significant amounts of ^{14}C-20:4 was transferred from diacyl-GPC to ether-containing lysophospholipids. 1-Alkyl-GPC was the most effective acceptor. The addition of CoA showed only small effect on the transfer of ^{14}C-20:4 to ether-containing lysophospholipids. On the other hand, the transfer rate to 1-acyl-GPE was markedly accelerated by CoA. The transfer rate to 1-acyl-GPE in the presence of CoA was comparable to that to 1-alkyl-GPC in the presence or absence of CoA. The transfer of ^{14}C-20:4 to 1-acyl-GPS or 1-acyl-GPI was, however, only small, with or without CoA. These results suggest that there is an acceptor selectivity and that there are at least two types of transfer, one is a CoA-independent reaction and the other is a CoA-dependent reaction.

The detailed natures of CoA-independent and COA-dependent transfer of fatty acids are still unclear. AcylCoA:lysophospholipid acyltransferase could be involved in the CoA-dependent reaction. Further studies are required to clarify which enzymes participate in the transacylation system.

Recently, it has been shown that PAF or lyso-PAF is rapidly metabolized to long chain fatty acid-containing alkylacyl-GPC in several types of cells (Cabot *et al.*, 1982; Touqui *et al.*, 1983; Pieroni *et al.*, 1983; Alam *et al.*, 1983; Chilton *et al.*, 1983a,b; Albert and Snyder 1983; Yamashita *et al.*, 1983; Malone *et al.*, 1985; Robinson *et al.*, 1985; Robinson and Snyder, 1985). The introduced fatty acyl residue is mainly 20:4 (Chilton *et al.*, 1983b; Malone *et al.*, 1985; Robinson *et al.*, 1985; Robinson and Snyder, 1985). PAF can be first deacetylated to yield lyso-PAF and then acylated. In this study, we suggest that lyso-PAF (1-alkyl-GPC) was transacylated with polyunsaturated fatty acids particularly with 20:4 derived from membrane lipids especially from diacyl-GPC (Figure 2). These transacylation systems may be very important in the regulation of polyunsaturated fatty acids such as 20:4 and lyso PAF which are the direct precursors of potent lipid mediators.

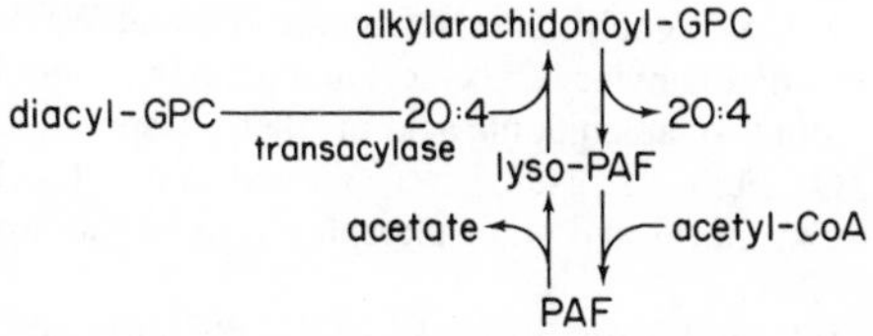

Figure 2. The metabolism of 1-*O*-alkyl-2-arachidonoyl-*sn*-glycero-3-phosphocholine, a putative source of potent lipid mediators

REFERENCES

Alam, I., Smith, J.B., and Silver, M.J. (1983). 'Metabolism of platelet-activating factor by blood platelets and plasma', *Lipids*, **18**, 534−538.

Albert, D.H., and Snyder, F. (1983). 'Biosynthesis of 1-alkyl-2-acetyl-*sn*-glycero-3-phosphocholine (platelet-activating factor) from 1-alkyl-2-acyl-*sn*-glycero-3-phosphocholine by rat alveolar macrophages, Phospholipase A₂ and acetyltransferase activities during phagocytosis and ionophore stimulation', *J. Biol. Chem.*, **258**, 97−102.

Cabot, M.C., Blank, M.L., Welsh, C.J., Horan, M.J., Cress, E.A., and Snyder, F. (1982). 'Metabolism of 1-alkyl-2-acetyl-*sn*-glycero-3-phosphocholine by cell cultures', *Life Sci.*, **31**, 2891−2898.

Chilton, F.H., O'Flaherty, J.T., Ellis, J.M., Swendsen, C.L., and Wykle, R.L. (1983a). 'Metabolic fate of platelet-activating factor in neutrophils', *J. Biol. Chem.*, **258**, 6357−6361.

Chilton, F.H., O'Flaherty, J.T., Ellis, J.M., Swendsen, C.L., and Wykle, R.L. (1983b). 'Selective acylation of lyso platelet activating factor by arachidonate in human neutrophils', *J. Biol. Chem.*, **258**, 7268−7271.

Malone, B., Lee, T-c., and Snyder, F. (1985). 'Inactivation of platelet activating factor by rabbit platelets; lyso-platelet activating-factor as a key intermediate with phosphatidylcholine as the source of arachidonic acid in its conversion to a tetraenoic acylated product', *J. Biol. Chem.*, **260**, 1531−1534.

Pieroni, G., and Hanahan, D.J. (1983). 'Metabolic behavior of acetyl glyceryl ether phosphorylcholine on interaction with rabbit platelets', *Arch. Biochem. Biophys.*, **224**, 485−493.

Robinson, M., and Snyder, F. (1985). 'Metabolism of platelet-activating factor by rat alveolar macrophages:lyso-PAF as an obligatory intermediate in the formation of alkylarachidonoyl glycerophosphocholine species', *Biochim. Biophys. Acta*, **837**, 52−56.

Robinson, M., Blank, M.L., and Snyder, F. (1985). 'Acylation of lysophospholipids by rabbit alveolar macrophages; Specificities of CoA-dependent and CoA-independent reactions', *J. Biol. Chem.*, **260**, 7889−7895.

Sugiura, T., and Waku, K. (1985). 'CoA-independent transfer of arachidonic acid from 1,2-diacyl-*sn*-glycero-3-phosphocholine to 1-*O*-alkyl-*sn*-glycero-3-phosphocholine (lyso platelet-activating factor) by macrophage microsomes', *Biochem. Biophys. Res. Commun.*, **127**, 384−390.

Sugiura, T., Masuzawa, Y., and Waku, K. (1985). 'Transacylation of 1-*O*-alkyl-glycero-3-phosphocholine (lysoplatelet-activating factor) and 1-*O*-alkenyl-glycero-3-phosphoethanolamine with docosahexaenoic acid (22:6ω3)', *Biophys. Rea. Commun.*, **133**, 574−580.

Sugiura, T., Onuma, Y., Sekiguchi, N., and Waku, K. (1982). 'Ether phospholipids in guinea pig polymorphonuclear leukocytes and macrophages: Occurrence of high levels of 1-*O*-alkyl-2-acyl-*sn*-glycero-3-phosphocholine', *Biochim. Biophys. Acta*, **712**, 515−522.

Sugiura, T., Nakajima, M., Sekiguchi, N., Nakagawa, Y., and Waku, K. (1983). 'Different fatty chain compositions of alkenylacyl, alkyacyl and diacyl phospholipids in rabbit alveolar macrophages: High amounts of arachidonic acid in ether phospholipids', *Lipids*, **18**, 125−129.

Sugiura, T., Katayama, O., Fukui, J., Nakagawa, Y., and Waku, K. (1984). 'Mobilization of arachidonic acid between diacyl and ether phospholipids in rabbit alveolar macrophages', *FEBS Lett.*, **165**, 273−276.

Touqui, L., Jacquemin, C., and Vargaftig, B.B. (1983). 'Conversion of ^{3}H-PAF acether by rabbit platelets is independent from aggregation: Evidence for a novel metabolite', *Biochem. Biophys. Res. Commun.*, **110**, 890−893.

Yamashita, M., Homma, H., Inoue, K., and Nojima, S. (1983). 'The metabolism of platelet activating factor in platelets and plasma of various animals' *J. Toxicol. Sci.*, **8**, 177−188.

New Horizons in Platelet Activating Factor Research
Edited by C. M. Winslow and M. L. Lee
© 1987 John Wiley & Sons Ltd.

6

Platelet Activating Factor Metabolism in Fetal Rabbit Lung Development

Dennis R. Hoffman and John M. Johnston

INTRODUCTION

We have previously identified 1-alkyl-2-acetyl-*sn*-glycero-3-phosphocholine (platelet activating factor, PAF) in the amniotic fluid obtained from women at term in active labor (Billah and Johnston, 1983). These data have recently been confirmed and extended (Nishihira *et al.*, 1984). There are at least three possible tissue sources of this PAF: fetal amnion, lung and kidney. We have demonstrated that PAF can be synthesized in human amnion and that PAF stimulates prostaglandin E_2 formation in amnion; however, PAF was apparently not released from this tissue (Billah *et al.*, 1985). PAF can be synthesized in adult rat kidney by both the acetyltransferase and choline phosphotransferase pathways (Lee and Snyder, 1985) and is released from adult rat kidney when perfused with the calcium ionophore, A23187 (Pirotzky and Benveniste, 1981). The metabolism of PAF in fetal tissue has not been investigated.

We had previously observed that the PAF, as well as its precursors, lyso-PAF and alkyl-acyl-GPC (1-alkyl-2-acyl-*sn*-glycero-3-phosphocholine), were associated with the surfactant-rich lamellar body fraction of amniotic fluid (Billah and Johnston, 1983). This was the first indication that fetal lung may release PAF into the amniotic fluid. Further support for the close association between PAF and surfactant produced by lung tissue was recently published by Prevost *et al.* (1984) and Kumar *et al.* (1985). These investigators reported the presence of PAF in rat and dog surfactant, respectively.

The objectives of our present investigation were:

1. To ascertain the specific activities of the enzymes involved in PAF metabolism in developing fetal lung;
2. To determine the concentration of PAF and its precursors in fetal lung during gestation.
3. To assess the possible role of PAF in the regulation of carbohydrate and lipid metabolism during lung development and the possible relationship of PAF formation in fetal lung to the initiation of parturition.

METHODS

Procedures for the isolation and quantitation of lipids and the determination of the specific activity of the PAF metabolic enzymes, lyso-PAF:acetyl-CoA acetyltransferase and PAF-acetylhydrolase, have been described previously (Billah and Johnston, 1983; Ban *et al.*, 1986). Glycogen was quantitated by the method of Chan and Exton (1976).

RESULTS AND DISCUSSION

Acetyltransferase has been postulated to be a regulatory enzyme of PAF metabolism (Lee and Snyder, 1985). The specific activity of the enzyme in microsomes prepared from fetal lung, liver and kidney was assayed during the later stages of gestation (Table 1). We found that:

1. The specific activity of acetyltransferase in lung was higher than liver or kidney at all time periods;
2. The enzyme activity in lung increased dramatically between days 21 and 24, and was maintained through day 31.

In contrast, the acetyltransferase activity in liver decreased with gestational age. The activity in fetal kidney increased to a lesser extent than that of fetal lung.

Table 1.   Specific Activity of Acetyltransferase in Microsomes of Various Fetal Rabbit Tissues During Gestation

| Tissue Source | Gestational Age (days) | | | |
	21	24	28	31
	(pM PAF formed min^{-1} mg^{-1}protein)			
Lung	116 ± 18	392 ± 41[1]	326 ± 16[1]	332 ± 46
Liver	68 ± 10	50 ± 15	47 ± 19	12 ± 3[1]
Kidney	68 ± 7	121 ± 8[1]	178 ± 12[1]	187 ± 14[1]

Values are the mean ± S.E.M. from a minimum of four determinations. [1]These values differ significantly from day 21 value of the respective tissue (p < 0.001).

Since a significant quantity of the PAF in amniotic fluid associated with the lamellar bodies containing surfactant which originates from the type II pneumonocytes, we investigated the PAF biosynthetic capabilities of this cell type. The specific activity of acetyltransferase was assayed in adult rat whole lung, type II pneumonocytes and alveolar macrophage. When the 600 × g supernatant was assayed, the highest specific activity of acetyltransferase was found in the type II cells, 579 ± 77 (mean ± S.E.M.) pM PAF formed min^{-1} mg^{-1} protein, compared to whole lung (322 ± 50) or macrophage (167 ± 32). On the basis of these results, we suggest that type II pneumonocytes are capable of synthesizing PAF.

Some investigators have suggested that PAF-acetylhydrolase, the enzyme which inactivates PAF, may be involved in the regulation of the physiological levels of PAF (Lee and Snyder, 1985). We assayed the acetylhydrolase activity in fetal rabbit lung between days 21 and 31 of gestation and observed no significant change in the activity of this enzyme 855 ± 21 (mean ± S.E.M.) pM PAF hydrolyzed min^{-1} mg^{-1} protein.

The concentrations of PAF, lyso-PAF and alkyl-acyl-GPC, were measured in fetal rabbit lung as a function of gestational age. PAF was found to increase from 12 to 35 fM mg^{-1} protein between days 21 and 31. Lyso-PAF and alkyl-acyl-GPC both decreased by 60 percent during gestation, from 1700 to 600 fM mg^{-1} protein and from 160 to 70 pM mg^{-1} protein respectively. This decrease may be explained by the possible packaging of these lipids in the lamellar bodies of type II pneumonocytes and, ultimately their release into the amniotic fluid due to fetal breathing movements.

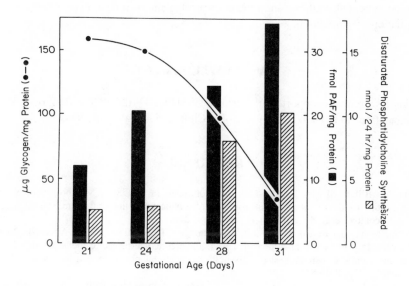

Figure 1. The relationship between the content of PAF and glycogen and the biosynthesis of disaturated phosphatidylcholine in the developing fetal rabbit lung. Disaturated phosphatidylcholine data are reproduced from Snyder *et al.*, 1981 by permission

Recently, Shukla *et al.* (1983) presented evidence that PAF may be involved in the stimulation of glycogen breakdown in the perfused adult rat liver. Others (Maniscalco *et al.*, 1978; Bourbon *et al.*, 1982) have suggested that in the fetal lung glycogen may supply, in part, the energy and the carbon source necessary for the biosynthesis of the glycerophospholipids of surfactant. Therefore, we have determined the glycogen content of rabbit lung during development *in utero* (Figure 1). As can be seen, the glycogen concentration of fetal lung decreases by 80 percent between days 24 and 31. The biosynthesis in fetal rabbit lung of disaturated-phosphatidylcholine (Snyder *et al.*, 1981), the characteristic phospholipid of surfactant, is also illustrated in Figure 1. There was a rapid and sustained increase in choline incorporation into disaturated-phosphatidylcholine commencing on day 24. Thus, the relationship between the increase of PAF, decrease in glycogen, and the increase in surfactant glycerophospholipid biosynthesis is consistant with the postulate that PAF may be involved in the regulation of fetal lung development.

We also suggest that the concept of packaging of PAF along with the other surfactant lipids into lamellar bodies for release into amniotic fluid is consistant with our previous findings that PAF is present in the amniotic fluid obtained from women in labor (Billah and Johnston, 1983). Furthermore, we suggest that maturation of the lung may be intimately involved in parturition since these tissues may be the source of the PAF found in amniotic fluid. This PAF, ultimately, may interact with amnion resulting in the increased synthesis and release of prostaglandin E_2 (Ban *et al.*, 1986) and the initiation of parturition.

ACKNOWLEDGMENT

This research was supported, in part, by USPH HD13912 and The Robert A. Welch Foundation. D.R.H. is a recipient of a Chilton Foundation Fellowship.

REFERENCES

Ban, C., Billah, M.M., Truong, C.T., and Johnston, J.M. (1986). 'Metabolism of platelet-activating factor (1-*O*-alkyl-2-acetyl-*sn*-glycero-3-phosphocholine) in human fetal membranes and decidua vera', *Arch. Biochem. Biophys.*, **246**, 9–18.

Billah, M.M., Di Renzo, G.C., Ban, C., Truong, C.T., Hoffman, D.R., Anceschi, M.M., Bleasdale, J.E., and Johnston, J.M. (1985).'Platelet-activating factor metabolism in human amnion and the responses of this tissue to extracellular platelet-activating factor', *Prostaglandins*, **30**, 841–850.

Billah, M.M., and Johnston, J.M. (1983). 'Identification of phospholipid platelet-activating factor (1-*O*-alkyl-2-acetyl-*sn*-glycero-3-phosphocholine) in human amniotic fluid and urine', *Biochem. Biophys. Res. Commun.*, **113**, 51–58.

Bourbon, J.R., Rieutort, M., Engle, M.J., and Farrell, P.M. (1982). 'Utilization of glycogen for phospholipid synthesis in fetal rat lung', *Biochim. Biophys. Acta*, **712**, 382–389.

Chan, T.M., and Exton, J.H. (1976). 'A rapid method for the determination of glycogen content and radioactivity in small quantities of tissue or isolated hepatocytes', *Anal. Biochem.*, **71**, 96–105.

Kumar, R., King, R.J., and Hanahan, D.J. (1985). 'Occurrence of glyceryl ethers in the phosphatidylcholine fraction of surfactant from dog lungs', *Biochim. Biophys. Acta*, **836**, 19–26.

Lee, T-c., and Snyder, F. (1985). 'Function, metabolism and regulation of platelet activating factor and related ether lipids'. In J.F. Kuo (ed.) *Phospholipid and Cellular Regulation*, CRC Press, Inc., Baco Raton, FL, pp. 1–39.

Maniscalco, W.M., Wilson, C.M., Gross, I., Gobran, L.S.A., Rooney, S.A., and Warshaw, J.B. (1978). 'Development of glycogen and phospholipid metabolism in fetal and newborn rat lung', *Biochim. Biophys. Acta*, **530**, 333–346.

Nishihira, J., Ishibashi, J., Imai, Y., and Muramatsu, T. (1984). 'Mass spectrometric evidence for the presence of platelet-activating factor (1-*O*-alkyl-2-acetyl-*sn*-glycero-3-phosphocholine) in human amniotic fluid during labor', *Lipids*, **19**, 907–910.

Pirotzky, E., and Beneveniste, J. (1981). 'Platelet-activating factor (PAF-acether) is released from isolated perfused rat kidney', *Int. Arch. Allergy Appl. Immun.*, **66 (Suppl. 1)**,176–177.

Prevost, M.C., Cariven, C., Simon, M.F., Chap, H., and Douste-Blazy, L.D. (1984). 'Platelet-activating factor (PAF-acether) is released into rat pulmonary fluid as a consequence of hypoxia', *Biochem. Biophys. Res. Commun.*, **119**, 58–63.

Shukla, S.D., Buxton, D.B., Olson, M.S., and Hanahan, D.J. (1983). 'Acetyl-glyceryl ether phosphorylcholine: A potent activator of hepatic phospho-inositide metabolism and glycogenolysis', *J. Biol. Chem.*, **258**, 10 212–10 214.

Snyder, J.M., Mendelson, C.R., and Johnston, J.M. (1981). 'The effect of cortisol on rabbit fetal lung maturation *in vitro*', *Devel. Biol.*, **85**, 129–140.

Origins of Platelet Activating Factor

New Horizons in Platelet Activating Factor Research
Edited by C. M. Winslow and M. L. Lee
© 1987 John Wiley & Sons Ltd.

7

Diversity in the Chemical Structures of Neutrophil-Derived Platelet Activating Factors

Janet C. Ludwig and R. Neal Pinckard

Platelet activating factor (PAF) is a potent lipid mediator of acute allergic and inflammatory reactions (cf. Benveniste *et al.*, 1981; Pinckard *et al.*, 1982; O'Flaherty, 1982) that is synthesized and released from a variety of stimulated inflammatory cells including the neutrophil, basophil, platelet and monocyte-macrophage (cf. Pinckard *et al.*, 1982). Basophil-derived PAF was chemically identified to be 1-*O*-hexadecyl (C_{16}:0) and octadecyl (C_{18}:0)-2-acetyl-*sn*-glycero-3-phosphocholine (AGEPC) (Hanahan *et al.*, 1980). In this chapter, the term PAF will be used to refer to the biologically derived molecules, whereas, AGEPC will refer only to the chemically defined material.

Subsequent to the discovery of the chemical structure of PAF, the availability of synthetic C_{16}:0 and C_{18}:0-AGEPC facilitated studies that demonstrated the wide spectrum of biological activities of this autacoid (Table 1). Structure-activity relationship studies have shown that even minor structural alterations in AGEPC result in profound changes in platelet stimulating activity (Table 2; Satouchi *et al.*, 1981a; Wykle *et al.*, 1981; Humphrey *et al.*, 1982; Surles *et al.*, 1985). These findings are of particular importance in view of the recent evidence that PAF synthesized from neutrophils, the principal cells of acute inflammation, is comprised not only of multiple saturated and unsaturated alkyl chain homologs of AGEPC in addition to C_{16}:0 and C_{18}:0, but 1-*O*-acyl analogs as well (Pinckard *et al.*, 1984; Mueller *et al.*, 1984b; Weintraub *et al.*, 1985; Satouchi *et al.*, 1985). In view of this extensive molecular heterogeneity of the class of biologically active acetylated phosphoglyceride autacoids, their collective roles in modulating acute and chronic inflammatory reactions must now be explored.

Many investigations have been directed towards identifying the enzymatic pathways involved in the synthesis and degradation of PAF by inflammatory cells (Benveniste *et al.*, 1982; Alonso *et al.*, 1982; Albert and Snyder, 1983; Mueller *et al.*, 1983). These studies, have demonstrated that the biosynthesis of PAF by various inflammatory

Table 1. *In Vitro* Biological Activities of AGEPC[1]

Platelet activation:	Secretion
	Aggregation
	Ca^{2+} uptake
	Phosphatidylinositol turnover
	Inhibition of adenylate cyclase
	Thromboxane synthesis
Neutrophil activation:	Chemotaxis
	Chemokinesis
	Aggregation
	Chemiluminescence
	Enhanced adherence
	Lysosomal enzyme release
	Superoxide anion production
	Lipoxygenase product synthesis
	Ca^{2+} uptake
Monocyte activation:	Chemotaxis
	Superoxide anion production
	Aggregation
	Oxidative burst
Cardiac alterations:	Arrythmias
	Negative inotropic effects
	Coronary artery vasoconstriction
Pulmonary alterations:	Contraction
	Edema
	Leukotriene production
	Perfusion pressure increase
	Inflation pressure increase
Smooth muscle contraction	
Hepatic alterations:	Vasoconstriction
	Glycogenolysis
	Phosphatidylinositol turnover

[1]   cf., Vargaftig *et al.*, 1981; O'Flaherty, 1982; Pinckard *et al.*, 1982; Snyder, 1982; Pinckard, 1983; Fisher *et al.*, 1984; this volume.

cells involves a two-step deacylation–acetylation reaction. Upon cell stimulation, phospholipase A_2 hydrolyzes an esterified fatty acyl residue in the *sn*-2 position of a putative precursor molecule, 1-*O*-alkyl-2-acyl-*sn*-glycero-3-phosphocholine, likely associated with the cellular membranes (Albert and Snyder, 1983; Mueller *et al.*, 1983; Swendsen *et al.*, 1983). In the event the fatty acyl *sn*-2 residue is arachidonate, it could then be metabolized by the cyclooxygenase and/or lipoxygenase pathways to yield other lipid mediators of inflammation. The other product of phospholipase

Table 2. Biological Activities of Various AGEPC Homologs and Analogs

Molecular species	Relative PAF activity (%)[1]
1-0-alkyl:	
C_{12}:0-AGEPC	8
C_{14}:0-AGEPC	11
C_{16}:0-AGEPC	100
C_{18}:1-AGEPC	50
C_{18}:0-AGEPC	27
C_{16}:0/C18:0-AGEPDME[2]	35
C_{16}:0/C18:0-AGEPMME[3]	4
C_{16}:0-AGEPE[4]	0.04
1-0-acyl:	
C_{12}:0-AGPC[5]	0.003
C_{16}:0-AGPC	0.3
C_{18}:0-AGPC	0.02

[1] PAF activity is expressed as a percentage relative to the platelet stimulating activity of C_{16}:0-AGEPC; C_{16}:0-AGEPC induced secretion of 50 per cent of the serotonin from washed rabbit platelets at 0.14 nM (final concentration) in 60 sec at 37 °C.
[2] 1-*O*-alkyl-2-acetyl-*sn*-glycero-3-phosphodimethylethanolamine.
[3] 1-*O*-alkyl-2-acetyl-*sn*-glycero-3-phosphomonomethylethanolamine.
[4] 1-*O*-alkyl-2-acetyl-*sn*-glycero-3-phosphoethanolamine.
[5] 1-*O*-acyl-2-acetyl-*sn*-glycero-3-phosphocholine.

A_2 action, 1-*O*-alkyl-*sn*-glycero-3-phosphocholine (lyso-GEPC) is acetylated by acetyltransferase and acetyl-CoA to form the highly potent inflammatory mediator AGEPC (Wykle *et al.*, 1980; Ninio *et al.*, 1982). A second biosynthetic pathway for AGEPC synthesis in various rat tissues has also been described and is catalyzed by cholinephosphotransferase which utilizes the substrates CDP-choline and 1-*O*-alkyl-2-acetyl-*sn*-glycero (Renooij and Snyder, 1981). While neutrophils contain cholinephosphotransferase, its activity is not increased upon cell stimulation as is the activity of acetyltransferase (Lee *et al.*, 1984; Wykle *et al.*, 1986). Thus, the 'major' pathway for the biosynthesis of neutrophil-derived PAF would appear to be the two-step phospholipase A_2 and acetyltransferase reactions. Related to the above, it should be noted that many of these studies designed to characterize the synthesis and degradation of PAF by inflammatory cells have been conducted using the exogenously added substrate, 1-*O*-hexadecyl-2-acyl-*sn*-glycero-3-phosphocholine or its lyso derivative. Thus, the metabolism of other, biologically active acetylated products derived from endogenous phospholipid substrate stores has not been addressed.

Biological inactivation of AGEPC results from the catabolic action of acetylhydrolase, a cytosolic enzyme that cleaves the acetyl group from AGEPC. This enzyme has been found in kidney, lung and brain, and in rabbit and human plasma as well as in neutrophils (Farr *et al.*, 1980; Blank *et al.*, 1981; Lee *et al.*, 1982). The plasma-derived acetylhydrolase has greater substrate specificity than phospholipase A_2 since it hydrolyzes only short chain fatty acyl moieties (five carbons or less) at the *sn*-2 position (Farr *et al.*, 1980); moreover, at least one methyl group must be present on the ethanolamine polar head group (Wardlow *et al.*, 1986). Thus, it is tempting to speculate that certain molecular species of PAF might have a reduced susceptibility to catabolic degradation by acetylhydrolase which would be expected to increase the pathological potential of the molecule.

While many of the above mechanisms for PAF synthesis and degradation are clearly established, little is known about the availability of endogenous substrates for these enzymes in stimulated cells. This question is of particular importance in view of the extensive number of alkyl chain homologs of AGEPC synthesized from the endogenous stores of neutrophil phospholipids (Pinckard *et al.*, 1984; Mueller *et al.*, 1984b; Weintraub *et al.*, 1985). Indeed, the molecular heterogeneity of neutrophil-derived PAF appears to be different from the reported pool of 1-*O*-alkyl-2-acyl-*sn*-glycero-3-phosphocholine in human neutrophils (Mueller *et al.*, 1984a). Thus, the biosynthesis of phospholipids with PAF activity generated from endogenous neutrophil precursor pools must be completely identified. The remainder of this chapter will review our recent findings on the synthesis of multiple molecular species of choline-containing PAFs as well as the newly described ethanolamine and/or methylated ethanolamine derivatives from stimulated human neutrophils and their possible role in the regulation of the albumin and calcium-dependent synthesis-release coupling mechanism of PAF.

CHARACTERIZATION OF NEUTROPHIL-DERIVED PAF

The characterization of platelet activating factor derived from endogenous stores of neutrophil phospholipids has presented several problems. First, the production of small quantities of the individual molecular species of PAF by stimulated neutrophils necessitated the development of highly sensitive analytical procedures for the purification, detection and structural identification of PAF. This was overcome by the development of sequential normal and reverse phase high performance liquid chromatography (HPLC) which has greatly improved the separation and recovery of individual molecular species of PAF (Jackson *et al.*, 1984). The methods for the detection and quantitation of the various PAF molecular species was the second obstacle in these studies. Many investigations have detected PAF by bioassay (platelet stimulation) (Hanahan *et al.*, 1980; Jackson *et al.*, 1984; Ludwig *et al.*, 1984; Doebber *et al.*, 1985), while others have monitored the incorporation of [^{3}H]acetate into various phospholipids during cell stimulation (Chap *et al.*, 1981; Mencia-Huerta *et al.*, 1982; Mueller *et al.*, 1984b). In view of the findings that AGEPC possesses a wide spectrum of biological activities in addition to platelet stimulation (Table 1), it is possible that PAF-like molecules with little or no platelet stimulating activity but with other biological activities might be produced by stimulated neutrophils. Thus, if only platelet stimulation were assessed, such molecules would not be detected. Although monitoring

[³H]acetate incorporation into PAF, which is based upon the findings that the acetate moiety is of critical importance for its inflammatory properties (Demopoulos *et al.*, 1979; Tence *et al.*, 1981), would overcome this problem, it would not provide evidence of bioactivity. Taking these considerations into account, we have utilized a combination of these detection techniques to more fully characterize neutrophil-derived PAF molecules.

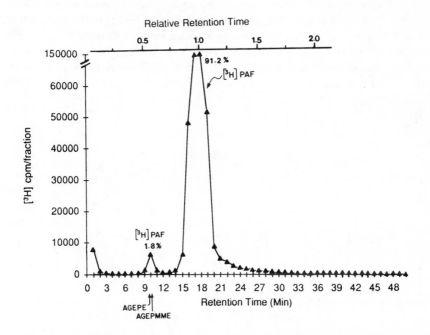

Figure 1.   Normal phase HPLC separation of ³H-labeled products from A23187-stimulated neutrophils. Relative retention time (RRT) was determined by dividing the peak elution time by the elution time of C_{16}:O-AGEPC. Neutrophils (5 × 10⁶ cells ml⁻¹) at 37 °C were stimulated in the presence of 920 μ Ci [³H] acetate (4.7 Ci Mmole⁻¹) by the addition of A23187 (2.5 μM, final concentration). After 20 min and subsequent centrifugation the pellet was lipid extracted and analyzed by normal phase HPLC. The total number of cells was 9.2 × 10⁷. Results are representative of three identical experiments

Normal phase HPLC of lipid extracts from human neutrophils stimulated with the calcium ionophore, A23187, in the presence of [³H]acetate, revealed two distinct peaks of radiolabeled products (Figure 1). The major peak of radioactivity (fractions 15−21) coeluted with synthetic AGEPC. The minor peak (fractions 8−11) coeluted with the synthetic standards of 1-*O*-alkyl-2-acetyl-*sn*-glycero-3-phosphoethanolamine (AGEPE) and its monomethylethanolamine derivative (AGEPMME) (J.C. Ludwig *et al.*, unpublished observations). Both peaks of radioactivity possessed platelet stimulating activity. Although, the biochemical role of these newly described ethanolamine and/or methylated ethanolamine-containing PAF molecules is unclear, they could represent intermediates in the biosynthesis of AGEPC. If the ethanolamine-containing derivatives were to be methylated during cell stimulation, their platelet-stimulating activities would dramatically increase, possibly up to 1000 fold (Satouchi *et al.*, 1981b). Alternatively, the ethanolamine-containing derivatives could play an important role in the inflammatory process since they are not catabolized by plasma acetylhydrolase (Wardlow *et al.*, 1986) and, thus, their *in vivo* biological effects would be sustained. While the biochemical functions of these acetylated molecules presently are unclear, these results demonstrate that, in addition to the previously described molecular heterogeneity in the *sn*-1 position of neutrophil-derived AGEPC molecules, structural diversity also exists with respect to the polar head group of the neutrophil-derived PAF molecules.

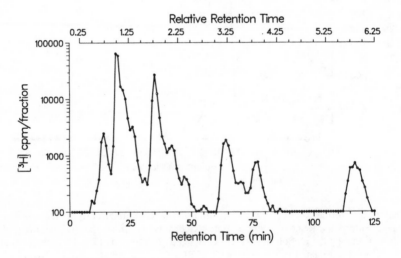

Figure 2. Reverse phase HPLC separation of ³H-labeled products obtained from the choline-containing region (fractions 15−20) of the normal phase HPLC shown in Figure 1. Results are representative of three identical experiments

Reverse phase HPLC separation of the acetylated choline-containing peak isolated by normal phase HPLC (fractions 15−21) (Figure 2) revealed the presence of 15 distinct [³H]acetate containing phospholipid peaks, all of which possessed platelet stimulating activity. Previously, we have identified six of these reverse phase HPLC peaks by fast atom bombardment (FAB) mass spectrometry (MS) to be the following alkyl chain AGEPC homologs: $C_{15}:0$, $C_{16}:0$, $C_{17}:0$, $C_{18}:0$, $C_{18}:1$ and $C_{22}:2$ (Weintraub *et al.*, 1985; J.C. Ludwig *et al.*, unpublished observations). Other independent studies (Mueller *et al.*, 1984b) have presented reverse phase HPLC evidence for the

$C_{16}:0$, $C_{17}:0$ (two isomers), $C_{18}:0$ and $C_{18}:1$ alkyl chain homologs of AGEPC in stimulated human neutrophils. In addition, the presence of the 1-*O*-acyl analogs of AGEPC has been demonstrated (Mueller *et al.*, 1984a; Satouchi *et al.*, 1985). Thus, these results indicate that stimulated human neutrophils synthesized at least fifteen different, choline-containing molecular species of PAF, six of which have been identified as alkyl chain homologs of AGEPC.

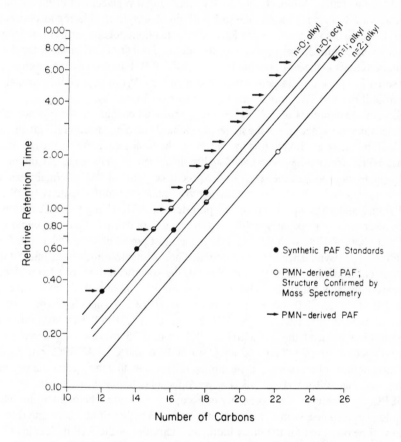

Figure 3. Relationship of *sn*-1 chain length to the relative retention time of choline-containing AGEPC homologs and analogs fractionated by reverse phase HPLC. The RRT for each molecular species was plotted against the carbon number of the fatty acid in the *sn*-1 position. The points represent synthetic standards and/or neutrophil-derived PAF identified by mass spectrometry and were connected for each homologous series of acetylated alkyl or acyl glycerophosophocholine molecule

Tentative identification of the remaining choline-containing PAF molecules may be faciliated by correlating their respective relative retention times (RRTs) on reverse phase HPLC to possible chain lengths of the molecules (Figure 3; Pinckard *et al.*, 1984). As previously observed (Patton *et al.*, 1982; Pinckard *et al.*, 1984), within a class of phospholipid there is a linear relationship between the $\log_{10}$ of the RRT on reverse phase HPLC and the length of the carbon chains in the *sn*-1 and *sn*-2 positions of the molecule. In addition, for each unsaturation within a carbon chain, there is a proportionate displacement of the line which is parallel to the more saturated series of molecules. Similarly, we have observed that replacement of the 1-*O*-alkyl linkage for a 1-*O*-acyl linkage in the *sn*-1 position of acetylated glycerophosphocholine also results in displacement of the RRT within this homologous series of molecules. Thus, using Figure 3, it is possible to predict the number of carbons and the degree of unsaturations in the *sn*-1 position from the RRT of PAF molecules in a given reverse phase HPLC peak on a large number of acetylated alkyl or acyl choline-containing neutrophil-derived PAF molecules (see arrows on Figure 3).

Structural alterations of AGEPC result in profound changes in the potency of the platelet stimulating activity of the molecule (Table 2) thereby making PAF quantitation difficult by bioassay. Taking this into account, the biological activity of each reverse phase HPLC fraction has been correlated to its content of [^{3}H]acetate. Assuming that [^{3}H]acetate incorporates into each of the precursor pools of PAF at equal rates, this calculation would indicate the specific activity (platelet stimulating activity) of each individual molecular species of neutrophil-derived PAF. Using this calculation for each reverse phase peak and graphing it as a function of its RRT (Figure 4) demonstrated that C_{16}:0-AGEPC with RRT of 1.00 is the most potent of the platelet stimulating PAF molecules synthesized by the stimulated human neutrophil. It is of interest that, the current findings suggest that, in general, the specific activity of each molecular species of the acetylated alkyl choline-containing PAF increased, the closer it eluted to C_{16}:0-AGEPC (RRT=1.00) on reverse phase HPLC. A specific example of this effect is seen in the case of C_{18}:0-AGEPC and C_{18}:1-AGEPC. The addition of one unsaturation reduced the $\log_{10}$(RRT × 10) from 1.25 to 1.04 and increased the specific activity from 1.01 to 3.66 for C_{18}:0-AGEPC and C_{18}:1-AGEPC, respectively. Because of these observations, it is tempting to speculate that the greater the structural similarity that an acetylated alkyl glycerophosphocholine molecule is to C_{16}:0-AGEPC, the greater will be its ability to occupy target cell receptor sites and induce a biological response such as platelet stimulation. Whether or not this same relationship will be observed for the other biological activities of the PAF molecules (Table 1) remains to be determined.

REGULATION OF PAF SYNTHESIS AND RELEASE

Results of previous studies have shown that the synthesis as well as the release of PAF from stimulated human neutrophils are dependent upon extracellular Ca^{2+} (Ludwig *et al.*, 1984) and albumin (Ludwig *et al.*, 1985). Extracellular Ca^{2+} is required for the release of newly synthesized PAF from stimulated neutrophils. In

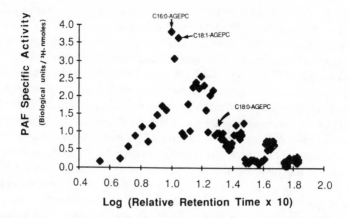

Figure 4.   Relationship of relative retention time to PAF specific activity separated by reverse phase HPLC as shown in Figure 2. The platelet stimulating activity for each reverse phase HPLC fraction was divided by its content of [^{3}H]acetate in order to calculate PAF specific activity. The RRT for each fraction was plotted as the log$_{10}$ of the RRT × 10 against the PAF specific activity

the absence of Ca^{2+} and the abrogation of the release of PAF, the synthesis of PAF by the neutrophils ceases abruptly. In addition to the Ca^{2+} requirement, PAF release is also dependent upon extracellular albumin. Similar to the Ca^{2+} effect, in the absence of albumin, there is no PAF release and further PAF synthesis does not occur. These findings suggest that the newly synthesized PAF that is not released causes feedback inhibition of further PAF synthesis likely located at the plasma membrane where PAF synthesis is thought to occur (Wykle *et al.*, 1986). The albumin effect upon PAF release may be explained by the possibility that albumin is acting as an acceptor molecule for PAF since the concentration of PAF synthesized by the neutrophil is below the critical micellar concentration of AGEPC (Kramp *et al.*, 1984). Albumin is, therefore, required to maintain PAF in solution and remove it from the neutrophil cell surface. Indeed, increasing the albumin concentration in the stimulated neutrophil preparation resulted in a 20-fold increase in PAF synthesis (Ludwig *et al.*, 1985). These same albumin concentrations have been shown to inhibit AGEPC-induced platelet stimulation (Hoppens *et al.*, 1983) possibly by preventing receptor site binding. Thus, while the mechanisms are not clearly defined, the synthesis and release of PAF are tightly coupled and dependent upon extracellular Ca^{2+} and albumin (Ludwig *et al.*, 1986).

SUMMARY

Platelet-activating factor synthesized by stimulated human neutrophils is comprised of multiple species of saturated and unsaturated AGEPC homologs (Pinckard *et al.*,

1984; Mueller *et al.*, 1984b; Weintraub *et al.*, 1985) as well as biologically active molecules containing polar head groups other that choline. Since these various neutrophil-derived PAF molecules stimulate platelets to different degrees (Table 2) and are degraded at different rates by acetylhydrolase (Wardlow *et al.*, 1986), the inflammatory role of PAF *in vivo* may be the result of complex biological interactions of several PAF molecules. Related to the synthesis-release coupling of PAF from stimulated neutrophils, extracellular factors such as albumin and Ca^{2+} may be a part of the mechanism responsible for the biosynthesis of this diverse family of PAF molecules. For example, PAF synthesis by neutrophils *in vitro*, which can be increased 20-fold by the addition of extracellular albumin (Ludwig *et al.*, 1985), may be due to a higher binding capacity of albumin for a particular molecular species of PAF such as C_{16}:0-AGEPC. This could result in the same number of PAF molecules being synthesized and released although there may be a shift towards the production of more potent platelet stimulating molecules. Similarly, the amount of extracellular Ca^{2+} available to the neutrophil during PAF synthesis and release may facilitate the availability of a particular precursor pool of PAF to the deacylation reaction of phospholipase A_2. Consequently, these albumin and Ca^{2+} influences might account for the apparent disparity between the proposed precursor pool of 1-*O*-alkyl-2-acyl-*sn*-glycero-3-phosphocholine of neutrophils (Mueller *et al.*, 1984a) and the molecular distribution of neutrophil-derived PAF (Pinckard *et al.*, 1984; Mueller *et al.*, 1984b; Weintraub *et al.*, 1985). Moreover, this apparent precursor pool selectivity may also be due to other biosynthetic pathways for PAF in addition to the deacylation-acetylation pathway of 1-*O*-alkyl-2-acyl-*sn*-glycero-3-phosphocholine. In conclusion, although the biosynthetic pathways and the effects of the various neutrophil-derived acetylated phosphoglycerides are presently unknown, diversity in the distribution of the multiple molecular species of PAF, with differing biological potencies, could regulate the pathogenesis of PAF-mediated inflammatory disease processes.

ACKNOWLEDGMENTS

These studies were supported by U.S. Public Health Service Grants AI 21818 and HL 22555 and the American Heart Association, Texas Affiliate. The authors thank Laida Garcia for preparing this manuscript.

REFERENCES

Albert, D.H., and Snyder, F. (1983). 'Biosynthesis of 1-alkyl-2-acetyl-*sn*-glycero-3-phosphocholine by rat alveolar macrophages. Phospholipase A_2 and acetyltransferase activities during phagocytosis and ionophore stimulation', *J. Biol. Chem.*, **258**, 97–102.
Alonso, F., Gil, M., Sanchez-Crespo, M., and Mato, J. (1982). 'Activation of 1-alkyl-2-lyso-glycero-3-phosphocholine', *J. Biol. Chem.*, **257**, 3376–3378.

Benveniste, J., Chignard, M., Le Couedic, J.P., and Vargaftig, B.B. (1982). 'Biosynthesis of platelet-activating factor (PAF-acether) II. Involvement of phospholipase A_2 in the formation of PAF-acether and lyso-PAF-acether from rabbit platelets', *Thrombos. Res.*, **25**, 375–385.

Benveniste, J., Jouvin, E., Perotzky, E., Arnoux, B., Mencia-Huerta, J.M., Roubin, R., and Vargaftig, B.B. (1981). 'Platelet-activating factor (PAF-acether): molecular aspects of its release and pharmacological actions', *Int. Archs. Allergy Appl. Immunol.*, **66 (Suppl.1)**, 121–126.

Blank, M.L., Lee, T-c., Fitzgerald, V., and Snyder, F. (1981). 'A specific acetyl hydrolase for 1-aikyl-2-acetyl-*sn*-glycero-3-phosphocholine (a hypotensive and platelet-activating lipid)', *J. Biol. Chem.*, **256**, 175–178.

Chap, H., Mauco, G., Simon, M.F., Benveniste, J., and Douste-Blazy, L. (1981). 'Biosynthethic labelling of platelet activating factor from radioactive acetate by stimulated platelets', *Nature*, **289**, 312–314.

Demopoulos, C.A., Pinckard, R.N., and Hanahan, D.J. (1979). 'Platelet-activating factor. Evidence for 1-*O*-alkyl-2-acetyl-*sn*-glycero-3-phosphocholine as the active component. A new class of lipid chemical mediators', *J. Biol. Chem.*, **254**, 9355–9358.

Doebber, T.W., Wu, M.S., Robbins, J.C., Choy, B.M., Chang, M.N., and Shen, T.Y. (1985). 'Platelet activating factor (PAF) involvement in endotoxin-induced hypotension in rats. Studies with PAF-receptor antagonist kadsurenone', *Biochem. Biophys. Res. Comm.*, **127**, 799-808.

Farr, R.S., Cox, C.P., Wardlow, M.L., and Jorgensen, R. (1980). 'Preliminary studies of an acid-labile factor (ALF) in human sera that inactivates platelet activating factor (PAF)', *Clin. Immunol. Immunopath.*, **15**, 318–330.

Fisher, R.A., Shukla, S.D., Debuysere, M.S., Hanahan, D.J., and Olson, M.S. (1984). 'The effect of acetylglyceryl ether phosphorylcholine on glycogenolysis and phosphatidyl inositol 4,5-bisphosphate metabolism in rat hepatocytes', *J. Biol.Chem.*, **259**, 8685–8688.

Hanahan, D.J., Demopoulos, C.A., Liehr, J., and Pinckard, R.N. (1980). 'Identification of platelet-activating factor isolated from rabbit basophils as acetyl glyceryl ether phosphorylcholine', *J. Biol.Chem.*, **255**, 5514–5516.

Hoppens, C.M., Ludwig, J.C., Castillo, R., McManus, L.M., and Pinckard, R.N. (1983). 'Albumin modulation of rabbit platelet-activation by 1-*O*-hexadecyl-2-acetyl-*sn*-glyceryl-3-phosphorylcholine (AGEPC)', *Fed. Proc.*, **42**, 693.

Humphrey, D.M., McManus, L.M., Satouchi, K., Hanahan, D.J., and Pinckard, R.N. (1982). 'Vasoactive properties of acetyl glyceryl ether phosphorylcholine (AGEPC) and AGEPC analogues', *Lab. Invest.*, **46**, 422–427.

Jackson, E.M., Mott, G.E., Hoppens, C., McManus, L.M., Ludwig, J.C., and Pinckard, R.N. (1984). 'High performance liquid chromotography of platelet-activating factors', *J. Lipid Res.*, **25**, 753–757.

Kramp, W., Pieroni, G., Pinckard, R.N., and Hanahan D.J. (1984). 'Observations on the critical micellar concentration of 1-*O*-alkyl-2-acetyl-*sn*-glyceryl-3-phosphorylcholine (PAF) and a series of its homologs and analogs', *Chem. Phys. Lipids*, **35**, 49–62.

Lee, T.-C., Lenihan, D.J., Malone, B., Roddy, L.L., and Wasserman, S.I. (1984). 'Increased biosynthesis of platelet-activating factor in activated human eosinophils', *J. Biol. Chem.*, **259**, 5526–5530.

Lee, T.-C., Malone, B., Wasserman, S.I., Fitzgerald, V., and Snyder, F. (1982). 'Activities of enzymes that metabolize platelet-activating factor (1-alkyl-2-acetyl-*sn*-glycero-3-phosphocholine) in neutrophils and eosinophils from humans and the effect of a calcium ionophore', *Biochem. Biophys. Res. Comm.*, **105**, 1303–1308.

Ludwig, J.C., Hoppens, C., McManus, L.M., Mott, G.E., and Pinckard, R.N. (1985). 'Modulation of platelet-activating factor (PAF) synthesis and release from human polymorphonuclear leukocytes (PMN): Role of extracellular albumin', *Arch. Biochem. Biophys.*, **241**, 337–347.

Ludwig, J.C., McManus, L.M., Clark, P.O., Hanahan, D.J., and Pinckard, R.N. (1984). 'Modulation of platelet-activating factor (PAF) synthesis and release from human polymorphonuclear leukocytes (PMN): Role of extracellular calcium', *Arch. Biochem. Biophys.*, **232.**, 102–110.

Ludwig, J.C., McManus, L.M., and Pinckard, R.N. (1986). 'Synthesis-release coupling of platelet-activating factors (PAF) from stimulated human neutrophils'. In I. Otterness, A. Lewis and R. Capetola (eds.) *Adv. Inflammation Res.* Raven Press, New York, Vol. 11, pp. 111–125.

Mencia-Huerta, J.M., Roubin, R., Morgat, L.-L., and Benveniste, J. (1982). 'Biosynthesis of platelet-activating factor (PAF-acether). III. Formation of PAF-acether from synthetic substrates by stimulated murine macrophages', *J. Immunol.*, **129**, 804–808.

Mueller, H.W., O'Flaherty, J.T., Greene, D.G., Samuel, M.P., and Wykle, R.L. (1984a). 1-*O*-alkyl-linked glycerophospholipids of human neutrophils: distribution of arachidonate and other acyl residues in the ether-linked and diacyl species', *J. Lipid Res.*, **25**, 383–388.

Mueller, H.W., O'Flaherty, J.T., and Wykle, R.L. (1984b). 'The molecular species distribution of platelet-activating factor synthesized by rabbit and human neutrophils', *J. Biol. Chem.*, **259**, 14 554–14 559.

Mueller, H.W., O'Flaherty, J.T., and Wykle, R.L. (1983). Biosynthesis of platelet-activating factor in rabbit polymorphonuclear neutrophils', *J. Biol. Chem.*, **258**, 6213–6218.

Ninio, E., Mencia-Huerta, J.M., Heymans, F., and Benveniste, J. (1982). 'Biosynthesis of platelet-activating factor. 1. Evidence for an acetyltransferase activity in murine macrophages', *Biochim. Biophys. Acta*, **710**, 23–31.

O'Flaherty, J.T. (1982). 'Biology of disease. Lipid mediators of inflammation and allergy', *Lab. Invest.*, **47**, 314–329.

Patton, G.M., Fasulo, J.M., and Robins, S.J. (1982). 'Separation of phospholipids and individual molecular species of phospholipids by high performance liquid chromatography', *J. Lipid Res.*, **23**, 190–196.

Pinckard, R.N., Jackson, E.M., Hoppens, C., Weintraub, S.T., Ludwig, J.C., McManus, L.M., and Mott, G.E. (1984). 'Molecular heterogeneity of platelet-activating factor produced by stimulated human polymorphonuclear leukocytes', *Biochem. Biophys. Res. Comm.*, **122**, 325–332.

Pinckard, R.N. (1983). Platelet-Activating Factor', *Hospital Practice*, **18**, 67–76.

Pinckard, R.N., McManus, L.M., and Hanahan, D.J. (1982). 'Chemistry and biology of acetyl glyceryl ether phosphorylcholine (platelet-activating factor)'. In G. Weissman (ed.) *Adv. Inflammation Res.* Raven Press, New York, Vol. 4, pp. 147–180.

Renooij, W., and Snyder, R. (1981). 'Biosynthesis of 1-alkyl-2-acetyl-*sn*-glycero-3-phospho-choline (platelet-activating factor and a hypotensive lipid) by cholinephosphotransferase in various rat tissues', *Biochim. Biophys. Acta*, **663**, 545–556.

Satouchi, K., Pinckard, R.N., and Hanahan, D.J. (1981a). 'Influence of alkyl ether chain length of acetyl glyceryl ether phosphorylcholine and its ethanolamine analog on biological activity towards rabbit platelets', *Arch. Biochem. Biophys.*, **211**, 683–688.

Satouchi, J., Pinckard, R.N., McManus, L.M., and Hanahan, D.J. (1981b). 'Modification of the polar head group of acetyl glyceryl ether phosphorylcholine and subsequent effects upon platelet activation', *J. Biol. Chem.*, **256**, 4425–4432.

Satouchi, K., Oda, M., Yasunaga, K., and Saito, K. (1985). 'Evidence for the production of 1-acyl-2-acetyl-*sn*-glyceryl-3-phosphorylcholine concomitantly with platelet-activating factor', *Biochem. Biophys. Res. Commun.*, **128**, 1409–1417.

Snyder, F. (1982). Platelet-activating factor (PAF), a novel type of phospholipid with diverse biological properties', *Ann. Reports Med. Chem.*, **17**, 243–252.

Surles, J.R., Wykle, R.L., O'Flaherty, J.T., Salzer, W.L., Thomas, M.J., Snyder, F., and Piantadosi, C. (1985). 'Facile synthesis of platelet-activating factor and racemic analogues containing unsaturation in the *sn*-1 alkyl chain', *J. Med. Chem.*, **28**, 73–78.

Swendsen, C., Ellis, J., Chilton, F., III, O'Flaherty, J., and Wykle, R. (1983). '1-*O*-alkyl-2-acyl-*sn*-glycero-3-phosphocholine: A novel source of arachidonic acid in neutrophils stimulated by the calcium ionophore A23187', *Biochem. Biophys. Res. Commun.*, **113**, 72–79.

Diversity in the Chemical Structures of Neutrophil-Derived PAFs   71

Tence, J., Michel, E., Coeffier, E., Polonsky, J., Godfroid, J.-J., and Benveniste, J. (1981). 'Synthesis and biological activity of some analogs of platelet-activating factor (PAF-acether)', *Agents Actions*, **11**, 558–559.

Vargaftig, B.B., Chignard, M., Mencia-Huerta, J.M., Arnoux, B., and Benveniste, J. (1981). 'Pharmacology of arachidonate metabolites and of platelet-activating factor (PAF-acether)'. In J.L. Gordon (ed.) *Platelets in Biology and Pathology*, Elsevier, New York, Vol. 2, pp. 373–406.

Wardlow, M.L., Cox, C.P., Meng, K.E., Greene, D.E., and Farr, R.S. (1986). 'Substrate specificity and partial characterization of the PAF-acylhydrolase in human serum that rapidly inactivates platelet-activating factor', *J. Immunol.*, **136**, 3441–3446.

Weintraub, S.T., Ludwig, J.C., Mott, G.E., McManus, L.M., Lear, C., and Pinckard, R.N. (1985). 'Fast atom bombardment-mass spectrometric identification of molecular species of platelet-activating factor produced by stimulated human polymorphonuclear leukocytes', *Biochem. Biophys. Res. Comm.*, **129**, 868–876.

Wykle, R.L., Malone, B., and Snyder, F. (1980). 'Enzymatic synthesis of 1-alkyl-2-acetyl-*sn*-glycero-3-phosphocholine, a hypotensive and platelet-aggregating lipid', *J. Biol. Chem.*, **255**, 10 256–10 260.

Wykle, R.L., Miller, C.H., Lewis, J.C., Schmitt, J.D., Smith, J.A., Surles, J.R., Piantadosi, C., and O'Flaherty, J.T. (1981). 'Sterospecific activity of 1-*O*-alkyl-2-*O*-acetyl-*sn*-glycero-3-phosphocholine and comparison of analogs in the degranulation of platelets and neutrophils', *Biochem. Biophys. Res. Commun.*, **100**, 1651–1658.

Wykle, R.L., Olson, S.C., and O'Flaherty, J.T. (1986). 'Biochemical pathways of platelet-activating factor synthesis and breakdown'. In I. Otterness, A. Lewis and R. Capetola (eds.) *Adv. Inflammation Res.*, Raven Press, New York, Vol. 11, pp. 71–81.

New Horizons in Platelet Activating Factor Research
Edited by C. M. Winslow and M. L. Lee
© 1987 John Wiley & Sons Ltd.

8

Generation of Platelet Activating Factor (PAF-Acether) from the Mononuclear Phagocytic System: Modulation and Pathophysiological Consequences

Mariano Sanchez Crespo, Julian Gomez-Cambronero, Sagrario Fernandez-Gallardo, Maria Luisa Nieto and Susana Velasco

INTRODUCTION

Platelet activating factor was initially described by Benveniste *et al.* (1972) as a substance released from IgE-stimulated basophils that could trigger the secretory response of rabbit platelets. This fact has been related to the pathogenic events which occur during the deposition of immune complexes in tissues, since rabbit basophils often appear to be sensitized with antibodies of identical specificity to those involved in soluble immune complexes, and this could account for the direct stimulation of these cells during immune-complex diseases (Benveniste *et al.*, 1972). According to these views, the generation of PAF-acether from IgE-stimulated basophils could be a crucial event in the induction of increased vascular permeability, which appears essential for extravascular deposition or immune complexes (Benveniste, 1974; Camussi *et al.*, 1982).

On the other hand, the primary function of the mononuclear phagocytic system is the ingestion and degradation of a number of potentially harmful biological materials, including soluble complexes (Arend and Mannik, 1971; Mannik and Arend, 1971). On this basis, one of the most relevant roles of resident macrophages in immune-complex-mediated diseases seems to be the prevention of tissue injury.

In the last years the research on PAF-acether has significantly enlarged, as regards its chemical structure (Demopoulos *et al.*, 1979; Benveniste *et al.*, 1979; Blank *et al.*, 1979), origin and biological actions and many of these findings are relevant to immune complex-mediated reactions, for instance, it has been shown that in several animal species, including man, polymorphonuclear leukocytes and macrophages rather than basophils are the sources of PAF-acether (Sanchez Crespo *et al.*, 1980;

Betz *et al.*, 1980). Platelets from some animal species as rat and mouse are not responsive to PAF-acether (Sanchez Crespo *et al.*, 1982; Namm *et al.*, 1982) and the absence of high affinity binding sites to PAF-acether has been described in rat platelets (Inarrea *et al.*, 1984). PAF-acether is a powerful stimulator of polymorphonuclear leukocytes (Goetzl *et al.*, 1980; Shaw *et al.*, 1981; O'Flaherty *et al.*, 1981), and therefore, the potential of these cells to induce tissue damage can be enhanced by PAF-acether. There are some reports showing that systemic infusion of PAF-acether reproduces the pathophysiology of shock state in rats, dogs, rabbits and baboons (Sanchez Crespo *et al.*, 1982; Bessin *et al.*, 1983a,b; McManus *et al.*, 1981; Halonen *et al.*, 1980), and this mediator induces the extravasation of protein-rich plasma when injected at low doses (Humphrey *et al.*, 1982a,b; Handley *et al.*, 1984a,b).

In this chapter we shall summarize some of the findings on the generation of PAF-acether from mononuclear phagocytes in order to achieve a comprehensive view of its regulation, pathophysiological consequences and possible pharmocological approaches.

GENERATION OF PAF-ACETHER BY THE MONONUCLEAR PHAGOCYTIC SYSTEM

The role of soluble aggregates of immunoglobulin G

Aggregates of immunoglobulin G are analogous to immune complexes as regards their ability to activate the complement system and to initiate cellular responses. For this reason they have been used as an appropriate research tool for the study of immune complex-mediated reactions. For our experiments, soluble aggregates of immunoglobulin G were prepared by heat aggregation according to the procedure described by Egido *et al.* (1982) and they were injected to normal mice through a jugular vein. The liver and the spleen of these animals were removed and treated to isolate the associated phospholipids. The intravenous infusion of IgG soluble immune aggregates was followed by the recovery from liver and spleen of a phospholipid fraction analogous to PAF-acether according to its biological properties, behaviour on thin layer chromatography and HPLC (high performance liquid chromatography), and sensitivity to the treatment by phospholipases A_2 and C (Inarrea *et al.*, 1983). By contrast, PAF-acether was not found in the spleen of control animals and their liver contained only 0.013 ± 0.006 ng g^{-1} of tissue (M $\pm$ S.D., n = 12). The generation of PAF-acether was time-dependent, starting as early as 1 min after the infusion and plateauing at 5 min. Some animals were depleted of mononuclear phagocytes by total irradiation with 700 rads and another group was treated with 0.05 mg of mepacrine to inhibit phospholipase A_2. In both groups of animals abrogation of PAF-acether release from the spleens and 80 percent reduction from the livers were observed.

The role of the liver as a source of PAF-acether has been recently studied by Buxton and co-workers (1984). These authors have confirmed in an isolated perfused liver the release of PAF-acether and its enhancement by soluble aggregates of IgG. Since PAF-acether is a potent glycogenolytic agent, this study has allowed the delineation of a cascade of interactions between Kuppfer cells and hepatocytes, whose role in immune-complex-mediated reactions remains to be elucidated.

Pathophysiological consequences

IgG−Fc receptors on mononuclear phagocytes play an important role in opsonization and phagocytosis (Newman and Johnston, 1979) and in the clearance of immune complexes (Lamers *et al.*, 1981). The role of the CR1 receptor (C3b receptor) on mononuclear phagocytes appears to be ancillary to the function of the Fc receptor, since it enhances the binding of the particle to the phagocyte, but not the ingestion of the particle in the absence of interaction with the Fc receptor (Scribner and Fahrney, 1976; Newman and Johnston, 1979). Furthermore, the clearance of preformed soluble immune complexes and the extravasation of protein-rich plasma which occur following infusion of these complexes are not modified in complement-depleted animals as compared to control animals (Arend and Mannik, 1971; Bockow and Mannik, 1981).

The list of products secreted by the mononuclear phagocytes has been enlarged with PAF-acether (Mencia-Huerta and Benveniste, 1979, 1981; Sanchez Crespo *et al.*, 1980; Arnoux *et al.*, 1980; Camussi *et al.*, 1983a,b) and this gives rise to the question of the role of this mediator in the physiological responses initiated by the stimulation of mononuclear phagocytes. On this basis we have studied extravasation, intravascular volume depletion and hypotension in rats and mice injected with soluble aggregates of IgG (Table 1).

Table 1. Extravasation and hypotension induced by PAF-acether and immunoglobulin G aggregates: effect of BN 52021

Challenge	BN52021	Hypotension mm Hg of fall	time of recovery	Extravasation
PAF-acether	nil	44.0 ± 3.2	4.6 ± 1.0 (3)	17.6 ± 1.5 (3)
$(0.5 \mu g\ kg^{-1})$	$5\ mg\ kg^{-1}$	10.6 ± 2.2^2	1.2 ± 0.4^2 (3)	6.2 ± 0.7^2(3)
PAF-acether	nil	92.5 ± 4.7	20.5 ± 0.2 (4)	36.0 ± 3.0 (5)
$(2.5 \mu g\ kg^{-1})$	$5\ mg\ kg^{-1}$	47.0 ± 4.9^2	5.7 ± 1.7^2 (7)	$18 \quad \pm 2.3^2$(5)
PAF-acether	nil	^{1}	$(3)^1$	$(3)^1$
$(10.0 \mu g\ kg^{-1})$	$5\ mg\ kg^{-1}$	73 ± 2.6	15.0 ± 3.2 (3)	31.6 ± 6 (2)
Aggregated IgG	−	80 ± 20	No recovery (3)	37.0 ± 5 (5)
$(40\ mg\ kg^{-1})$	$5\ mg\ kg^{-1}$	23 ± 8^2	1.6 ± 0.688(3)	$17 \quad \pm 3^2$(5)

BN 52021 or vehicle were intravenously injected 15 minutes prior to the challenge. Number in parentheses indicates the number of rats included in each group of experiments.
[1] Sudden death occurred upon injection of the challenge.
[2] Indicates p < 0.05 (Reproduced from Sanchez Crespo *et al.*, 1985, by permission)

Vessel hyperpermeability leading to the loss of protein-rich plasma (extravasation) was measured by using ^{125}I-BSA (bovine serum albumin) as an intravascular probe in a group of rats injected with different concentrations of soluble aggregates of IgG.

Under these circumstances, up to 36 percent of the ^{125}I-BSA was extravasated in the group of animals which had been injected with a dose of aggregates of 40 mg per kg. This extravasation occurred in a progressive manner up to 30 min after the injection of the aggregates and was blunted by previous treatment of the animals with a specific antagonist of PAF-acether, the compound BN 52021 (IHB-IPSEN, Research laboratories, Le Plessis-Robinson, France) at a concentration of 1−5 mg kg^{-1} of body weight (Sanchez Crespo et al., 1985). Similar findings have been obtained by other groups with other pharmacological antagonist of PAF-acether. Hwang and colleagues (1985) have recently shown that the compound L-652,731 (Merck, Sharp & Dohme, Research Laboratories, Rahway, NJ, USA) at a concentration of 10−20 mg kg^{-1} reduced the extravasation and the secretion of N-acetyl-glucosaminidase induced by the infusion of immune complexes, and Hellewell and Williams (1985) have been able to inhibit the Arthus reaction by two chemically unrelated selective antagonists of the PAF-acether receptor, 48740 RP (Rhone Poulenc Sante, Vitry-sur-Seine, France) and L-652,731. Although these authors have not measured the generation of PAF-acether in their experiments, the most likely interpretation of this study also supports a role for PAF-acether in the pathogenesis of immune-aggregate-induced changes. When the extravasation produced by immune aggregates was compared to that observed in response to PAF-acether, a more protracted pattern has been observed in the case of immune-aggregates, which is consistent with the requirement of a time-lag to generate the endogenous mediator. Since PAF-acether has been found to be a potent hypotensive substance (Blank et al., 1979; Sanchez Crespo et al., 1982), arterial pressure was recorded in a group of rats following intravenous injection of soluble aggregates of IgG. The hypotension induced by IgG immune-aggregates was more protracted and long-lasting than that induced by sublethal doses of PAF-acether, but was also blunted by BN 52021. Interestingly, recovery of the basal arterial pressure could be observed when BN 52021 was injected after the challenge with both substances (Sanchez Crespo et al., 1985). Furthermore, Van Valen and co-workers (1985) have recently reported the reversal of two immune-aggregate-induced phenomena: hypotension and mesenteric artery blood flow reduction by the compound SRI 63-072.

The variation of the intravascular volume in response to soluble aggregates of IgG was studied in mice by using homologous blood red cells labeled with ^{51}Cr. The depletion of the intravascular volume was preceded by the generation of PAF-acether by the organs of the mononuclear phagocytic system, and the most likely explanation for this contraction could be the development of extravasation mediated by the PAF-acether released from the organs of the mononuclear phagocytic system, in fact, depletion of mononuclear phagocytes by total irradiation and pharmacological blockade of phospholipases by mepacrine induced abrogation of both aggregate-induced vascular volume depletion and release of PAF-acether from the spleen (Inarrea et al., 1983). Since the description of the release of PAF-acether from endothelial cells in culture by Camussi et al. (1983a) it should be also considered this origin for the PAF-acether generated in the reactions above mentioned, however, this possibility has not been as yet demonstrated.

MODULATION OF THE BIOSYNTHESIS OF PAF-ACETHER IN SPLENIC MICROSOMES

The role of calcium ions

Soon after the description of the chemical structure of PAF-acether, the specific enzymes involved in its biosynthesis have been documented in several rat organs (Wykle *et al.*, 1980; Renooij and Snyder, 1981). Among these enzymes, the acetyltransferase which catalyzes the acetylation of the lyso form of PAF-acether has been thought to play an essential role in the regulation of the biosynthesis of this mediator. Thus, signals which induce the release of PAF-acether from polymorphonuclear leukocytes and macrophages enhance this enzyme activity (Alonso *et al.*, 1982; Lee *et al.*, 1982; Ninio *et al.*, 1983; Albert and Snyder, 1983). A variety of results support the concept that calcium ions play a role in the process of PAF-acether synthesis. This evidence includes:

1. The addition of the cationophore A23187 to intact cells activates acetyltransferase (Sanchez Crespo *et al.*, 1983; Ninio *et al.*, 1983; Albert and Snyder, 1983; Gomez-Cambronero *et al.*, 1984; Lee *et al.*, 1984).
2. Zymosan-mediated activation of acetyltransferase from rat peritoneal macrophages and human eosinophils depends on the presence of extracellular calcium (Gomez-Cambronero *et al.*, 1985; Lee *et al.*, 1984; Ninio *et al.*, 1983) and is preceded by an influx of this ion into the cell, furthermore, the magnitude of this influx correlates well with the magnitude of acetyltransferase activation (Gomez-Cambronero *et al.*, 1983.
3. Angiotensin and vasopressin, two hormones whose actions are mediated by calcium ions, stimulate PAF-acether synthesis in endothelial cells (Camussi *et al.*, 1983a,b).

Based on these results we planned the study of the effect of calcium ions on the last regulatory step of the biosynthesis of PAF-acether. We selected as a preparation for this study splenic microsomes based on the following reasons:

1. They are the richest preparation on acetyltransferase as compared to microsomes from other organs (Wykle *et al.*, 1980).
2. They constitute a more purified fraction than tissular homogenates.
3. The spleen is the largest reservoir of phagocytes and since lymphoid cells do not contain acetyltransferase activity (Jouvin-Marche *et al.*, 1984) all the enzyme activity present in the preparation is accounted for by the resident macrophages.

In these experiments, the addition of calcium ions to isolated rat spleen microsomes stimulated acetyltransferase activity up to seven-fold. The effect of the addition of calcium ions was very fast and could be reversed by the addition of EGTA. This effect of Ca^{2+} was dose-dependent with a maximum between 0.1 μM and 10 μM

Ca^{2+} (Figure 1). The effect of Ca^{2+} was on the apparent K_m for acetyl-CoA without any significant effect on the Vmax of the acetylation reaction (1200 pM min⁻¹mg⁻¹ protein). When microsomes were isolated in the presence of 5 mM EGTA to remove endogenous calmodulin, the stimulation of acetyltransferase by calcium ions could be observed as in the experiments omitting EGTA. The addition of exogenous calmodulin (1−10 μM) did not affect the stimulation of acetyltransferase induced by calcium ions. In order to test whether the effect of calcium is mediated by protein phosphorylation, acetyltransferase activity was assayed both in the presence and absence of Mg-ATP. Under these conditions no effect of Mg-ATP could be observed on the acetylation reaction (Table 2). All these data suggested that calcium ions modulate acetyltransferase activity by a mechanism independent of calmodulin and also of protein phosphorylation (Gomez-Cambronero *et al.*, 1985a).

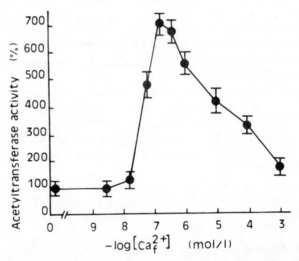

Figure 1.   Effect of calcium ions on acetyltransferase activity from rat splenic microsomes: dose-dependency. The enzyme was assayed in the presence of 2mM EGTA and different concentrations of $CaCl_2$ to obtain the desired concentrations of calcium ions. Results are expressed as percentages of the activity obtained in the absence of exogenous added $CaCl_2$. Values represent mean ± S.D. of six independent experiments in duplicate. 100 percent = 250 pmol min⁻¹ mg⁻¹ protein (Reproduced from Gomez-Cambronero *et al.*, 1985a, by permission)

The role of a phosphorylation-dephosphorylation mechanism

Early observations on acetyltransferase have shown that acetyltransferase activity is enhanced several fold in stimulated cells, in addition, it has been shown that stimulation of macrophages and polymorphonuclear leukocytes did not affect the properties of acetyltransferase nor its kinetic parameters (Ninio *et al.*, 1983; Sanchez Crespo *et al.*, 1983). On this basis it has been suggested that some kind of covalent modification of the enzyme might occur during cell stimulation. Lenihan and Lee (1984) recently obtained data with rat spleen microsomes to support such a notion, since the results obtained with incubations of spleen microsomes, Mg^{2+}-ATP and alkaline phosphatase indicated that acetyltransferase could be phosphorylated for expression of maximum activity. Since diolein and phosphatidylserine, but not exogenous calmodulin, produced a further enhancement of acetyltransferase, it was proposed that protein kinase C (calcium-phospholipid-dependent protein kinase) could be involved in the process. In view of these data and taking into account previous studies on the role of cyclic AMP in the activation of polymorphonuclear leukocytes and in the modulation of the release of PAF-acether, we decided to study the possible effect of cyclic AMP-dependent protein kinase on acetyltransferase activity. Preincubation of rat spleen microsomes with 10 μM Mg^{2+}-ATP in the presence of the catalytic subunit of cyclic AMP-dependent protein kinase (PrKA) increased up to three-fold acetyltransferase activity. This stimulation was optimal with a concentration of PrKA of about 30 units ml^{-1}. In parallel experiments, with $[\gamma$-^{32}P]ATP, phosphorylation of spleen microsomes by PrKA was also transient and followed a similar kinetics to that of acetyltransferase activation.

Table 2.   Effect of different additions on acetyltransferase activity

Addition	Enzyme activity percent of control
None	100
10 μM Mg-ATP	106 $\pm$ 3
200 μM Ca^{2+}	702 $\pm$ 30
200 μM Ca^{2+} + 1 μM Calmodulin	723 $\pm$ 40
200 μM Ca^{2+} + 10 μM Calmodulin	690 $\pm$ 53
200 μM Ca^{2+} + 10 μM Mg-ATP	696 $\pm$ 35

Microsomes were isolated in the presence of 5 mM EGTA, and acetyltransferase activity was assayed in the presence of different additions. Data represent the mean $\pm$ S.D. of three independent experiments in duplicate (Reproduced from Gomez-Cambronero *et al.*, 1985a by permission)

The ATP derivate AMP-PNP could not replace ATP for the activation of acetyltransferase and the heat-stable inhibitor of PrKA prevented the activation of the acetylation reaction. The action of the PrKA was dependent on the time of incubation prior to the addition of the substrates of the reaction, maximum stimulation being observed when microsomes were preincubated for 5 min at 37 °C before the initiation of the acetylation reaction (Figure 2). The addition of nitrophenol-4-phosphate to the incubation mixture resulted in both a more prolonged activation of the acetyltransferase, and in a maintained phosphorylation of the microsomes which suggested that the transient activation of the enzyme observed in the presence of Mg^{2+}-ATP and the PrKA is due to the action of phosphoprotein-phosphatases (Gomez-Cambronero *et al.*, 1985b).

Table 3.   Effect of different additions on acetyltransferase activity

Addition	Enzyme activity percent of control
None	100
Mg-ATP 10 μM	95 ± 6
PrKA 30 U ml^{-1}	93 ± 3
Mg-ATP 10 μM + PrKA 30 U ml^{-1}	258 ± 26
Mg-AMPPNP 10 μM + PrKA 30 U ml^{-1}	105 ± 11
Mg-ATP 10 μM + PrKA 30 U ml^{-1} + PrKI 250 μg	106 ± 13

Spleen microsomes were incubated for 5 min at 37 °C in the presence of the additives indicated. At the end of this period the acetylation reaction was started by addition of the substrate. PrKI, heat stable protein kinase inhibitor. PrKa, catalytic subunit of the cyclic AMP dependent protein kinase. AMPPNP, adenylyl-imidodiphosphate. PrKA was incubated with PrKI for 10 min at 4 °C before its addition to the microsomes. Results are the mean ± S.D. of three independent experiments in duplicate. 100 percent corresponds to 98 pM PAF-acether min^{-1} mg^{-1} protein (Reproduced from Gomez-Cambronero et al., 1985a by permission)

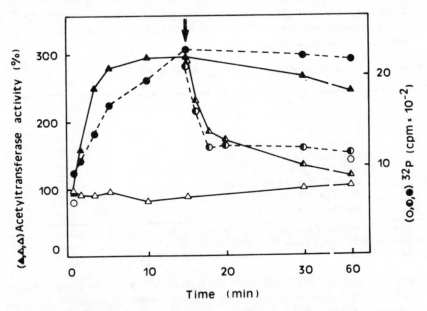

Figure 2.   Effect of nitrophenyl 4-phosphate and alkaline phosphatase on the activation of acetyltransferase by the catalytic subunit of cyclic AMP-dependent protein kinase. Rat spleen microsomes containing 10 μM Mg-ATP were incubated in the presence (●, ▲, ○, △) or absence (◐, ◭) of 30 U ml^{-1} protein kinase and 100 μM nitrophenyl phosphate. After 15 min incubation, alkaline phosphatase (15 U ml^{-1}) was added (arrow) to two sets of samples (◐, ◭). At the times indicated acetyltransferase (△, ▲, ▲) or microsome phosphorylation (○, ◐, ●) were measured. Results are the means of three independent experiments in duplicate. 100 percent corresponds to 98 pmol PAF-acether min^{-1} mg^{-1} protein (Reproduced from Gomez-Cambronero et al., 1985b, by permission)

ACKNOWLEDGMENTS

This study has been supported by grants from 'C.A.I.C.Y.T.', 'Fondo de Investigaciones Sanitarias' and 'Fundacion Alvarez de Toledo'.

REFERENCES

Albert, D.H., and Snyder, F. (1982) 'Biosynthesis of 1-alkyl-2-acetyl-*sn*-glycero-3-phosphocholine (Platelet-activating factor) from 1-alkyl-2-acyl-*sn*-glycero-3-phosphocholine by rat alveolar macrophages', *J. Biol. Chem.*, **258**, 97–102.

Alonso, F., Sanchez Crespo, M., and Mato, J.M. (1982). 'Modulatory role of cyclic AMP in the release of Platelet-activating factor from human polymorphonuclear leukocytes', *Immunology*, **45**, 493–500.

Alonso, F., Garcia-Gil, M., Sanchez Crespo, M., and Mato, J.M. (1982). 'Activation of 1-alkyl-2-lyso-glycero-3-phosphocholine:acetyl-CoA transferase during phagocytosis in human polymorphonuclear leukocytes', *J. Biol. Chem.*, **257**, 3376–3378.

Arend, W.P., and Mannik, M. (1971). 'Studies on antigen-antibody complexes. II. Quantitation of tissue uptake of soluble complexes in normal and complement-depleted rabbits', *J. Immunol.*, **107**, 63–75.

Arnoux, B., Duval, D., and Benveniste, J. (1980). 'Release of platelet-activating factor (paf-acether) from alveolar macrophages by the calcium ionophore A23187 and phagocytosis', *Eur. J. Clin. Invest.*, **10**, 437–441.

Benveniste, J., (1974). 'Platelet-activating factor, a new mediator of anaphylaxis and immune-complex deposition from rabbit and human basophils', *Nature*, **294**, 581–582.

Benveniste, J., Egido, J., and Gutierrez-Millet, V. (1976). 'Evidence for the involvement of the IgE-basophil system in acute-serum sickness', *Clin. Exp. Immunol.*, **26**, 449–456.

Benveniste, J., Henson, P.M., and Cochrane, C.G. (1972). 'Leukocyte-dependent histamine release from rabbit platelets. The role of IgE, basophils and a platelet-activating-factor', *J. Exp. Med.*, **136**, 1356–1377.

Benveniste, J., Tence, M., Varenne, P., Bidault, J., Boullet, C., and Polonski, J. (1979). 'Semi-synthese et structure proposee du facteur activant les plaquettes (P.A.F.); PAF-acether, un alkyl ether analogue de la lysophosphatidylcholine', *C.R. Acad. Sci. (D) (Paris)*, **289**, 1037–1040.

Bessin, P., Bonnet, J., Apffel, D., Soulard, C., Desgroux, L., and Benveniste, J. (1983a). 'Acute circulatory collapse caused by platelet-activating factor (paf-acether) in dogs', *Eur. J. Pharmacol.*, **86**, 403–413.

Bessin, P., Bonnet, J., Thibandeau, D., Agier, B., Beaudet, Y., and Gilet, F. (1983b). 'Pathophysiology of shock states caused by paf-acether in dogs and rats'. In J. Benveniste and B.A. Arnoux, (eds.) *Platelet-activating factor and structurally related ether lipids*, Elsevier Science Publishers B.V., Amsterdam, pp. 343–356.

Betz, S.J., Lotner, G.Z., and Henson, P.M. (1980). 'Generation and release of platelet-activating factor (PAF) from enriched preparations of rabbit basophils; failure of human basophils to release PAF', *J. Immunol.*, **125**, 2749–2755.

Blank, M.L., Snyder, F., Byers, L.W., Brooks, B., and Muirhead, E.E. (1979). 'Antihypertensive activity of an alkyl ether analog of phosphatidylcholine', *Biochem. Biophys. Res. Commun.*, **90**, 1194–1200.

Bockow, B., and Mannik, M. (1981). 'Clearance and tissue uptake of immune complexes in complement-depleted and control mice', *Immunology*, **42**, 497–504.

Buxton, D.B., Hanahan, D.J., and Olson, M.L. (1984). 'Stimulation of glycogenolysis and platelet-activating factor production by heat aggregated immunoglobulin G in the perfused liver', *J. Biol. Chem.*, **259**, 13 758–13 761.

Camussi, G., Aglietta, M., Malavasi, F., Tetta, C., Piacibello, W., and Bussolino, F. (1983a). 'The release of platelet-activating factor from human endothelial cells in culture', *J. Immunol.*, **131**, 2397–2403.

Camussi, G., Bussolino, F., Tetta, C., Piacibello, W., and Aglietta, M. (1983b). 'Biosynthesis and release of platelet-activating factor from human monocytes', *Int. Arch. Allergy Appl. Immunol.*, **70**, 245–251.

Camussi, G., Mencia-Huerta, J.M., and Benveniste, J. (1977). 'Release of platelet-activating factor and histamine. I. Effect of immune complexes, complement and neutrophils in human and rabbit mastocytes and basophils', *Immunology*, **33**, 523–534.

Camussi, G., Tetta, C., DeRegibus, M.C., Bussolino, F., Segoloni, G., and Vercellone, A. (1982). 'Platelet-activating factor (PAF) in experimentally-induced rabbit acute serum sickness: role of basophil-derived PAF in immune complex deposition', *J. Immunol.*, **128**, 86–94.

Demopoulos, C.A., Pinckard, R.N., and Hanahan, D.J. (1979). 'Platelet-activating factor. Evidence for 1-*O*-alkyl-2-acetyl-*sn*-glyceryl-3-phosphorylcholine as the active component (a new class of lipid chemical mediators)', *J. Biol. Chem.*, **254**, 9355–9358.

Egido, J., Sancho, J., Rivera, F., and Sanchez Crespo, M. (1982). 'Handling of soluble IgA aggregates by the mononuclear phagocytic system in mice. A comparison with IgG aggregates', *Immunology*, **46**, 1–7.

Goetzl, E.J., Derian, C.K., Tauber, A.I., and Valone, F.H. (1980). 'Novel effects of 1-*O*-hexadecyl-2-acetyl-*sn*-glycero-3-phosphorylcholine mediators in human leukocyte function: Delineation of the specific roles of the acyl substituents', *Biochem. Biophys. Res. Commun.*, **94**, 881–888.

Gomez-Cambronero, J., Inarrea, P., Alonso, F., and Sanchez Crespo, M. (1984). 'The role of calcium ions in the process of acetyltransferase activation during the synthesis of platelet-activating factor', *Biochem. J.*, **219**, 419–424.

Gomez-Cambronero, J., Nieto, M., Mato, J.M., and Sanchez Crespo, M. (1985a). 'Modulation of acetyltransferase activity in rat splenic microsómes. I. The role of calcium ions', *Biochim. Biophys. Acta*, **845**, 511–515.

Gomez-Cambronero, J., Nieto, M., Velasco, S., Mato, J.M., and Sanchez Crespo, M. (1985c). 'Regulation by calcium ions and cyclic AMP of lyso-platelet-activating factor:acetyltransferase from rat splenic microsomes'. In *Advances in Inflammation Research*. Raven Press, New York, (in press).

Gomez-Cambronero, J., Velasco, S., Mato, J.M., and Sanchez Crespo, M. (1985b). 'Modulation of acetyltransferase activity in rat splenic microsomes. II. The role of catalytic subunit of cyclic AMP-dependent protein kinase', *Biochim. Biophys. Acta*, **845**, 516–519.

Halonen, M., Palmer, J.D., Lohman, I.C., McManus, L.M., and Pinckard, R.N. (1980). 'Respiratory and circulatory alterations induced by acetyl glyceryl ether phosphorylcholine (AGEPC), a mediator of IgE anaphylaxis in the rabbit', *Am Rev. Resp. Dis.*, **122**, 915–924.

Handley, D.A., Arbeeny, C.M., Lee, M.L., Van Valen, R.G., and Saunders, R.N. (1984a). 'Effect of platelet-activating factor on endothelial permeability to plasma macromolecules', *Immunopharmacology*, **8**, 137–142.

Handley, D.A., Van Valen, R.G., Melden, M.K., and Saunders, R.N. (1984b). 'Evaluation of dose and route effects of platelet-activating factor-induced extravasation in the guinea pig', *Throm. Haemostas.*, **52**, 34–36.

Hellewell, P.G., and Williams, T.J. (1985). 'Suppression of inflammatory oedema in rabbit skin by two paf antagonists'. *GREMI Symposium. Paris*, **June 1985**, (abstract).

Humphrey, D.M., Hanahan, D.J., and Pinckard, R.N. (1982a). 'Induction of leukocytic infiltrates in rabbit skin by acetyl glyceryl ether phosphorylcholine', *Lab. Invest.*, **47**, 227–234.

Humphrey, D.H., McManus, L.M., Satouchi, K., Hanahan, D.J., and Pinckard, R.N. (1982b). 'Vasoactive properties of acetyl glyceryl ether phosphorylcholine and analogues', *Lab. Invest.*, **46**, 422–427.

Hwang, S.-B., Biftu, T., Doebber, T.W., Lam, M.H.T., Wu, M.S., and Shen, T.Y. (1985). 'A synthetic pseudolignan derivative as potent and specific paf-acether receptor antagonist. Is there a case for paf-acether antagonists', *GREMI Symposium, Paris*, **June 1985**, (abstract).

Inarrea, P., Alonso, F., and Sanchez Crespo, M. (1983). 'Platelet-activating factor: an effector substance of the vasopermeability changes induced by the infusion of immune aggregates in the mouse', *Immunopharmacology*, **6**, 7–14.

Inarrea, P., Gomez-Cambronero, J., Nieto, M., and Sanchez Crespo, M. (1984). 'Characteristics of the binding of platelet-activating factor to platelets of different animal species', *Eur. J. Pharmacol.*, **105**, 309–315.

Inarrea, P., Gomez-Cambronero, J., Pascual, J., Ponte, M.C., Hernando, L., and Sanchez Crespo, M. (1985). 'Synthesis of paf-acether and blood volume changes in Gram-negative sepsis', *Immunopharmacology*, **9**, 45–52.

Jouvin-Marche, E., Ninio, E., Beaurain, G., Tence, M., Niaudet, P., and Benveniste, J. (1984). 'Biosynthesis of paf-acether (platelet-activating factor). Precursors of paf-acether and acetyltransferase activity in human leukocytes', *J. Immunol.*, **133**, 892–898.

Lamers, J.L., De Groot, E.R., and Roos, D. (1981). 'Phagocytosis and degradation of DNA-anti-DNA complexes by human phagocytes. I. Assay conditions, quantitative aspects and differences between human blood monocytes and neutrophils', *Eur. J. Immunol.*, **11**, 757–764.

Lenihan, D.J., and Lee, T-c. (1984). 'Regulation of platelet-activating factor synthesis: modulation of 1-alkyl-2-lyso-*sn*-glycero-3-phosphocholine:acetyl-CoA acetyltransferase by phosphorylation and dephosphorylation in rat splenic microsomes', *Biochem. Biophys. Res. Commun.*, **120**, 834–839.

Lee, T-c., Lenihan, D.J., Malone, B., Roddy, L.L., Wasserman, S.I. (1984). 'Activities of enzymes that metabolize platelet activating factor (1-alkyl-2-acetyl-*sn*-glycero-3-phosphocholine) in neutrophils and eosinophils from humans and the effect of a calcium ionophore', *Biochem. Biophys. Res. Commun.*, **105**, 1303–1308.

Mannik, M., and Arend, W.P. (1971). 'Fate of preformed immunocomplexes in rabbits and rhesus monkeys', *J. Exp. Med.*, **134**, 19S–31S.

McManus, L.M., Hanahan, D.J., Demopoulos, C.A., and Pinckard, R.N. (1980). 'Pathobiology of the intravenous infusion of acetyl glyceryl ether phosphorylcholine (AGEPC), a synthetic platelet-activating factor (PAF) in the rabbit', *J. Immunol.*, **124**, 2919–2924.

McManus, L.M., Pinckard, R.N., Fitzpatrick, F.A., O'Rourke, R.A., Crawford, M.H., and Hanahan, D.J. (1981). 'Acetyl glyceryl ether phosphorylcholine. Intravascular alterations following intravenous infusion in the baboon', *Lab. Invest.*, **45**, 303–307.

Mencia-Huerta, J.M., and Benveniste, J. (1979). 'Platelet-activating factor and macrophages. I. Evidence for the release from rat and mouse macrophages and not from mastocytes', *Eur. J. Immunol.*, **9**, 409–415.

Mencia-Huerta, J.M., and Benveniste, J. (1981). 'Platelet-activating factor and macrophages. II. Phagocytosis associated release of paf-acether from rat peritoneal macrophages', *Cell. Immunol.*, **57**, 281–292.

Namm, D.H., Tadepalli, A.S., and High, J.A. (1982). 'Species specificity of the platelet responses to 1-O-alkyl-2-acetyl-sn-glycero-3-phosphocholine', *Thromb. Res.*, **25**, 341−350.

Newman, S.L., and Johnston, R.B., Jr. (1979). 'Role of binding through C3b and IgG in poly-morphonuclear neutrophil function: Studies with trypsin generated C3b', *J. Immunol.*, **123**, 1839−1846.

Ninio, E., Mencia-Huerta, J.M., and Benveniste, J. (1983). 'Biosynthesis of platelet-activating factor (paf-acether) V. Enhancement of acetyltransferase activity in murine peritoneal cells by calcium ionophore A23187', *Biochim. Biophys. Acta*, **751**, 298−304.

Ninio, E., Mencia-Huerta, J.M., Heymans, F., and Benveniste, J. (1982). 'Biosynthesis of platelet-activating factor. I. Evidence for an acetyltransferase activity in murine macro-phages', *Biochim. Biophys. Acta*, **710**, 23−31.

O'Flaherty, J.T., Wykle, R.L., Miller, C.H., Lewis, J.C., Waite, M., Bass, D.A., McCall, C.E., and DeChatelet, L.R. (1981). '1-O-alkyl-2-acetyl-sn-glyceryl-3-phosphoryl-choline: A novel class of neutrophil stimulants', *Am. J. Pathol.*, **103**, 70−78.

Pinckard, R.N., Farr, R.S., and Hanahan, D.J. (1979). 'Physicochemical and functional ident-ity of platelet-activating factor (PAF) released *in vivo* during IgE anaphylaxis with PAF released *in vitro* from IgE sensitized basophils', *J. Immunol.*, **123**, 1847−1857.

Pirotzki, E., Page, C.P., Roubin, R., Pfister, A., Paul, W., and Benveniste, J. (1984). 'PAF-acether-induced plasma exudation is independent of platelets and neutrophils in rat skin', *Microcirculation*, **1**, 107−122.

Renooij, W., and Snyder, F. (1981). 'Biosynthesis of 1-alkyl-2-acetyl-sn-glycero-3-phospho-choline (platelet-activating factor and a hypotensive lipid) by cholinephosphotransferase in various rat tissues', *Biochim. Biophys. Acta*, **663**, 545−556.

Sanchez Crespo, M., Alonso, F., and Egido, J. (1980). 'Platelet-activating factor in anaphyl-axis and phagocytosis. I. Release from human peripheral polymorphonuclears and mono-cytes during the stimulation by ionophore A23187 and phagocytosis but not from degranulating basophils', *Immunology*, **40**, 645−655.

Sanchez Crespo, M., Alonso, F., Inarrea, P., Alvarez, V., and Egido, J. (1982). 'Vascular actions of synthetic PAF-acether (A synthetic platelet-activating factor) in the rat: Evidence for a platelet independent mechanism', *Immunopharmacology*, **4**, 173−185.

Sanchez Crespo, M., Alonso, F., Inarrea, P., and Egido, J. (1981). 'Non-platelet-mediated vascular actions of 1-O-alkyl-2-acetyl-sn-glyceryl-3-phosphocholine (a synthetic PAF)', *Agents Actions*, **11**, 565−566.

Sanchez Crespo, M., Alonso, F., and Mato, J.M. (1983). 'Role of an acetyltransferase reaction in the biosynthesis of paf-acether in human polymorphonuclear leukocytes'. In J. Benveniste and B.A. Arnoux, (eds.) *Platelet-activating factor and structurally related ether lipids*, Elsevier Science Publishers B.V., Amsterdam, pp. 269−275.

Sanchez Crespo, M., Fernandez-Gallardo, S., Nieto, M.L., Baranes, J., and Braquet, P. (1985). 'Inhibition of the vascular actions of immunoglobulin G aggregates by BN 52021, a highly specific antagonist of paf-acether', *Immunopharmacology*, (in press).

Sancho, J., Rivera, F., Sanchez Crespo, M., and Egido, J. (1982). 'The effect of the injection of a synthetic platelet-activating factor (PAF-acether) on the fate of IgG aggregates in mice', *Immunology*, **47**, 643−650.

Scribner, D.J., and Fahrney, D. (1976). 'Neutrophil receptors for IgG and complement: Their roles in the attachment and ingestion phases of phagocytosis', *J. Immunol.*, **116**, 892−897.

Shaw, J.O., Pinckard, R.N., Ferrigni, K.S., McManus, L.M., and Hanahan, D.J. (1981). 'Activation of human neutrophils with 1-O-hexadecyl/octadecyl-2-acetyl-sn-glyceryl-3-phosphorylcholine (platelet-activating factor)', *J. Immunol.*, **124**, 1482−1489.

Van Valen, R.G., Melden, M.K., Lee, M.L., Saunders, R.N., and Handley, D.A. (1985). 'Reversal by SRI 63-072 of endotoxin and immune-aggregate-induced hypotension in the rat', *Symposium New Horizons in Platelet-Activating Factor Research. Hilton Head Island*, **1985**. Abstract number 8.

Wykle, R.L., Malone, B., and Snyder, F. (1980). 'Enzymatic synthesis of 1-alkyl-2-acetyl-*sn*-glycero-3-phosphocholine, a hypotensive and platelet-activating phospholipid', *J. Biol. Chem.*, **255**, 10 256–10 260.

New Horizons in Platelet Activating Factor Research
Edited by C. M. Winslow and M. L. Lee
© 1987 John Wiley & Sons Ltd.

9

Erythrocyte-Bound Immune Complexes Stimulate the Release of Platelet Activating Factor by Human PMN Leukocytes

G. Virella and T.A. Sherwood

INTRODUCTION

The pathogenic consequences of immune complex (IC) formation depend on the triggering of inflammatory processes. This is believed to be the consequence of a complex set of interactions that includes the activation of the complement system and the release of pharmacologically active substances from a variety of cells. Of particular consequence appears to be release of platelet activating factor (PAF), which seems to play a critical role in determining immune complex deposition in rabbit acute serum sickness (Camussi *et al.*, 1982) and which appears to be able to mediate a variety of effects of possible relevance in inflammation, including the induction of platelet aggregation and release of vasoactive amines (Pinckard *et al.*, 1979; Benveniste *et al.*, 1979), a direct effect on vascular permeability (Bjork *et al.*, 1983; Cusack, 1980; Worthen *et al.*, 1983) and chemotactic and activating effects on neutrophils (O'Flaherty *et al.*, 1981; Shaw *et al.*, 1981).

In man it has been shown that PAF is produced by neutrophils and since these phagocytic cells are known to secrete their enzymatic contents as a consequence of interactions with immune complexes (IC) (Henson, 1971; Becker and Henson, 1973; Henson and Oades, 1975) it would appear logical that the same interactions would lead to the release of PAF. However, Camussi *et al.*, (1977) studied the effect of the interaction between soluble IC and PMN and concluded that such interaction could not induce PAF release. We demonstrated for the first time that, similar to what had been described by Henson and his co-workers with regard to enzymatic release, the interaction of neutrophils and surface-bound IC would result in PAF release (Virella *et al.*, 1982). In our initial work we bound *in vitro* made or purified IC to artificial substrates, such as Sepharose beads. In looking for a biological system able to be involved in IC presentation to phagocytic cells we decided to investigate the possibility that erythrocyte (RBC)-adsorbed IC could trigger the release of PAF from human PMN leukocytes.

MATERIALS AND METHODS

Separation of polymorphonuclear leukocytes

We used a modification of Rocklin's procedure (1980) which combines 6 percent dextran sedimentation, centrifugation in Ficoll–Paque, (Pharmacia Fine Chemicals), and red-cell lysis using a solution of 0.15 M NH_4Cl, 0.1 mM ethylenediamine tetraacetic acid (EDTA) and 0.01 M $NaHCO_3$. The final PMN suspension contained PMN at 95 percent or better purity, neutrophils being the predominant cell type (90 percent).

Preparation of washed rabbit platelets

Rabbit blood was collected by arterial puncture in 3.8 percent trisodium citrate-acid citrate-dextran solution (six parts blood to one of anticoagulant) and processed as described by Ardlie et al. (1970). The final platelet suspension was prepared in Tyrodes Ca^{2+}, Mg^{2+}-bovine serum albumin (BSA) (0.35 percent), pH 7.35, and adjusted to 500 000 mm^{-3}. To this suspension we added apyrase prepared according to Molnar and Lorand (1961) at a ratio of 2 μl ml^{-1} of platelet suspension.

Testing for PAF activity in PMN supernatants

The ability of PMN supernatants to induce platelet aggregation was measured by mixing 0.2 cm^3 of a 5×10^5 μl^{-1} rabbit platelet suspension and 0.3 cm^3 of the supernatant being tested in a warmed (37 °C) and stirred cuvette with continuous recording of light transmission during a 4 min period in a Payton dual channel aggregometer. For each supernatant tested, we determined 1 min and maximal aggregation, expressed as percent increase of light scattering.

Inhibition studies were carried out with phospholipase, according to Benveniste et al. (1977). Briefly, the PMN supernatant was adjusted to pH 8.0 and a 10 mM content of $CaCl_2$; 0.5 U ml^{-1} of phospholipase A_2 (Sigma Chemical Co.) was then added, incubated at 37 °C for 30 min, and kept in an ice bath until testing.

Isolation of PAF from PMN supernatant

The procedure of Pinckard et al. (1979) was followed. The PMN supernatants were extracted in methanol: chloroform: water (1:1:0.8 v/v), the chloroform phases were removed and concentrated and methanol was added to a final concentration of 10 percent. The extract was separated by thin layer chromatography on silica gel H, 250 μm thick, using as solvent a mixture of chloroform: methanol: water (65:35:6 v/v). The separation was stopped after the solvent front moved 17–18 cm from origin. Phosphatidyl ethanolamine, sphingomyelin, phosphatidyl inositol, lysolecithin and egg lecithin were used as controls. At the end of the run, the plates were air dried and the PAF-contained lanes sectioned into 1 cm squares and scraped. The scraped silica gel was mixed with 2 ml of chloroform: methanol: water (1:2:0.8 v/v), and processed as described by Pinckard *et al.* (1979). The dried fractions were reconstituted with Tyrodes Ca^{+2}-BSA. The remaining silica gel plate was placed in a mercuric vapor chamber to locate the control lipids. Rf for control lipids and purified PAF were calculated according to Dryer (1970).

Preparation of insoluble IC and soluble IC

Tetanus toxoid (TT) (Lederle Laboratories and Wyeth Laboratories) and hyperimmune anti-tetanus toxoid (anti-TT) sera prepared in rabbits by us were used to prepare TT-anti-TT IC. A series of tubes with a 1:10 dilution of rabbit anti-TT (antibody concentration: 42 to 48 U ml^{-1}) was prepared, and increasing amounts of TT were added to the tubes. For complement dependency studies, similar preparations were made using heat-inactivated anti-TT (diluted 1:10 in PBS and heated at 56 °C for 30 min) (HIATT) or anti-TT diluted 1:10 in PBS-EDTA. A tube with the same dilution of anti-TT and no TT was used as the antibody control. The antigen-antibody mixtures were incubated overnight at 4 °C and centrifuged at 2,000 × g for 5 min to separate insoluble IC from soluble IC. The relative concentration of soluble IC was estimated by measuring the light scattering of the supernatants in a Hyland laser PDQ nephelometer (sensitivity settings 1/1-3, course/fine), the supernatant dispersing the most light being selected for experiments with soluble IC. The highest readings were obtained at three to seven fold antigen excess and at about 100–160 fold antibody excess over equivalence, respectively.

Binding of soluble IC to HRBC and presentation to PMN leukocytes

Soluble TT-anti-TT IC at antigen or antibody excess, were mixed with 100 × 10^6 washed HRBC in the presence or absence of complement and incubated at 37 °C for 30 min on a rocking platform. The red cells were washed 3 × (2,000 × g for 2 min) using Tyrodes Ca^{2+}, Mg^{2+}, or PBS-EDTA (1×) followed by Tyrodes Ca^{2+}, Mg^{2+} (2 ×) depending on whether complement was present or absent in the system. After the final wash, IC-HRBC pellets were resuspended in 0.5 ml Tyrodes Ca^{2+}, Mg^{2+}-BSA followed by subsequent addition of an equal volume of PMN (10 × 10^6 cells ml^{-1}) in the same buffer and incubated as above. Following this last incubation, the tubes were spun (2,000 × g for 5 min) and the supernatants retained and frozen immediately until testing for PAF activity.

Table 1. Study of the complement requirement for PMN stimulation by surface-bound IC

			Effects of PMN super-natants on rabbit platelets		
			1 min	Max	Serotonin release
IC	C	Substrate	(%)[1]	(%)[1]	(%)[2]
TT/ATT	+	RBC	40 ± 20[3,4]	50 ± 22[3,4]	3.5 ± 2.6[3]
TT/ATT	−	RBC	32 ± 22[3,5]	36 ± 21[3,5]	3.3 ± 3.2[3]
ATT/PBS	+	RBC	5 ± 5[3]	9 ± 9[3]	0[3]

[1] Expressed as percent increase of light scattering using as references the original platelet suspension (0 percent) and the buffer used in the final platelet suspension (100%).
[2] Release of ^{14}C-labeled serotonin expressed as percentage of the total serotonin incorporated in 100 μl of platelet suspension.
[3] n = 4.
[4] p < 0.01 compared to ATT/PBS; NS when experiments with or without complement are compared by the Student's t-test.
[5] p < 0.05 compared to ATT/PBS; NS when experiments with or without complement are compared by Student's t-test.

Table 2. Isolation of PAF by thin layer chromatography from supernatants of zymosan and immune complex-RBC-stimulated PMN

	Aggregation		
TLC Fraction[1]	1 min (%)	Maximal (%)	Serotonin release (%)
(a) Zymosan stimulated PMN			
No.3	0	0	0.1
No.4	33	33	2.6
No.5	72	82	30.0
No.6	0	0	0
(b) IC-RBC-stimulated PMN			
No.1	0	0	
No.2	0	0	1
No.3	6	6	0
No.4	17	45	0
No.5	0	0	3

[1] Lysolecithin separated at about 3 cm from origin: sphingomyelin separated at about 5 cm from origin: 1 cm fractions were cut and eluted from the TLC plate and counted from the origin. The PAF activity was recovered most at 5 cm from origin, in a position intermediate between lysolecithin and sphingomyelin that has been reported to be characteristic of PAF.

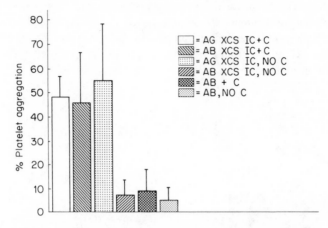

Figure 1.   Maximal platelet aggregation induced with supernatants of PMN leukocytes incubated with homologous erythrocytes (RBC) to which we had previously adsorbed soluble TT-anti-TT IC prepared at different antigen−antibody ratios and incubated with RBC in the presence or absence of complement (C). As negative controls we used RBC incubated with anti-TT alone, in the presence or absence of C. Statistical comparisons (by Student's t-test) between the aggregating activity of PMN supernatants after incubation with RBC-IC and negative controls showed significant differences between RBC-Ag excess IC + C and controls ($p < 0.01$), RBC-Ag excess, no C and controls ($p < 0.05$), RBC-Ab excess IC + C and controls ($p < 0.05$) and RBC-Ab excess IC + C and RBC-Ab excess IC, no C ($p < 0.05$). No significant difference was observed between RBC-Ag excess IC + C and RBC-Ag excess IC, no C. The values shown in the diagram correspond to the mean ± 1 S.D.

RESULTS

Stimulation of human PMN by soluble IC bound to HRBC

Human PMN were effectively stimulated to release PAF by homologous RBC preincubated with soluble IC (Table 1). As shown in Table 1, stimulation of PMN by IC-RBC was complement independent although higher values were seen when RBC coated with opsonized IC were added to PMN leukocytes. We also compared the stimulatory effects of RBC coated with soluble IC prepared at either antigen or antibody excess on PMN. The results shown in Figure 1 indicate that both IC prepared at antigen excess or antibody excess are capable of provoking platelet aggregating activity release from PMN after binding to HRBC. The abrogation of this activity after preincubation of IC-RBC stimulated PMN supernatants with phospholipase A_2

suggested that PAF was the mediator responsible for platelet aggregation (Figure 2). While the binding of IC prepared at antibody excess and subsequent interaction with PMN are complement-dependent, IC prepared at antigen excess bind to erythrocytes and stimulate PAF release from PMN whether previously incubated with a source of complement or not (Figure 1).

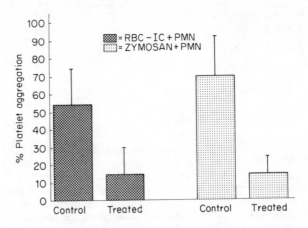

Figure 2.　Effects of preincubation with phospholipase on the platelet aggregating activity of PMN supernatants obtained by incubating PMN leukocytes with RBC coated with TT-anti-TT IC prepared at antigen excess ($n = 5$) and by incubating PMN with zymosan ($n = 5$). The decrease of activity was significant in both cases ($p < 0.02$ and < 0.01, respectively, by Student's t-test). The values shown in the diagram correspond to the mean $\pm$ S.D.

Isolation of PAF from IC-RBC stimulated PMN supernatants

As shown in Table 2, PAF was isolated from supernatants of PMN stimulated with IC-HRBC. The RF values calculated for the PAF preparation were intermediate to that of lysolecithin (0.17) and sphingomyelin (0.27), as described by Pinckard *et al.* (1979) and Camussi *et al.* (1982).

DISCUSSION

Inflammatory processes appear to be a consequence, at least in part, of the release of stored intracellular enzymes from phagocytic cells which attack extracellular substrates of ground substance, adversely affecting the microcirculation of tissue (Houck, 1968). In the case of IC-mediated inflammation, it is believed that neutrophil infiltration at sites of deposition of complement fixing IC results in the release of tissue degradative enzymes (Weissmann *et al.*, 1982; in addition, monocytes appear capable, in such instances, of releasing neutral proteases (Ragsdale and Arend, 1979). IC which are bound to surfaces, such as articular cartilage in rheumatoid arthritis (Ohno and Cooke, 1978; Shunichi *et al.*, 1980) are believed to be better stimuli of the secretion of phagocytic cell granule contents than the same complexes presented in suspension (Henson, 1971; Henson *et al.*, 1979). Our previous findings (Virella *et al.*, 1982, 1983) using PAF release as an indicator of PMN leukocyte stimulation, showed that soluble IC bound to the surfaces of non-phagocytosable Sepharose beads, but not soluble IC themselves, were very effective *in vitro* as stimuli for the release of PAF.

The initial phase of IC-induced inflammatory processes appears to involve those events which promote increased vascular permeability, allowing for extravascular deposition of IC. Once deposited, complement-fixing IC can attract, via complement activation and generation of C5a, phagocytic cells resulting in subsequent tissue destruction. Conceivably, as a consequence of recognition of red cell bound IC, human PMN are able to release PAF which in turn induces platelet aggregation and the release of vasoactive amines. In addition, PAF itself is capable of increasing microvascular permeability (Bjork *et al.*, 1983), in skin (Cusack, 1980) as well as in lung (Worthen *et al.*, 1983). The resultant increase in vascular permeability believed to precede IC deposition in tissues could thus be explained by these events. Furthermore, massive platelet aggregation in the microvascular bed is likely to play a direct pathogenic role.

Our studies seem to establish beyond reasonable doubt that the presentation of red-cell bound IC to neutrophils *in vitro* results in the release of PAF. The effect of supernatants of neutrophils incubated with RBC-IC on platelets was abrogated by phospholipase (Benveniste *et al.*, 1977), and the active mediator was isolated through the general lipid extraction and thin layer chromatography protocol that was proposed for PAF isolation by Pinckard *et al.* (1979).

The adsorption of IC to RBC appears mediated both by complement-dependent and complement-independent mechanisms. Binding through CR1 receptors is the main binding mechanism for IC prepared at Ab excess, while IC prepared at Ag excess are efficiently bound through non-complement dependent mechanisms which do not appear to involve specific receptors. Furthermore, it appears that stimulation of PAF release is mainly a function of the interaction of RBC bound IC with Fc receptors on the neutrophil since it can be induced with equal efficiency by IC prepared and adsorbed to RBC in the presence or absence of complement.

Our studies suggest a potentially adverse effect for IC-RBC interactions which is in direct contrast with the protective effect initially proposed by Siegel *et al.* (1981) and by Wilson *et al.* (1982) and which received experimental support in the investigations of Cornacoff *et al.* (1983). These authors demonstrated that radiolabeled BSA-rabbit anti-BSA complexes infused intravenously into baboons and rhesus monkeys were rapidly bound by erythrocytes. Within 5 min after the infusion of IC, most of the IC was removed from the red cells as they passed through the liver, probably by the phagocytic Kuppfer cells, although this was not proven. It was further shown that IC-coated RBC were not sequestered by any organ. To date, this remains the strongest argument for a beneficial role of IC-RBC interactions, which would represent a clearance mechanism for soluble IC.

Investigations not reported in this article carried out in our laboratory (Sherwood and Virella, 1986) have shown two additional interesting facts concerning the interaction between human neutrophils and IC-coated RBC: in the first place, the RBC are not phagocytized; secondly, the IC appear to be transferred from the RBC membrane to the neutrophil membrane and eventually ingested. It thus appears that a mechanism for elimination of RBC-adsorbed IC may exist in humans, similar to that described by Cornacoff *et al.* (1983) in baboons. However, the final outcome of the interaction between RBC-bound IC and phagocytic cells in man is not very clear, since it appears very plausible that deleterious effects secondary to the release of mediators such as PAF may ensue.

ACKNOWLEDGMENTS

The authors are indebted to Dr Peter Winocour for the generous gift of apyrase and invaluable guidance in the process of preparation of rabbit platelets, and to the Editorial Office staff of the Department of Basic and Clinical Immunology and Microbiology at the Medical University of South Carolina for their collaboration in preparing this manuscript.

Research supported in part by the Juvenile Diabetes Foundation and by the South Carolina Appropriation for Biomedical Research.

REFERENCES

Ardlie, N.G., Packham, M.A., and Mustard, J.F. (1970). 'Adenosine disphospate-induced platelet aggregation in suspensions of washed rabbit platelets', *Br. J. Haematol.*, **19**, 7–17.

Becker, E.L., and Henson, P.M. (1973). '*In vitro* studies of immunologically induced secretion of mediators from cells and related phenomena', *Adv. Immunol.*, **17**, 93–193.

Benveniste, J., Le Couedic, J.P., Polonsky, J., and Tence, M. (1977). 'Structural analysis of purified platelet-activating factor by lipases', *Nature*, **269**, 170–171.

Benveniste, J., Tence, M., Varenne, P., Bidault, J., Boullet, C., and Polonsky, J. (1979). 'Semi-synthese et structure proposee du facteur activant des plaquettes (PAF)-acether, un alkyl ether analogue de la lysophosphatidylcholine', *C.R. Acad. Sci. Paris*, **289**, 1037–1040.

Bjork, J., Lindblom, L., Gerdin, B., Smedegard, G., Arfors, K.E., and Benveniste, J. (1983). 'Paf-acether (platelet activating factor) increases microvascular permeability and affects endothelium-granulocyte interaction in microvascular beds', *Acta Physiol. Scand.*, **199**, 305–308.

Camussi, G., Mencia-Huerta, J.M., and Benveniste, J. (1977). 'Release of platelet-activating factor and histamine. I. Effect of immune complexes, complement and neutrophils on human and rabbit mastocytes and basophils', *Immunology*, **33**, 523–534.

Camussi, G., Tetta, C., Deregibus, M.C., Bussolino, F., Segoloni, G., and Vercellone, A. (1982). 'Platelet-activating factor (PAF) in experimentally-induced rabbit acute serum sickness: role of basophil-derived PAF in immune complex deposition', *J. Immunol.*, **128**, 86–94.

Cornacoff, J.B., Hebert, L.A., Smead, W.L., Vanaman, M.E., Birmingham, D.J., and Waxman, F.J. (1983). 'Primate erythrocyte-immune complex-clearing mechanism', *J. Clin. Invest.*, **71**, 236–247.

Cusack, N.J. (1980). 'Platelet-activating factor', *Nature*, **285**, 193.

Dryer, R.L. (1970). 'The lipids', In N.W. Tietz (ed.) *Fundamentals of Clinical Chemistry*, Saunders, Philadelphia, p. 302.

Henson, P.M. (1971). 'The immunologic release of constituents from neutrophil leukocytes. I. The role of antibody and complement on nonphagocytosable surfaces or phagocytosable particles', *J. Immunol.*, **107**, 1535–1546.

Henson, P.M., Hollister, J.R., Musson, R.A., Webster, R.O., Spears, P., Henson, J.E., and McCarthy, K.M. (1979). 'Inflammation as a surface phenomenon: initiation of inflammatory processes by surface-bound immunologic components' In Weissman, Samuelsson and Paoletti, (eds.) *Advances in Inflammation Research*, Raven Press, New York, Vol. 1, p. 341.

Henson, P.M., and Oades, Z.G. (1975). 'Stimulation of human neutrophils by soluble and insoluble immunoglobulin aggregates. Secretion of granule constituents and increased oxidation of glucose', *J. Clin. Invest*, **56**, 1053–1061.

Houck, J.C. (1968). 'A personal overview of inflammation', *Biochem. Pharmacol.*, **Supplement 17**, 1–3.

Molnar, J., and Lorand, L. (1961). 'Studies on apyrases', *Arch. Biochem. Biophys.*, **93**, 353–363.

O'Flaherty, J.T., Lees, C.J., Miller, C.H., McCall, C.E., Lewis, J.C., Love, S.H., and Wykle, R.L. (1981). 'Selective desensitization of neutrophils: further studies with 1-*O*-alkyl-*sn*-glycero-3-phosphocholine analogues', *J. Immunol.*, **127**, 731–737.

Ohno, O., and Cooke, T.D. (1978). 'Electron microscopic morphology of immunoglobulin aggregates and their interactions in rheumatoid articular collagenous tissues', *Arthritis Rheum.*, **21**, 516–527.

Pinckard, R.N., Farr, R.S., and Hanahan, D.J. (1979). 'Physicochemical and functional identity of rabbit platelet-activating factor (PAF) released *in vivo* during IgE anaphylaxis with PAF released *in vitro* from IgE sensitized basophils', *J. Immunol.*, **123**, 1847–1857.

Ragsdale, C.G., and Arend, W.P. (1979). 'Neutral protease secretion by human monocytes. Effect of surface-bound immune complexes', *J. Exp. Med.*, **149**, 954–968.

Rocklin, R.E. (1980). 'Production and assay of macrophage inhibitory factor', In N.R. Rose and H. Friedman (eds.) *Manual of Clinical Immunology* (2nd edn.,), American Society for Microbiology, p. 246.

Siegel, I., Liu, T.L., and Gleicher, N. (1981). 'The red-cell immune system', *Lancet*, **2**, 556–559.

Shaw, J.O., Pinckard, R.N., Ferrigni, K.S., McManus, L.M., and Hanahan, D.J. (1981). 'Activation of human neutrophils with 1-*O*-hexadecyl/octadecyl-2-acetyl-*sn*-glycero-3-phosphorylcholine (platelet activating factor)', *J. Immunol.*, **127**, 1250–1255.

Sherwood, T.A., and Virella, G. (1986). 'The binding of immune complexes to human red cells: complement requirements and fate of the RBC-bound IC after interaction with human phagocytic cells', *Clin. Exp. Immunol.*, (in press).

Shunichi, S., Jasin, H.E., and Ziff, M. (1980). 'Absence of immunoglobulins in rheumatoid cartilage-pannus junctions', *Arthritis Rheum.*, **23**, 816–821.

Virella, G., Espinoza, A., Patrick, H., and Colwell, J.A. (1982). 'Polymorphonuclear leukocytes release a factor(s) that induces platelet aggregation and ATP release after interaction with insoluble and surface-fixed immune complexes', *Clin. Exp. Immunol.*, **49**, 684–694.

Virella, G., Lopes-Virella, M.F.L., Shuler, C., Sherwood, T., Espinoza, G.A., Winocour, P., and Colwell, J.A. (1983). 'Release of PAF by human polymorphonuclear leukocytes stimulated by immune complexes bound to Sepharose particles and human erythrocytes', *Immunology*, **50**, 43–51.

Weissman, G., Serhan, C., Korchak, H.M., and Smolen, J.E. (1982). 'Neutrophils: release of mediators of inflammation with special reference to rheumatoid arthritis, *Ann. N.Y. Acad. Sci.*, **389**, 11-24.

Wilson, J.G., Wong, W.W., Schur, P.H., and Fearon, D.T. (1982). 'Mode of inheritance of decreased C3b receptors on erythrocytes of patients with systemic lupus erythematosus', *N. Eng. J. Med.*, **307**, 981–986.

Worthen, G.S., Goins, A.J., Mitchel, B.C., Larsen, G.L., Reeves, J.R., and Henson, P.M. (1983). 'Platelet-activating factor causes neutrophil accumulation and edema in rabbit lungs', *Chest*, **Supplement 83**, 13S–15S.

New Horizons in Platelet Activating Factor Research
Edited by C. M. Winslow and M. L. Lee
© 1987 John Wiley & Sons Ltd.

10

Processing of Platelet Activating Factor by Interstitial and Alveolar Epithelial Cells from Rat Lungs

R. Kumar, R.J. King, and D.J. Hanahan

Platelet activating factor (PAF) is a potent mediator of several cellular functions, which include platelet and polymorphonuclear neutrophil aggregation, the production of thromboxane B and superoxide ions, and the contraction of smooth muscle. Further, it induces both cardiovascular and pulmonary responses when injected intravenously (Snyder, 1985; Halonen *et al.*, 1980, 1981; Pinckard *et al.*, 1982).

PAF is synthesized and released by a variety of cells including neutrophils, basophils, monocytes, endothelial cells and alveolar macrophages (Snyder, 1985; Pinckard *et al.*, 1982; Benveniste and Vargaftig, 1983). Several of these cells are normally present in the parenchyma of the lungs, and more are recruited to the lungs under abnormal conditions. In recent studies we found that glycerylether phosphocholine, which is a product of PAF metabolism, comprises about 6 percent of the phosphatidylcholine fraction of the surfactant isolated from the lavage fluid of dogs and rabbits. PAF-like activity was also observed in the surfactant of these animals (Kumar *et al.*, 1985). Stenmark and co-workers (1985) have reported the presence of PAF-like activity in the lavage fluid of nine out of nine infants with bronchopulmonary dysplasia. We have found that surfactant obtained from premature baboons of 140 days gestation age which were ventilated for six days with 100 percent oxygen had detectable PAF-like activity, whereas no such activity was observed in 140 days animals that were not ventilated (R. Kumar, R.J. King and D.J. Hanahan, unpublished observations). It is, therefore, evident that PAF may be released into alveolar fluid, even under conditions not associated with severe lung injury. Since picomolar quantities of PAF are sufficient to initiate potentially important cardiopulmonary reactions (Halonen *et al.*, 1981), we felt that it was of interest to determine how PAF might be metabolized by lung cells. We had three objectives for these experiments. First, to determine whether alveolar epithelial type II cells and lung fibroblasts were capable of metabolizing PAF to less toxic compounds. Secondly, to identify the principal products of this metabolism. Finally, to begin experiments on the capacity of alveolar type II cells to synthesize PAF.

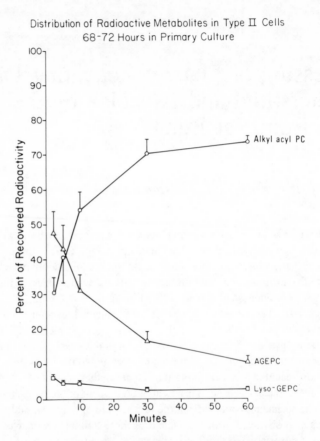

Figure 1. Intracellular distribution of metabolites of AGEPC in type II cells expressed as the percent of total recovered activity at each time point. Shown are the means and standard errors for the experiments

METABOLISM OF PAF

Alveolar epithelial type II cells and lung fibroblasts were purified from mixed rat lung cells by differential adherence in culture (Dobbs and Mason, 1978). Adherent cells consisted of about 90 percent type II cells, as indicated by their characteristic appearance associated with lamellar inclusions and staining with a modified Papanicolaou procedure (Kikkawa and Yoneda, 1974). Greater than 95 percent of the cells excluded trypan blue. 1-*O*-[³H]-alkyl-2-acetyl-*sn*-glycero-3-phosphocholine [³H-AGEPC, 18:0] was bound to bovine serum albumin (2.5 mg percent) and presented to the cells at a concentration of 1×10^{-9} M. The cells were incubated in RPMI 1640 containing 0.05 percent albumin at 37 °C for times varying from 2 to 60 min, the cellular lipids were extracted, and the incorporation of radioactivity into AGEPC, acyl-GEPC and lyso-GEPC was analyzed at the time intervals. The uptake of [³H]AGEPC by type II cell was linear with time from 5 to 60 min, with average rates of 660 and 450 fM 10^{-6} cells h⁻¹ for cells in primary culture for 48–72 h. Further analysis of the intracellular counts indicated that AGEPC was rapidly metabolized and by 10 min 60 percent of the AGEPC was converted into long chain acyl GEPC (50 percent), and lyso-GEPC (10 percent) (Figure 1). By 60 min radioactivity in AGEPC was less than 10 percent of the total intracellular activity. Lyso-GEPC remained at about 10 percent throughout the incubation period. Approximately 10 percent of the total radioactivity was consistently present in the neutral lipid fraction, but was not analyzed further. The uptake of [³H]AGEPC by fibroblasts was very similar to that seen with type II cells, but the *h* of metabolism was slower. Thus, in fibroblasts, AGEPC constituted 85 percent of the cellular counts after 10 min. By 60 min about 50 percent of the counts were present in the long chain acyl GEPC.

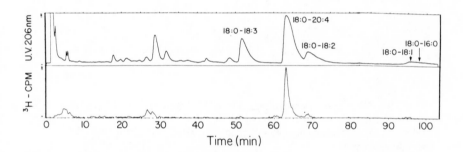

Figure 2.   HPLC separation of 1-O-[³H]alkyl-2 acyl-PC from alveolar epithelial type II cells. Glycerylether standards containing fatty acids at the *sn*-2 position were added to the sample and their elution is shown in the upper tracing. A Waters C-18 radial pack cartridge was used and eluted with a solvent system of methanol-acetonitrile-200 mM choline chloride in water (83:10:7 V/V) at a flow rate of 1 ml min⁻¹

In order to characterize the composition of the alkyl-acyl GEPC produced from the metabolism of AGEPC, the PC fraction was recovered from the TLC plate, mixed with synthetic analogs of 1-*O*-octadecyl-2-acyl-3-PC containing fatty acids of various chain length at the *sn*-2 position (16:0, 18:2, 18:3, 20:4), and analyzed by HPLC (Patton *et al.*, 1982). We found that 74 percent of the total counts from type II cells were eluted with the alkyl ether standards, of which about 90 percent had the mobility with 1-*O*-alkyl-2-arachidonyl-*sn*-glycero-3-phosphocholine. The remaining counts were distributed in small amounts in the 18:3, 18:2 and 18:1 or 16:0 glyceryl ethers.

About 10—15 percent of the total counts were in compounds eluting with diacyl phosphatidylcholine, but these were not identified (Figure 2). The distribution of radioactivity was not markedly different when the experiments were carried out in lung fibroblasts.

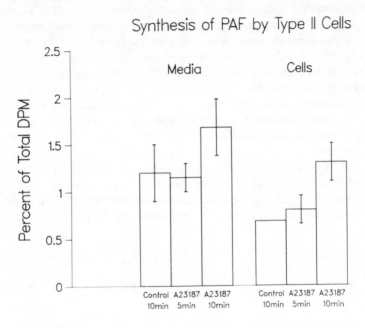

Figure 3. Type II cells were prelabeled with [³H]-lyso-GEPC for 4 h, and then incubated for 5 and 10 min with 2 × 10⁻⁶ M A23187. Cells in media were separately extracted and analyzed for radioactivity incorporated into AGEPC. Error bars are the ranges for two experiments

SYNTHESIS OF PAF BY TYPE II CELLS

Our final series of experiments studied the synthesis and release of PAF by type II cells in primary culture. We have, to date, carried out two types of experiments evaluating the capacity of type II cells in primary culture to synthesize and release AGEPC. In one set type II cells were presented with [³H]lyso-GEPC in a medium of RPMI 1640 with 0.05 percent BSA. After 4 h the medium was removed, new medium was added, and either 2 × 10⁻⁶M A23187 (in 5 μl ethanol) or 5 μl ethanol (control) was given to the cells. After 5 and 10 min the cells and media were separately recovered, and the lipids extracted. Part of the sample was applied to silica gel 60 plate for separation of lipids, using a solvent system of 60:35:6 (C/M/W). The phospholipids were identified by external standards added to the sample, scraped directly into counting vials and quantified by scintillation counting. The remainder of the sample was run on TLC (without added external standards) and the AGEPC fraction was eluted from the silica gel by Bligh—Dyer extraction. This was evaporated, suspended in 0.05 percent BSA/saline, and assayed for PAF-activity by platelet aggregation.

The incorporation of [^{3}H]lyso GEPC into AGEPC is shown in Figure 3. Under basal conditions, type II cells in primary culture incorporate about 0.7 percent of the precursor into material with the R_f of AGEPC. When presented with 2×10^{-6}M A23187, this incorporation doubles to about 1.3 percent of the incorporated radioactivity. About 1.2 percent of the radioactive material in the medium has the R_f of AGEPC, and its release is increased to 1.8 percent by a 10 min exposure to A23187. AGEPC fractions from the 5 min A23187 medium, 5 min A23187 cells, and 10 min A23187 cell induced irreversible aggregation of platelets, both in the absence and presence of 10 μM indomethacin. Control cells and medium from about 5×10^5 cells did not show this activity.

The second set of studies quantified by bioassay the amount of PAF present in type II cells and medium after 10 min of stimulation with 4×10^{-6} M A23187. The ionophore was presented to the cells ($2-3 \times 10^6$ cells) in 0.05 percent BSA/RPMI 1640, and the lipid in the cells and medium were separately extracted after 10 min incubation at 37 °C. The AGEPC fraction was isolated by TLC, and quantified by platelet aggregation and the release from platelets of ^{3}H-labeled serotonin. We found that control cells contained 0.13 $\pm$ 0.11 (S.E.) pmoles of PAF-activity per 10^6 cells, and released less than 5 percent of their activity into the medium. When the cells were stimulated with the calcium ionophore, cellular activity increased by ten-fold, and the medium had activities nearly equal to that found intracellularly. Although these results are interesting in that they suggest that type II cells may synthesize PAF, perhaps for use in the regulation of some metabolic activity, we cannot yet rule out that a contamination by 1—2 percent alveolar macrophages might not have contributed to our observed results. Experiments are underway using lectins specific for alveolar macrophages and type II cells, respectively, by which we might detect the presence of small amounts of contaminating cells.

In conclusion, type II cells in primary culture have the capacity to hydrolyze PAF. Lung fibroblasts share this capability but the time course of metabolism is slower. Nearly 90 percent of the alkyl-acyl GEPC contained arachidonic acid at the *sn*-2 position. Type II cells may synthesize PAF, and may release it into the medium in response to calcium ionophores.

REFERENCES

Benveniste, J., and Vargaftig, B.B. (1983). 'Platelet-activating factor: An ether lipid with biological activity'. In H.K. Mangold and F. Paltauf (eds.), *Ether Lipids*, Academic Press, New York, pp. 356—376.

Dobbs, L.G., and Mason, R.J. (1978). 'Pulmonary alveolar Type II cells isolated from fats:

release of phosphatidylcholine in response to beta-adrenergic stimulation', *J. Clin. Invest.*, **63**, 378–387.

Halonen, M., Palmer, J.D., Lohman, I.C., McManus, L.M., and Pinckard, R.N. (1980). 'Respiratory and circulatory alterations induced by acetyl glycerylether phosphorylcholine (AGEPC), a mediator of IgE anaphylaxis in the rabbit', *Amer. Rev. Resp. Dis.*, **122**, 915–924.

Halonen, M., Palmer, J.D., Lohman, I.C., McManus, L.M., and Pinckard, R.N. (1981). 'Differential effects of platelet depletion on the cardiovascular and pulmonary alterations of IgE anaphylaxis and AGEPC infusion in the rabbit', *Amer. Rev. Resp. Dis.*, **124**, 416–421.

Kikkawa, Y., and Yoneda, K. (1974). 'The type II epithelial cell of the lung. 1. Method of isolation', *Lab. Invest.*, **30**, 76–84.

Kumar, R., King, R.J., and Hanahan, D.J. (1985). 'Occurrence of glycerylethers in the phosphatidylcholine fraction of surfactant from dog lungs', *Biochim. Biophys. Acta*, **836**, 19–26.

Patton, G.M., Fasulo, J.M., and Robins, J. (1982). 'Separation of phospholipids and individual molecular species of phospholipids by high performance liquid chromatography', *J. Lipid Res.*, **23**, 190–196.

Pinckard, R.N., McManus, L.M., Halonen, M., and Hanahan, D.J. (1982). 'Immuno pharmacology of acetyl glycerylether phosphorylcholine'. In C. Lenfant and H. Newball (eds.) *Immuno-pharmacology of the lung.* Marcel Dekker, Inc., New York, pp. 73–107.

Snyder, F. (1985). 'Chemical and biochemical aspects of platelet-activating factor: A novel class of acetylated ether-linked choline phospholipids', *Med. Res. Review*, **5**, 107–140.

Stenmark, K.R., Eyzaguirre, M., Remigo, L., Secome, J., and Benson, P.M. (1985). 'Recovery of platelet-activating factor and leukotrienes from infants with severe bronchopulmonary dysplasia: Clinical improvement with cromolyn treatment', *Amer. Rev. Res. Dis.*, **131**, a236.

New Horizons in Platelet Activating Factor Research
Edited by C. M. Winslow and M. L. Lee
© 1987 John Wiley & Sons Ltd.

11

Molecular Mechanisms in the Action of Platelet Activating Factor and Other Mediators of Inflammation

P.M. Lad, C.V. Olson, I.S. Grewal, S.J. Scott, D.B. Learn, P.A. Smiley and M. Frolich-Lafrance

INTRODUCTION

Platelet activating factor (PAF) is a potent phospholipid mediator of anaphylaxis. Its *in vivo* effects include hypotension, neutropenia and thrombocytopenia (Pinckard *et al.*, 1983; Henson, 1981; Goetzl *et al.*, 1980; Ingraham *et al.*, 1982). *In vitro* studies show that PAF causes the release of serotonin from platelets and promotes multiple inflammatory responses including chemotaxis, enzyme release, superoxide generation and aggregation by activating the human neutrophil. Thus its behavior in the neutrophil system is strikingly similar to that of the bacterial chemotactic peptide, f-met-leu-phe (FMLP) as well as agents such as C5a and IgG. Several receptors for hormones and neurotransmitters are regulated by guanine nucleotides through N (or G) proteins (generally defined as Ni and Ns, linked to inhibitory and stimulatory receptors respectively) (Lad *et al.*, 1977a, 1983). The involvement of these regulatory proteins with neutrophil receptors was therefore suspected. The binding studies of the FMLP receptor (Koo and Snyderman, 1983) pointed to a GTP-sensitive regulation of this receptor as well. Our initial studies were directed at the effects of β-adrenergic and prostaglandin receptors which are coupled to the Ns protein (Lad *et al.*, 1984a,b). Intracellular cyclic AMP is elevated and cell function is inhibited in a manner which is sensitive to the receptor occupied and the level of cyclic AMP generated (Lad *et al.*, 1985). As the Ns component is not a candidate for any primary transduction associated with the FMLP receptor, the obvious other choice was the Ni protein. A powerful probe for this protein is available from the work of Okajima *et al.* (1984, 1985) who have shown that pertussis toxin specifically modifies the Ni protein in several cell systems. In the past year it has become clear both from our studies and those of other investigators (Lad *et al.*, 1985b,c,d,e,f; Verghese *et al.*, 1985; Becker *et al.*, 1985; Shefcyk *et al.*,

1985; Cockcroft *et al.*, 1985; Smith *et al.*, 1985; Bokoch and Gilman, 1984) that this pertussis toxin sensitive Ni protein plays a pivotal role in the regulation of multiple receptors and transduction systems in the human neutrophil. The results presented below describe some of our recent findings.

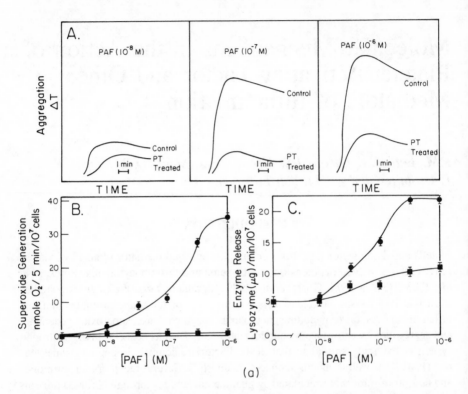

Figure 1.   A.   Effects of pertussis toxin pretreatment on PAF mediated aggregation (panel A), superoxide generation (panel B), and enzyme release (panel C). Human neutrophils were pretreated with or without pertussis toxin and tested for various functional responses as indicated. The details of cell preparations, toxin pretreatment and function tests were carried out as reported previously (Lad *et al.*, 1985c). Bars (panels B and C) denote the S.E.M. of triplicate determinations, and the experiments are representative of cells derived from three separate normal donors.

RESULTS

Inhibition of cell function by pertussis toxin

As shown in Figure 1A and B the neutrophil functional responses of chemotaxis, enzyme release, superoxide generation and aggregation are inhibited after incubation with pertussis toxin (PT). Both the PAF and the FMLP receptors are affected as are the C5a and Fc receptors. In addition, receptor mediated cell surface capping via the lectin Concanavalin-A (Con-A) is also abolished. Because multiple functions and multiple receptors are affected, the question arises as to which process might not be regulated by a PT substrate. Two exceptions have been noted:

1. Receptors which produce their functional effects by crosslinking, such as the Con-A and Fc γ-receptors, are less susceptible to the effects of pertussis toxin.
2. Phagocytosis of opsinized or non-opsinized particles is immune to the effect of the toxin.

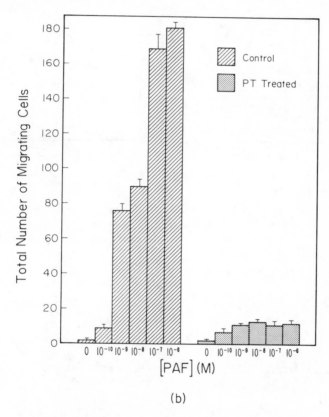

(b)

B. Effects of pertussis toxin pretreatment on PAF mediated chemotaxis. Control (buffer treated) and toxin treated neutrophils were tested for chemotaxis at the levels of PAF indicated. Chemotaxis was carried out in a modified Boyden chamber filter assay (Lad *et al.*, 1985c) 10^6 cells were included in each chamber and the number of cells which had migrated a distance > 20 μm were counted in four separate fields. Bars denote S.E.M. of triplicate determinations, and the experiment is representative of cells derived from three separate normal donors

These results indicate the following: receptors and actions which depend on extensive crosslinking of cell surface sites are less dependent on Ni; while monovalent ligands or those which involve relatively low degrees of crosslinking (capping) are controlled via Ni.

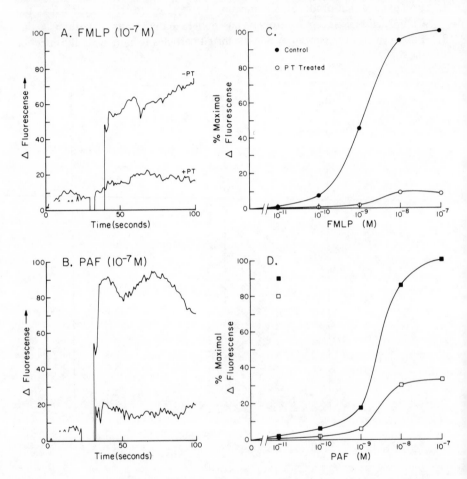

Figure 2.   Receptor-mediated changes in the fluorescence of quin2 loaded cells. Neutrophils were treated with PT and loaded with quin2 as reported previously (Lad *et al.*, 1985e). The cells were then exposed to FMLP (10^{-7} M) (Panel A) and PAF (10^{-7} M) (Panel B) and the changes in fluorescence were monitored. The fluorescence in arbitrary units (100) corresponds to 355 nM of Ca^{2+} as determined by a precalibration curve. Panels C and D are fluorescence readings at the 100 s mark for different concentrations of the two ligands. The fluorescence change noted with 10^{-7} M FMLP was 30 percent of that observed after analysis of the cells with 0.1 percent Triton. These results are representative of four experiments carried out on different normal donors. The break in fluorescence signal in Figures 3A and B corresponds to the time of addition of the ligand and mixing

Regulation of the receptor

A simple prediction from the above results is that the receptors affected in the function tests be regulated by guanine nucleotide and the phenomenon observed in other receptor systems be established for these receptors; namely, that pertussis toxin treatment uncouples the receptor from the regulatory protein. Results with the FMLP receptor, (Koo *et al.*, 1983; Okajima and Ui; 1984; Lad *et al.*, 1984b) suggest that:

1. GTP regulates the binding of FMLP to its receptor.
2. PT treatment is associated with the abolition of this regulation of the receptor by guanine nucleotide, as well as the loss of agonist induced guanine nucleotide exchange.

Thus the early step which is altered, and from which the loss of cell function is derived, is the interaction of the receptor in question with the Ni GTP-binding protein.

Associated transduction mechanisms of FMLP and PAF receptors

Traditionally, the Ns protein was thought to be involved in the stimulation of adenylate cyclase, while the Ni protein was thought to be associated with the inhibition of this enzyme. More recently a novel role for the Ni protein has been indicated in the regulation of intracellular calcium levels. Thus, the interaction of Ns and Ni to cyclic AMP and calcium related events should be investigated further. The major transduction effect associated with Ni is the modulation of calcium levels; both the mobilization of internal calcium and the influx of extracellular calcium (Figure 2). Several distinct measurements of calcium movement are possible and have now been carried out (Naccache *et al.*, 1977a,b; Korchak *et al.*, 1984; Tsien *et al.*, 1982). Calcium influx using isotopic calcium is decreased in response to PT, and using channel blockers, both dependent and independent Ni mediated responses can be discerned. Alterations in the fluorescence properties of Quin2 (a dye which measures intracellular calcium by chelation) loaded cells are observed in response to FMLP and PAF, and are abolished by toxin treatment. The alterations in the fluorescence of chlorotetracycline (CTC) (Figure 3) a probe which measures 'membrane' associated calcium, are similarly diminished as a result of pertussis toxin's action. Thus, regardless of the measure of calcium related transduction, inhibition is observed, suggestive of 'Ni' influence. Adenylate cyclase inhibition (Figure 4) occurs only at high concentrations of the agonist and is disrupted by the toxin. Prior stimulation of the cyclase system with Ns linked agonists is required to observe this inhibition.

Regulation of functions and receptors by phorbol ester

Phorbol-12-myristate-13-acetate (PMA) is known to affect multiple cell functions probably by the activation of kinase C. It is a useful probe in the human neutrophil

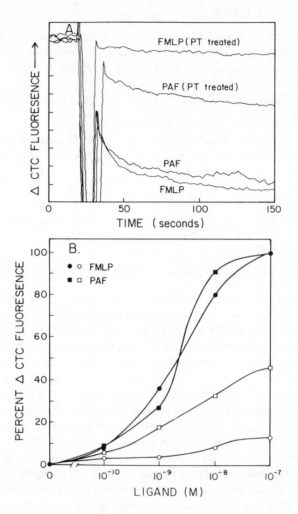

Figure 3. PT mediated inhibition of FMLP and PAF stimulated release of membrane bound calcium by chlorotetracycline. Neutrophils (1×10^8 cells ml^{-1} in modified HBSS) were pretreated with buffer or PT for 60 min at 37 °C, diluted ten-fold in PBS, and incubated with 50 μM chlorotetracycline (CTC) for 20 min at 37 °C. The cells were washed twice (150 g for 15 min at 4 °C), resuspended in PBS (1×10^7 cells ml^{-1}) and kept at room temperature. The assay was as follows: 1 ml of the cell suspension was added to 2.5 ml of buffer (150 nM NaCl, 5 mM KCl, 1.3 mM CaCl$_2$, 1.2 mM Mg Cl$_2$, and 10 mM N-2-hydroxyethyl-piperazine-N-2-ethane sulfonic acid (HEPES), pH = 7.4), incubated at 37 °C for 5 min, and transferred to a 1 cm cuvette. The ligand was added (35 μl), and the decrease in fluorescence followed for 150 s. The excitation wavelength was 390 nM and the emission 560 nM. In panel A, a characteristic fluorescence profile for buffer and PT treated cells is shown as stimulated by FMLP (10^{-7} M) and PAF (10^{-7} M). Panel B shows the dose–response for FMLP and PAF, for buffer (closed symbols) and PT treated (open symbols) cells as measured at the 15 s mark (Lad *et al.*, 1985c)

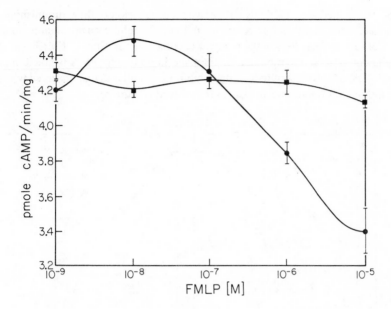

Figure 4. FMLP Mediated Adenylate Cyclase Inhibition. Neutrophil plasma membranes were pretreated with PT ($\bigcirc$), and in buffer without added toxin, as reported previously (Lad *et al.*, 1985b). Adenylate cyclase was then measured in the presence of forskolin (10^{-5} M) in order to enhance basal activity and thus permit easier detection of inhibition. Basal values were 0.6 pM min^{-1} mg^{-1} and were essentially unaltered by the treatment with PT. Bars denote the S.E.M. of triplicate measurements. The experiments were repeated twice with purified plasma membranes, twice with whole homogenates and in the presence of forskolin as well as PGE$_1$ + GTP

because it serves to augment some functions (enzyme release and superoxide generation) and inhibit others (capping and chemotaxis). A comparison of its stimulatory and inhibitory functions can be used to better identify the role of kinase C in neutrophil function. Our initial efforts were directed at understanding the role of PMA in the regulation of cell functions. Two classes of functions were tested; those which involved the use of cytochalasin B, such as enzyme release and superoxide generation, and those in which the function is observed naturally in the absence of this agent. Our results indicate the following: PMA promotes the reactions of enzyme release and superoxide generation. Preincubation with PMA at levels too low to elicit these functions can also augment the reactions of enzyme release and superoxide generation from other receptors, such as those for FMLP. In contrast to these function tests, the functions of capping and chemotaxis are inhibited by PMA, and the inhibition is observed at very low concentrations (0.1 ng ml^{-1}). Finally, when phagocytosis is studied, no inhibition is observed, regardless of the particle presented to the cells. At the level of transduction, the central feature of PMA is that it enhances the effects of Ns mediated cyclic AMP increases (see below) while diminishing Ni mediated calcium mobilization. As shown in Figure 4, inhibition of calcium mobilization is observed regardless of the receptor occupied. Thus, Con-A, FMLP and PAF have all been observed to mobilize calcium and inhibition by PMA is noted in each instance. The order of magnitude of the inhibition is similar to that observed with the toxin, although different mechanisms are involved (Figure 5).

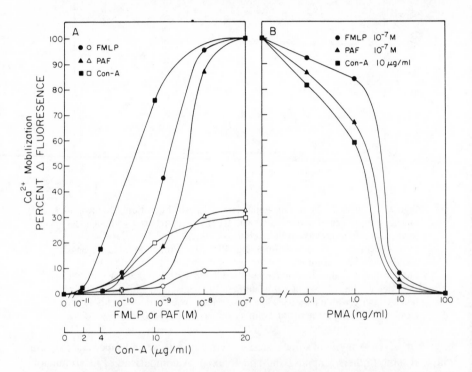

Figure 5.   Effect of PT and PMA on calcium mobilization. Human neutrophils, loaded with the fluorescent calcium chelator quin2, were pretreated with buffer (closed symbols), PT (open symbols) (panel A), or PMA (panel B), under conditions described in previous reports (Lad *et al.*, 1985e). The magnitude of the fluorescence enhancement in response to the different ligands was monitored continuously and the value at the 200 s (FMLP or PAF) or 400 s (Con-A) mark is presented in the above figures. The concentration of intracellular calcium corresponding to the 100 percent mark was 250 nM (FMLP), 225 nM (PAF) and 280 nM (Con-A)

Role of phosphorylation

The profiles of protein phosphorylation are being evaluated using three types of systems which include (a) ^{32}P loaded intact cells, (b) γ-^{32}P ATP loaded permeablized cells and (c) isolated membranes. The experiments using the second type of system are shown in Figure 6. A high molecular weight protein 220K is phosphorylated in response to PAF in a dose dependent manner. Proteins of molecular weight, 67K and 60K are also phosphorylated. These are similar to those reported by workers with guinea pig neutrophils (White *et al.*, 1984; Huang *et al.*, 1983, 1984; Okamura *et al.*, 1984). The identities of these proteins are as yet unknown and their possible association with the cytoskeleton is currently being further explored; particularly as vimentin has been proposed as a target protein for the phosphorylation pathway from the FMLP receptor. Of particular interest is whether the same proteins are phosphorylated by PMA (a promoter and inhibitor of cell function) as by PAF or FMLP.

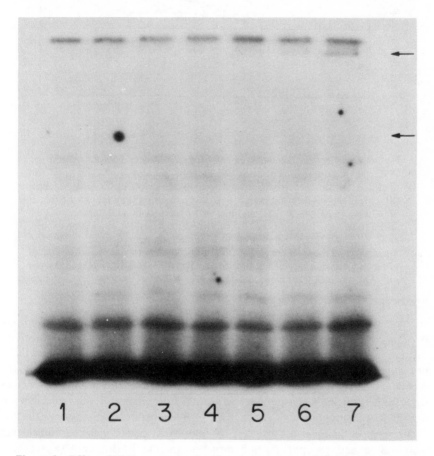

Figure 6. Effect of PAF on protein phosphorylation. Autoradiography of 11 percent SDS polyacrylamide gels of PAF dose dependence of protein phosphorylation is shown. Neutrophils were exposed to various concentrations of PAF for 1 min. at 37 °C, then loaded with $[\gamma^{32}p]$ ATP (100 μCi gel^{-1} 5 × 10^7 cells) in buffer containing 0.1 percent Triton, 10 mM Mg^{2+} 20 μM, Zn^{2+} and 1 mM PMSF for 1 min, digested with nucleases for 1 min, after which the reaction was stopped by boiling in SDS. The peptide phosphorylation detected above background phosphorylation is designated by the arrow ($\leftarrow$)

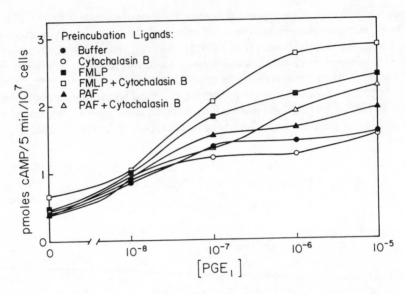

Figure 7. Effect of Preincubation of Neutrophils with FMLP and PAF on PGE₁, mediated cAMP generation. Neutrophils (80 μl of 3 × 10⁷ cells ml⁻¹ in modified HBSS) were preincubated with buffer, FMLP (10⁻⁶ M) or PAF (10⁻⁶ M) in the absence and presence of cytochalasin B (10 μg ml⁻¹) for 5 min at 37 °C. PGE₁ (10⁻⁸ to 10⁻⁵ M) and methyl-isobutyl-xanthine (1 mM) were then added (final volume 200 μl) and the cells were incubated for an additional 5 min at 37 °C. The reaction was stopped with the addition of ice cold TCA (200 μl of 5 percent) and the cells pelleted at 2500 g for 15 min at 4 °C. A 200 μl aliquot of each supernatant was then neutralized with 50 μl of NaOH (0.5 N) and assayed for cAMP by RIA (Lad *et al.*, 1985a)

Ns–Ni interactions

We have mentioned earlier that the Ns protein is involved in the increase in cyclic AMP and the Ni protein is predominantly involved in the elevation of intracellular calcium. Evidence that these pathways interact is presented in the experiments shown in Figure 7. Pretreatment of neutrophils with either FMLP or PAF causes a dose dependent increase in the subsequent stimulation of cyclic AMP via receptors coupled to the Ns protein. When the converse process was examined, it was found that pretreatment of neutrophils with either PGE₁ or β-adrenergic agonists, particularly in the presence of the phosphodiesterase inhibitor MIX, caused a decrease in calcium mobilization and phosphoinositide turnover via the FMLP or PAF receptors (Figure 8).

Identity of the putative 'Ni' protein

The traditional role of Ni is in the inhibition of adenylate cyclase. The discovery of target enzymes other than cyclase has led to the obvious question of whether the same

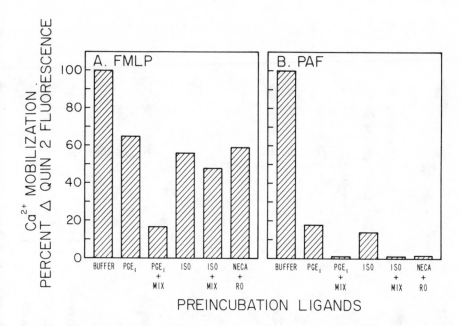

PREINCUBATION LIGANDS

Figure 8. Inhibition of FMLP and PAF stimulated calcium mobilization by Ns associated receptors. Neutrophils were loaded with quin2 as described in the legend to Figure 3. The cells (1 ml of 1 × 10^7 cells ml^{-1}) were diluted into 2.5 ml of HEPES buffer containing PGE_1 (10^{-5} M) or isoproterenol (10^{-4} M) in the absence or presence of methyl-isobutyl-xanthine (MIX) (1 mM), or N-ethyl carboxyamide adenosine (NECA) (10^{-4} M) in the presence at RO 20-1724, and preincubated for 5 min at 37 °C. FMLP (10^{-7} M) or PAF (10^{-7} M) was then added and the fluorescence monitored for 200 s. Preincubation with NECA alone shows no inhibition (Lad *et al.*, 1985a)

protein is involved in multiple transduction mechanisms (e.g. phospholipase C, A_2, and cyclase). The idea of a family of proteins has been advocated by several investigators although the nature of this familial grouping is unclear. Our own approach (Figure 9) has been to carry out the peptide mapping of the Ni component in the human neutrophil and compare this to the properties of the pertussis toxin substrates from the human erythrocyte, human platelet and mouse lymphoma (AC-) plasma membranes. In each of these systems, distinct functions have been associated with the Ni protein. Three types of experiments are involved. First, ADP-ribosylation, followed by peptide mapping, reveals that there is a resistance to Ni proteolysis in the modified state, except with papain and *S. aureus* proteases. Secondly, if the sequence is reversed and the ribosylation follows proteolysis, then the 41K band is completely abolished; suggesting that in the non-ADP-ribosylated state Ni is indeed susceptible to proteolysis. Finally, when Cleveland gels (protease digestion of the denatured 41K protein from SDS gels) are carried out, marked proteolysis is observed with all proteases; however, the pattern obtained is similar to that in the proteolysis-post-ADP-

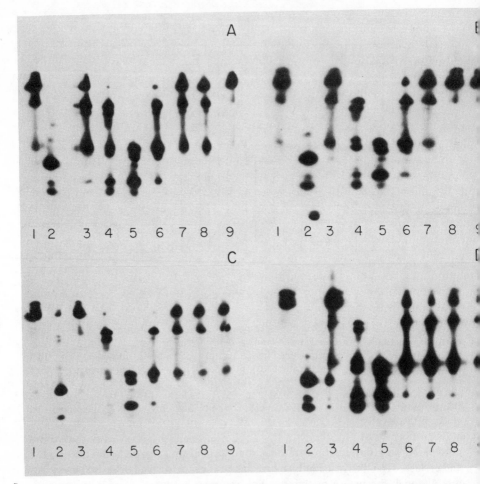

Figure 9.   Cleveland gel analysis of the pertussis toxin substrate. The purified plasma membranes of human erythrocytes (A), platelet (B), neutrophil (C), and mouse lymphoma AC⁻ (D), were ADP-ribosylated with pertussis toxin (3 μg 100 μ⁻¹ membrane protein) in the presence of [α-³²P]NAD, and other agents as described previously. The 41K labeled band was identified by wet-gel autoradiography and then subjected to proteolysis. The proteases (5 ng lanes 2–9) are *S. aureus* (2), endoprotease (3), chymotrypsin (4), papain (5), elastase (6), thermolysin (7), pepsin (8), carboxypeptidase A (9). The second gel was autoradiographed in the presence of an enhancer (Autofluor) and photographed

ribosylation experiments. These observations suggest that the sites available to proteolysis are not markedly enhanced in the denatured state. Of most interest is the fact that all three properties are noted in the pertussis toxin substrate in the erythrocyte, platelet, neutrophil, and the lymphoma AC-membrane. These results imply that the Ni protein is significantly conserved in cells of different types and in the evolutionary sense as well. The divergences in protein sequences, if present, are likely to be such that the protease sensitive sites are not involved.

Role of phospholipid turnover

The primary mechanism proposed for the mobilization of intracellular calcium is that of Berridge (1984). According to this view, the hydrolysis of phosphoinositides by a membrane bound phospholipase-C results in the production of the intracellular iono-phore IP_3 and possibly cyclic IP_3. Our preliminary experiments were directed at the role of this pathway as related to the activation of phospholipase A_2. (Bokoch and Gilman, 1984; Smith *et al.*, 1985; Okajima *et al.*, 1984, 1985). The experiments suggest a rapid decline (Figure 10) in the levels of PIP_2 (10−20 s) followed by a slower replenishment (2−5 min). A PAF dependent decrease in PIP_2 is observed in these experiments. Direct measurement of IP_3 and by the concomitant measure of the release of arachidonate to judge the possible activation of phospholipase A_2 and its inhibition by agents such as PT or PMA, is now in progress to confirm these results.

The quantal nature of second messenger action

Calcium and cyclic AMP are two second messengers that are involved in the initiation and regulation of FMLP and PAF mediated responses. How do these second messenger levels relate to the regulation of cell function? At least with respect to cyclic AMP, the answer to this question is quite complex. Our results indicate that occupancy of the appropriate Ns linked cell surface receptor will lead to a diminution in specific responses. As shown in Table 1, occupancy of the β-adrenergic receptor to levels which would account for only partial occupancy of this receptor and a small activation of cyclase, are sufficient to completely inhibit superoxide generation. (Lad *et al.*, 1985a). By contrast, complete occupancy of the PGE_1 receptor, which is associated with maximal activation of cyclase, together with the inhibition of cyclic AMP phosphodiesterase is required to inhibit enzyme release. Under conditions which are effective for inhibition of enzyme release, chemotaxis is very poorly inhibited and capping is unaffected. These results suggest that the type of function initiated from a particular receptor may have unique requirements for modulation via specific messengers. With regard to calcium, the situation is still less clear. For example, the question of whether FMLP and PAF share the same pool of intracellular calcium and whether the amount of calcium released correlates in simple fashion with the cell function initiated, are matters which are still to be resolved. Our results suggest that chemotaxis and capping are initiated with relatively low levels of intracellular calcium, that phagocytosis requires even less, while much higher levels are required for the initiation of enzyme release and superoxide generation.

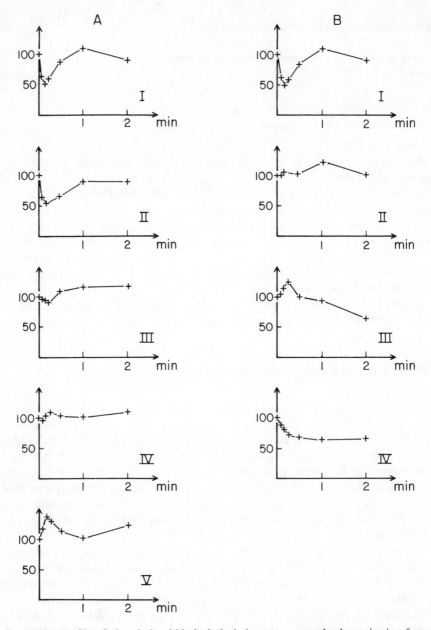

Figure 10. Profile of phosphoinositide hydrolysis in response to platelet activating factor. Panel A represents the changes in PIP_2 level in response to different concentrations of PAF measured as ^{32}P labeled PIP_2. Neutrophils were prelabeled with ^{32}P (1 h 37 °C, 500 μCi 10^{-8} neutrophils ml^{-1}). The cells were then stimulated with PAF and aliquots were removed at the indicated time intervals. The phospholipids are extracted, PIP_2 separated by TLC and the radioactivity of PIP_2 measured and compared with the value before stimulation. PAF concentration: (1) 10^{-6} M, (2) 10^{-7} M (3) 10^{-8} M (4) 10^{-9} M (5) (10^{-10} M). Panel B represents the effect on PAF stimulated PIP_2 turnover by preincubation with (1) buffer (control) (2) pertussis toxin (1 μg ml^{-1} 130 min), (3) PMA (100 μg ml^{-1} 10 min), (4) PGE_1 (10^{-6} M, 10 min)

Table 1. Comparison of agonists acting at the prostaglandin and β-adrenergic receptors in the modulation of adenylate cyclase, intracellular cyclic AMP, enzyme release and superoxide production

Ligands	Cyclase activation	Intracellular cyclic AMP	Inhibition of enzyme release	Inhibition of superoxide production
Isoproterenol	4×10^{-7} M [1.5]	5×10^{-8} M [1.4]	[1] (0)	6×10^{-10} M (52%)
Isoproterenol (-methylisobutylxanthine)	n.a.	1×10^{-8} M [2]	[1] (0)	[2]
Prostaglandin E$_1$	6×10^{-7} M [4]	7×5.10^{-8} M [1.3]	[1] (0)	7.5×10^{-9} M (100%)
Prostaglandin E$_1$ (-methylisobutylxanthine)	n.a.	5×10^{-8} M [11]	$(5-9) \times 10^{-8}$ M (40%)	[2]

Methylisobutylxanthine was present at 100 μM. Numbers in the second and third column refer to the apparent K_{act} for activation: the number in square parentheses refers to fold activation. n.a. denotes measure not applicable or not done.

[1] The effect is too small to be adequately quantified. For the adenylate cyclase assay, cytosolic phosphodiesterases have been removed, and cyclic AMP is added to the assay to prevent degradation of cyclic AMP due to membrane-bound phosphodiesterases.

[2] Complete inhibition was observed in the presence of methylisobutylxanthine alone in the absence of hormone. The apparent K_{act} was computed as the concentration which gives 50 percent of the maximal effect observed in the presence of the given ligand. Numbers in the fourth and fifth column refer to the apparent K_I for inhibition; the number in round parentheses refers to percent inhibition

DISCUSSION

The results presented imply that the GTP-binding protein Ni is a key regulatory element in the actions of multiple mediators of inflammation including PAF. PT modifies a single GTP-binding subunit of 41K, with attendant uncoupling of the receptor from the regulatory subunit resulting in the loss of guanine nucleotide exchange and receptor promoted GTPase activities in the isolated plasma membrane. In agreement with this concept, several receptor promoted functions are inhibited in intact cells. A possible weakness in the argument is that the effect in whole cells might arise from a different mechanism from that seen in isolated membranes. This objection cannot be entirely overcome, although the membranes isolated after whole cell treatment with toxin show properties which are very similar to purified membranes post-treated with toxin.

The possible transduction mechanisms associated with Ni remain only partially clear. Mobilization of intracellular calcium seems likely, although a smaller effect on adenylate cyclase cannot be ruled out. Similarly, multiple calcium related steps are affected by the toxin. These results point to two important areas:

1. The Ni protein is probably pleiotropic in nature governing more than one transduction system.
2. Regulation involves multiple calcium related steps including calcium influx, dissociation of membrane bound calcium and mobilization of intracellular calcium.

As these steps are related to each other, unique inhibitors (perhaps by acting at steps distal to Ni) which can distinguish between these processes will be required before the exact cellular physiology of the receptor−Ni complex becomes clear. The answer of whether the Ni protein mediating calcium related events is the same as the protein inhibiting adenylate cyclase is as yet unclear. Two mutually exclusive possibilities are that they are completely distinct proteins and that they possess substantial homology with relatively minor differences. Our results point to the second possibility for the following reasons:

1. The molecular weight of Ni in the neutrophil is very close to the platelet and human erythrocyte Ni proteins which have been previously shown to attenuate adenylate cyclase.
2. The uncoupling of the receptor from Ni (at least for the FMLP receptor) is similar to the observations for cyclase linked receptors.
3. The disposition of protease sensitive sites toward a wide panel of proteases is also conserved in all 'Ni' systems.

The possibility of a divergence of sequences within the conserved sites is currently being explored further.

An important observation relates to the reciprocal interactions between the Ns and Ni proteins and the structural relationships between them; cyclic AMP is an inhibitor of calcium mobilization via Ni while intracellular calcium apparently augments the elevation of cyclic AMP via Ns. The results presented here suggest that interactions may occur between the Ns and Ni components probably through second messengers. In addition, the Ns protein may share or attenuate some of the properties of the Ni protein, the only clear distinguishing feature being the susceptibility to ADP-ribosylation by cholera rather than PT. Our results suggest that ADP-ribosylation protects Ns from proteolysis in a manner similar to that observed with pertussis toxin and Ni.

Generally the postulated sequence following FMLP receptor occupancy and in part for PAF is that the hydrolysis of PIP_2 inositides leads to the production of IP_3 and diglyceride. Calcium, in conjunction with the released diglyceride, activate kinase C. This sequence is at best vastly oversimplified and is unlikely to be correct in detail. Notable arguments against it are:

1. Phorbol esters (potent activators of kinase C) inhibit rather than activate calcium mobilization by Ni-linked receptors.
2. The inhibitor of kinase C, polymyxin B, has no effect on FMLP functions.
3. The effects of PAF and FMLP in those function tests which do not involve cytochalasin B are inhibited rather than promoted by PMA.
4. PMA mediated kinase C activation may give rise to covalent modification of the receptors themselves, of the associated GTP-binding proteins, or of possible combinations.
5. Where similar effects of phorbol esters and PAF are observed, the concentrations of PMA required are very high.

Considered together these results suggest that the same kinase C is not involved in the actions of PMA and R-Ni complexes (White *et al.*, 1984; Naccache *et al.*, 1985; Volpi *et al.*, 1985). Whether distinct kinase C enzymes are involved remains unknown. However, the possibility of a target for intracellular calcium other than the activation of kinase C should be seriously considered (e.g. direct activation of calmodulin sensitive kinases or other enzymes) and is currently being studied.

REFERENCES

Becker, E.L., Kermode, J.C., Naccache, P.H., Yassin, R., Marsh, M.L., Munoz, J.J., and Shaafi, R.I. (1985). 'The inhibition of neutrophil granule enzyme secretion and chemotaxis by pertussis toxin', *J. Cell. Biol.*, **1985**, 1641–1646.
Berridge, M.J. (1984). 'Inositol triphosphate and diacylglycerol as second messengers', *Biochem. J.*, **220**, 345–360.
Bokoch, G.M., and Gilman, A.G. (1984). 'Inhibition of receptor-mediated release of arachidonic acid by pertussis toxin', *Cell*, **39**, 301–308.
Cockcroft, S., Barrowman, M.M., and Gomperts, B.D. (1985). 'Breakdown and synthesis of

polyphosphoinositides in f-met-leu-phe stimulated neutrophils', *FEBS Letters*, **181**, 259–263.

Goetzl, E.J., Derian, C.K., Tanber, A.I., and Varlene, F.N. (1980). 'Novel effects of 1-*O*-hexadecyl-2-acyl-*sn*-glycero-3-phosphorycholine mediators on human leukocyte function; delineation of the specific roles of the acyl substituents', *Biochem. Biophys. Res. Commun.*, **941**, 881–888.

Henson, P.M. (1981). 'Platelet-activating factor as a mediator of neutrophil-platelet interactions in inflammation', *Agents and Actions*, **11**, 545–546.

Huang, C.K., Hill, J.M., Bormann, B.J., Mackin, W.M., and Becker, E.L. (1983). 'Endogenous substrates for cyclic AMP-dependent and calcium-dependent protein phosphocylation in rabbit peritoneal neutrophils', *Biochim. Biophys. Acta*, **760**, 126–135.

Huang, C.K., Hill, J.M., Bormann, B.J., Mackin, W.M., and Becker, E.L. (1984). 'Chemotactic factors induced vimentin phosphorylation in rabbit peritoneal neutrophil', *J. Biol. Chem.*, **259**, 1386–1389.

Ingraham, L.M., Gates, T.D., Allen, J.M., Higgins, C.P., Baehner, R.L., and Boxer, L.A. (1982). 'Metabolic, membrane and functional responses of human polymorphonuclear leukocytes to platelet-activating factor', *Blood*, **59**, 1259–1266.

Koo, C., Lefkovitz, R.J., and Snyderman, R. (1983). 'Guanine nucleotides modulate the binding affinity of the oligopeptide chemoattractant receptor on human polymorphonuclear leukocytes', *J. Clin Invest.*, **72**, 748–753.

Korchak, N.M., Rutherford, L.E., and Weissman, G. (1984). 'Stimulus response coupling in the human neutrophil: Temporal analysis of changes in cytosolic calcium and calcium efflux', *J. Biol. Chem.*, **259**, 4070–4074.

Lad, P.M., Yamamura, H., and Rodbell, M. (1977a). 'GTP stimulates and inhibits adenylate cyclase through distinct regulatory processes', *J. Biol. Chem.*, **252**, 7964–7971.

Lad, P.M., Welton, A.F., and Rodbell, M. (1977b). 'Evidence for distinct sites in the regulation of the glucagon receptor and of adenylate cyclase activity', *J. Biol. Chem.*, **252**, 5942–5948.

Lad, P.M., Reisinger, D.M., and Smiley, P.A. (1983). 'Ligand requirements for the relaxation of adenylate cyclase from activated and inhibited states', *Biochemistry*, **22**, 3278–3284.

Lad, P.M., Glovsky, M.M., Richards, J.H., Learn, D.B., Reisinger, D.M., and Smiley, P.A. (1984a). 'Identification of receptor regulatory proteins, membrane glycoproteins, and functional characteristics of adenylate cyclase in vesicles derived from the human neutrophil', *Mol. Immunol.*, **21**, 627–629.

Lad, P.M., Glovsky, M.M., Smiley, P.A., Klempner, M., Reisinger, D.M., and Richards, J.H. (1984b). 'The beta adrenergic receptor in the human neutrophil plasma membrane: receptor-cyclase uncoupling is associated with amplified GTP-activation', *J. Immunol.*, **132**, 1466–1472.

Lad, P.M., Goldberg, B.J., Smiley, P.A., and Olson, C.V. (1985a). 'Receptor-specific threshold effects of cyclic AMP are involved in the regulation of enzyme release and superoxide production from human neutrophils', *Biochim. Biophys. Acta*, **846**, 286–295.

Lad, P.M., Olson, C.V., and Smiley, P.A. (1985b). 'Association of the FMLP receptor in human neutrophils with a GTP-binding protein sensitive to pertussis toxin', *Proc. Nat. Acad. Sci. (USA)*, **82**, 869–873.

Lad, P.M., Olson, C.V., and Grewal, I.S. (1985c). 'Platelet activating factor mediated effects on human neutrophil function are inhibited by pertussis toxin', *Biochem. Biophys. Res. Commun.*, **129**, 632–638.

Lad, P.M., Glovsky, M.M., Richard, J.H., Smiley, P.A., and Backstrom, B. (1985d). 'Regulation of human neutrophil guanylate cyclase by metalions, free radicals and the muscarinic cholinergic receptor', *Mol. Immunol.*, **22**, 731–739.

Lad, P.M., Olson, C.V., Grewal, I.S., and Scott, S.J. (1985e). 'A pertussis-toxin sensitive GTP-binding protein in the human neutrophil regulates multiple receptors, calcium mobilization and lectin-induced capping', *Proc. Nat. Acad. Sci. (USA)*, **82**, 8643−8647.

Lad, P.M., Olson, C.V., Grewal, I.S., Frolich, M., Smiley, P.A., and Scott, S.J. (1985f). 'Role of GTP binding proteins in the regulation of the human neutrophil in progress in leukocyte biology'. In J. Oppenheim (ed.) *Proceedings of the RES/LCC conference*, Alan R. Liss, New York, 373−378.

Naccache, P.H., Showell, H.J., Becker, E.L., and Sha'afi, R.I. (1977a). 'Transport of sodium, potassium and calcium across rabbit polymorphonuclear leukocyte membranes. Effect of chemotactic factor', *J. Cell Biol.*, **73**, 428−444.

Naccache, P.H., Showell, H.J., Becker, E.L., and Sha'afi, R.I. (1977b). 'Changes in ionic movements across rabbit polymorphonuclear leukocyte membranes during lysosomal enzyme release. Possible ionic basis for lysosomal enzyme release', *J. Cell Biol.*, **75**, 635−649.

Naccache, P.H., Molski, T.F.P., Borgeat, P., White, J.R., and Sha'afi, R.I. (1985) 'Phorbol esters inhibit the f-met-leu-phe and leukoteiene B4-stimulated calcium mobilization and enzyme secretion in rabbit neutrophils', *J. Biol. Chem.*, **260**, 2125−2131.

Nishizuka, Y. (1984). 'Role of Kinase C in cell surface signal transduction and tumour promotion', *Nature (London)*, **308**, 693−698.

Okajima, F., and Ui, M. (1984). 'ADP-ribosylation of the specific membrane protein by Islet-activating protein, pertussis toxin, associated with inhibition of a chemotactic peptide induced arachidonate release in neutrophils', *J. Biol. Chem.*, **259**, 13 863−13 871.

Okajima, F., Katada, T., and Ui, M. (1985). 'Coupling of the guanine nucleotide regulatory protein to chemotactic peptide receptors in neutrophil membranes and its uncoupling by islet-activating protein, pertussis toxin. A possible role of the toxin substrate in Ca^{2+}-mobilizing receptor-mediated signal transduction', *J. Biol. Chem.*, **260**, 7226−7233.

Okamura, N., Ohashi, S., Nagahisa, N., and Ishibashi, S. (1984). 'Changes in protein phosphorylation in guinea pig polymorphonuclear leukocytes by treatment with membrane-perturbing agents which stimulate superoxide anion production', *Arch. Biochem. Biophys.*, **228**, 270−277.

Pinckard, R.N., McManus, L.M., and Hanahan, D.J. (1983). 'Chemistry and biology of acetyl, glyceryl ether phosphorylcholine (platelet activating factor)', *Adv. Inflamm. Res.*, **4**, 147−169.

Shefcyk, J., Yassin, R., Volpi, M., Molkski, T.F., Naccache, P.H., Munoz, J.J., Becker, E.L., Feinstein, M.B., and Sha'afi, R.I. (1985). 'Pertussis but not cholera toxin inhibits the stimulated increase in actin association with cytoskeleton in rabbit neutrophils; role of the "G proteins" in stimulus-response coupling', *Biochem. Biophys. Res. Commun.*, **126**, 1174−1181.

Smith, C.D., Lane, B.C., Kusaka, I., Verghese, M.W., and Snyderman, R. (1985). 'Chemoattractant receptor induced hydrolysis of phosphotidylinositol 4,5, bisphosphate in human polymorphonuclear leukocyte membranes. Requirement for a guanine nucleotide regulatory protein', *J. Biol. Chem.*, **260**, 5875−5878.

Tsien, R.Y., Pozzan, T., and Rink, T.J. (1982). 'Calcium homeostasis in intact lymphocytes cytoplasmic free calcium monitored with a new intracellular trapped fluorescent indicator', *J. Cell Biol.*, **94**, 325−334.

Verghese, M.W., Smith, C.D., and Snyderman, R. (1985). 'Potential role for a guanine nucleotide regulatory protein in chemoattractant receptor mediated polyphosphoinositide metabolism, Ca^{++} mobilization and cellular responses by leukocytes', *Biochem. Biophys. Res. Commun.*, **127**, 450−457.

Volpi, M., Naccache, P.H., Molski, T.F.P., Shefcyk, J., Huang, C.K., Marsh, M.L., Munoz,

J., Becker, E.L., and Sha'afi, R.I. (1985). 'Pertussis toxin inhibits f-met-leu-phe but not phorbolester stimulated changes in rabbit neutrophils: Role of G proteins in excitation-response coupling', *Proc. Nat. Acad. Sci. (USA)*, **82**, 2708–2712.

White, J.R., Huang, C.K., Hill, J.M., Naccache, P.M., Becker, E.L., and Sha'afi, R.I. (1984). 'Effects of phorbol 12-myristate 13-acetate and its analogue 4 alpha-phorbol 12, 13-didecanoate on protein phosphorylation and lysosomal enzyme release in rabbit neutrophils', *J. Biol. Chem.*, **259**, 8605–8611.

New Horizons in Platelet Activating Factor Research
Edited by C. M. Winslow and M. L. Lee
© 1987 John Wiley & Sons Ltd.

12

Reversal by SRI 63−072 of Endotoxin and Immune Aggregate-Induced Hypotension in the Rat

Ronald G. Van Valen, Robert N. Saunders, Mark L. Lee and Dean A. Handley

INTRODUCTION

Platelet activating factor (PAF) is an ether phospholipid which is recognized to induce a broad range of biological responses. Intravenously administered synthetic PAF (C_{18}) does produce a selective activation of inflammatory and mononuclear phagocytic systems with possible involvement of the endothelium as well (Altura *et al.*, 1985; Kasuya *et al.*, 1984). The resultant cardiovascular and pulmonary effects have been characterized in a wide variety of animal species (Tanaka *et al.*, 1983; Kamitani *et al.*, 1984).

Within the past few years however, attention has focused upon several animal models of endogenous PAF production, including gram-negative sepsis (Inarrea *et al.*, 1985), endotoxin challenge (Terashita *et al.*, 1985) and soluble immune aggregate administration (Sanchez Crespo *et al.*, 1982).

The objective of this study was to evaluate the antagonist of PAF, SRI 63-072, following endotoxin or soluble immune aggregate-induced systemic hypotension and depressed blood flow in the rat. The results of these studies further support the role of endogenous PAF in vascular shock models.

MATERIALS AND METHODS

Endotoxin (ET) from *E. coli* lipopolysaccharides (0111-B, Sigma Inc., St Louis, MO) was prepared fresh daily and given at $3-30$ mg kg^{-1} i.v. to establish a dose−response profile. Human IgG (Cohn fraction II, III) was purchased from Sigma Inc. (St Louis, MO) and was heat aggregated (A-IgG) to form large molecular weight complexes (Sanchez Crespo *et al.*, 1982). These soluble aggregates were separated from the smaller immune complexes using differential centrifugation (100,000 × g, 3h). The supernatant was partitioned, adjusted to 10–50 mg protein ml^{-1} in tris-Tyrode's buffer (Spector, 1978) and used to establish a dose-response curve. Sizing confirmed the fraction to be 0.9–1.9 10^6 molecular weight. SRI 63-072 was administered i.v. in tris-Tyrode's buffer 1–6 min after inducer challenge.

Male Sprague–Dawley rats (250–270 g) were anesthetized with sodium pentobarbital (50 mg kg^{-1} i.p.) and the common carotid artery was cannulated for direct arterial pressure measurements using a Gould 2400S physiograph. Blood flow of the mesenteric artery was monitored on a calibrated electromagnetic flowmeter (probe EP102.5, Carolina Medical Electronics, Inc.). Mean arterial pressures (MAP) were calculated from recordings and blood flow rates were expressed as percent of controls. All values are mean ± 1 S.D. for 3–5 animals per treatment. The ED$_{50}$ value for SRI 63-072 was obtained using the inhibitory profile from A-IgG challenge (three animals per dose).

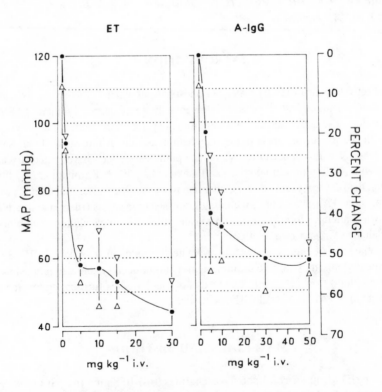

Figure 1. Dose–response profiles of systemic hypotension induced in the rat by endotoxin (1A) or soluble immune aggregates of A-IgG (1B). Values (mean ± 1 S.D.) are expressed as actual MAP (mmHg) and as percent change from controls

RESULTS

Endotoxin will produce a characteristic dose-response depression $(3-30$ mg kg^{-1} i.v.) in carotid arterial pressure (Figure 1A). At 15 mg kg^{-1}, ET more consistently depressed arterial pressure and mesenteric artery blood flow than at other doses tested. There was an immediate onset of hypotension of 54 ± 8 percent and recovery was complete within 6 min. SRI 63-072 at 1.0 mg kg^{-1} i.v., when given $2-4$ min after ET, produces rapid recovery of MAP and blood flow to near control values (Figure 2A). Similar results with SRI 63-072 were observed in the reversal of hypotension induced by 100 ng kg^{-1} PAF in the rat (Handley *et al.*, 1986).

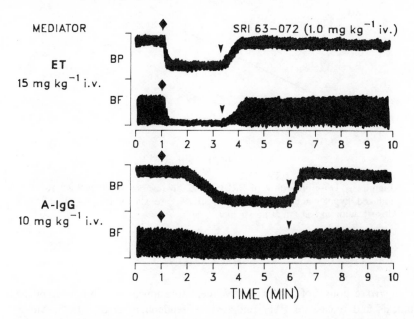

Figure 2.   The injection time (t = 1 min; ♦) is denoted for endotoxin at 15 mg kg^{-1} and soluble aggregates of A-IgG at 10 mg kg^{-1} on carotid blood pressure (bp) and mesenteric arterial blood flow (bf). Administration of SRI 63−072 at 1.0 mg kg^{-1} i.v. (▼) will reverse all depressed wave forms to near baseline control values

Intravenous delivery of soluble immune aggregates (A-IgG) at $3-50$ mg kg^{-1} produced consistent dose-related blood pressure reductions (Figure 1B). In comparison to ET (or PAF), A-IgG does not induce immediate hypotension. Instead, we observed a protracted onset followed by a progressive rate of decrease in MAP (Figure 2B) and a prolonged stabilized period (greater than 7 min; data not shown) at 40 ± 9 percent MAP. However, only a slight depression of the mesenteric artery blood flow was seen at these dosages of A-IgG. Administration of $0.01-0.1$ mg kg^{-1} SRI 63-072 produced immediate reversal of A-IgG-induced MAP with and ED$_{50}$ of 0.05 mg kg^{-1} i.v. (Figure 3).

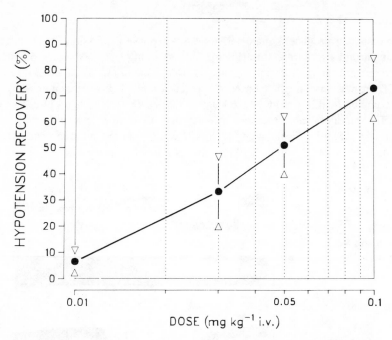

Figure 3.   Dose−response of SRI 63−072 on reversal of 10mg kg^{-1} A-IgG-induced hypotension. The mean ± S.E.M. are shown for $n = 3$ animals dose^{-1}, with an ED$_{50}$ of 50μg kg^{-1} i.v.

DISCUSSION

The *in vivo* responses of several putative mediators appear to be produced by the bio-synthesis and release of PAF. Endotoxin (Freudenberg *et al.*, 1985; Maier and Hahnel, 1984) and soluble immune aggregates (Inarrea *et al.*, 1983; Mannik, 1980) are stimuli for the mononuclear phagocytic system, hepatic macrophages (Kupffer cells) and complement pathways (Kunkel *et al.*, 1981; Morrison and Ulevitch, 1978). Endotoxin has also been reported to increase endogenous phospholipase A$_2$ levels in heart (Liu *et al.*, 1983) and liver (Conde *et al.*, 1981) and to secondarily decrease membrane lipid fluidity (Liu *et al.*, 1983). In addition, A-IgG tissue deposition and subsequent activation of Fc receptors mediate the interaction with neutrophils, plate-lets and certain T and B lymphocyte populations (Mannik, 1980). These induced res-ponses may be in part or wholly responsible for the PAF-like episodes of systemic hypotension (Gonzalez-Crussi and Hsueh, 1983; Terashita *et al.*, 1985; Sanchez Crespo *et al.*, 1985) and the intense peripheral vasoconstriction of the mesenteric arterioles and metarterioles (Altura *et al.*, 1985) as evidenced by depressed blood flow.

However, apparent differences among these mediators are clear. In contrast to the rapid onset of hypotension observed for ET (or PAF), a delayed induction of hypotension occurred with A-IgG treatment. Similar findings have been reported elsewhere (Sanchez Crespo *et al.*, 1985). The relative difference in onset may be due to a more pyrogenic nature of ET over that of A-IgG (Dinarello, 1983) or the involvement of second messengers. Likewise different vascular beds may be involved, as evidenced by the ability of ET (and PAF) but not A-IgG, to affect mesenteric blood flow. The duration of hypotensive activity following A-IgG challenge (>10 min) may reflect a prolongation of PAF release in comparison to that observed for ET.

The reversal or attenuation of systemic hypotension and depressed mesenteric blood flow following SRI 63-072 and other PAF inhibitors (CV-3988, Terashita *et al.*, 1985; BN 52021, Sanchez Crespo *et al.*, 1985) is suggestive of antagonism of the PAF-like effects. The possibility also exists for a mechanism involving membrane-lipid reorganization (Liu *et al.*, 1982).

In conclusion, PAF and endotoxin reduce blood pressure and blood flow in rats. Soluble aggregates of IgG only affect blood pressure. Our studies indicate that the competitive receptor antagonist SRI 63-072 effectively reverses these vascular effects. Whether PAF acts directly, through a second messenger, or synergistically with other mediators, the observed reversal by SRI 63-072 further implicates a role for PAF in various endotoxemic shock states and immune complex-induced vascular diseases.

ACKNOWLEDGMENTS

The authors wish to gratefully acknowledge Ms. Sonya Beasley for competent manuscript preparation.

REFERENCES

Altura, B.M., Gebrewold, A., and Burton, R.W. (1985). 'Failure of microscopic metarterioles to elicit vasodilator responses to acetylcholine, bradykinin, histamine and substance P after ischemic shock, endotoxemia and trauma: possible role of endothelial cells', *Microcirculation, Endothelium, and Lymphatics*, **2**, 121–127.

Conde, G., Garcia-Barreno, P., Municio, A.M., and Suarez, A. (1981). '*In vitro* and *in vivo* effect of *Escherichia coli* endotoxin on mitochondrial phospholipase A_2 activity', *Febs. Lett.*, **127**, 115–120.

Dinarello, C.A. (1983). 'Molecular mechanisms in endotoxin fever', *Agents Actions*, **13**, 470–486.

Freudenberg, N., Freudenberg, M.A., Bandara, K., and Galamos, C. (1985). 'Distribution and localization of endotoxin in the reticulo-endothelial system (RES) and in the main vessel of the rat during shock', *Path. Res. Pract.*, **179**, 517–527.

Gonzalez-Crussi, F., and Hsueh, W. (1983). 'Experimental model of ischemic bowel necrosis. The role of platelet-activating factor and endotoxin', *Am. J. Pathol.*, **112**, 127–135.

Handley, D.A., Van Valen, R.G., Melden, M.K., Flury, S., Lee, M.L., and Saunders, R.N.

(1986). 'Inhibition and reversal of endotoxin-, aggregated IgG- and paf-induced hypotension in the rat by SRI 63-072, a paf receptor antagonist', *Immunopharmacology*, 12, 11–16.

Inarrea, P., Gomez-Cambronero, J., Pascual, J., del Carmen Ponte, M., Hernando, L., and Sanchez Crespo, M. (1985). 'Synthesis of paf-acether and blood volume changes in gram-negative sepsis', *Immunopharmacology*, 9, 45–52.

Kamitani, T., Katamoto, M., Tatsumin, M., Katsuta, K., Ono, T., Kikuchi, H., and Kumada, S. (1984). 'Mechanism(s) of the hypotensive effect of synthetic 1-O-octadecyl-2-O-acetyl-glycero-3-phosphorylcholine', *Eur. J. Pharmacol.*, 98, 357–366.

Kasuya, Y., Masuda, Y., and Shigenobu, K. (1984). 'Possible role of endothelium in the vasodilator response of rat thoracic aorta to platelet activating factor (PAF)', *J. Pharma. Dyn.*, 7, 138–142.

Kunkel, S.L., Fantone, J.C., and Ward, P.A. (1981). 'Complement mediated inflammatory reactions'. In H.L. Ioachiom (ed.) *Pathobiology Annual* Raven Press, New York, pp. 127–155.

Liu, M.S., and Takeda, H. (1982). 'Endotoxin-induced stimulation on phospholipase A activities in dog hearts', *Biochem. Med.*, 28, 62–69.

Liu, M.S., Ghosh, S., and Yang, Y. (1983). 'Change in lipid fluidity induced by phospholipase A activation: a mechanism of endotoxin shock', *Life Sci.*, 33, 1995–2002.

Maier, R.V., and Hahnel, G.B. (1984). 'Potential for Endotoxin-activated Kuppfer's cells to induce microvascular thrombosis', *Arch. Surg.*, 119, 62–67.

Mannik, M. (1980). 'Physicochemical and functional relationships of immune complexes', *J. Invest. Dermatol.*, 74, 333–338.

Morrison, D.C., and Ulevitch, R.J. (1978). 'The effects of bacterial endotoxins on host mediation systems: A review', *Am. J. Pathol.*, 93, 526–617.

Sanchez Crespo, M., Alonso, F., Inarrea, P., Alvarez, V., and Egido, J. (1982). 'Vascular actions of synthetic paf-acether (a synthetic platelet-activating factor) in the rat: Evidence for a platelet independent mechanism', *Immunopharmacology*, 12, 173–185.

Sanchez Crespo, M., Fernandes-Gallardo, S., Nieto, M.L., Baranes, J., and Braquet, P. (1985). 'Inhibition of the vascular actions of immunoglobulin G aggregates by BN 52021, a highly specific antagonist of paf-acether', *Immunopharmacology*, 10, 69–74.

Spector, T. (1978). 'Refinement of the coomassie blue method of protein quantitation', *Anal. Biochem.*, 86, 142–146.

Tanaka, S., Kasuya, Y., Masuda, Y., Shigenoba, K. (1983). 'Studies on the hypotensive effects of platelet activating factor (paf 1-O-alkyl-2-acetyl-sn-glyceryl-3-phosphorylcholine) in rats, guinea pigs, rabbits and dogs', *J. Pharm. Dyn.*, 6, 866–873.

Terashita, Z., Imura, Y., Nishikawa, K., and Sumida, S. (1985). 'Is platelet activating factor (paf) a mediator of endotoxin shock?', *Eur. J. Pharmacol.*, 109, 257–261.

Cellular and Tissue Responses of Platelet Activating Factor

New Horizons in Platelet Activating Factor Research
Edited by C. M. Winslow and M. L. Lee
© 1987 John Wiley & Sons Ltd.

13

Interactions of Platelet Activating Factor with other Lipid Mediator Systems in Neutrophils

J.T. O'Flaherty and Jun Nishihira

INTRODUCTION

Polymorphonuclear neutrophils (PMN), when stimulated, produce platelet activating factor (PAF), diacylglycerols and metabolites of arachidonic acid such as 5-L-hydroxy-E,Z,Z,Z,Z-eicosatetraenoic acid (5-HETE) and leukotriene B_4 (LTB_4) (Betz and Henson, 1980; Mueller *et al.*, 1984; Samuelsson, 1982; Takenawa *et al.*, 1983; Chilton *et al.*, 1982; Walsh *et al.*, 1981). Based on their capacities to stimulate PMN, these lipids may be secondary messengers that link cell stimulation with ensuing functional responses. Individually, however, they possess insufficient potency to explain many cellular responses. It seems more likely that the lipids act in concert under conditions in which they have overlapping and sometimes complementary effects. Here, we review our studies on these co-operative interactions.

LIPID BIOACTIVITIES

PAF (O'Flaherty *et al.*, 1981; Shaw *et al.*, 1981; Smith *et al.*, 1984), diacylglycerols (Fujita *et al.*, 1984; O'Flaherty *et al.*, 1984, 1985), and LTB_4 (Ford-Hutchinson *et al.*, 1980; Palmblad *et al.*, 1983; Rollins *et al.*, 1983) stimulate various PMN responses. Under the same assay conditions, 5-HETE is relatively or completely inactive. Nevertheless, 5-HETE enhances the bioactions of each lipid agonist. Its most potent effects are expressed upon PAF in the cytochalasin B-dependent degranulation assay where 500 nM of 5-HETE increases the potency of PAF by a factor of approximately 100 and raises the optimal response magnitude by approximately 50 percent (O'Flaherty *et al.*, 1983a). The 5-HETE is ten-fold and 100-fold, respectively, less effective in enhancing the actions of diacylglycerols and LTB_4 (O'Flaherty *et al.*,

1983b), and has no effects on responses to chemotactic peptides or calcium ionophore A23187. [In preliminary studies, we find the 5-L-HETE similarly enhances oxidative metabolism responses elicited by the lipids (personal observations).] Various other arachidonate metabolites, including several HETEs, are mostly or completely without effect (O'Flaherty *et al.*, 1983a, 1983b). Thus, 5-HETE is a structurally-specific, stimulus-selective potentiator of PMN function. Its spectrum of action appears restricted to those stimuli that are natural products of PMN.

Diacylglycerols are relatively weak agonists of PMN function (O'Flaherty *et al.*, 1984; 1985b). They are much more powerful in enhancing various actions of PAF, LTB$_4$, chemotactic peptides and A23187 (O'Flaherty *et al.*, 1984; Robinson *et al.*, 1984; Dale and Penfield, 1984; Dewald *et al.*, 1984; Dewald and Baggiolini, 1985). The diacylglycerols are particularly effective upon PAF and LTB$_4$, enhancing their potencies in the degranulation assay by ten- to 30-fold and increasing their optimal effects by 50–75 percent (O'Flaherty *et al.*, *et al.*, 1984). Alkyl ether glycerols, although structurally similar to diacylglycerols, neither directly stimulate nor enhance stimulated PMN function (O'Flaherty *et al.*, 1984, 1985b). Thus, diacylglycerols are structurally-specific activators of PMN. Unlike 5-HETE, they possess significant direct actions and enhance responses to virtually all stimuli. The bioactivity they express is synergistic with those of most other agents.

These studies indicate that seemingly inactive (e.g. 5-HETE) or weak (e.g. diacylglycerols) compounds can have unexpected bioactivities when considered within the context of the stimulated cell. They suggest that functional responses may be multiply mediated. That is, stimulated PMN produce several intracellular signals. Some of these directly elicit function. Others enhance the response or co-operate synergistically. Such interactions allow any particular messenger to be involved in promoting function at very low concentrations. We find, for instance, very prominent PMN degranulation responses to 3 μM diacylglycerol, 50 nM 5-HETE, 1 nM LTB$_4$ and 2 nM PAF, when these lipids are used in combination. Individually, the lipids induce little or no response at these concentrations.

MECHANISMS OF ACTIONS

PAF (Hwang *et al.*, 1983), diacylglycerols (O'Flaherty *et al.*, 1985b; Nishihira and O'Flaherty, 1985) and LTB$_4$ (Kreisle and Parker, 1983; Goldman and Goetzl, 1984; Lin *et al.*, 1984; O'Flaherty *et al.*, 1985a) activate PMN by binding with specific receptors. PMN contain approximately 130,000 high affinity (K_d=0.9 nM) diacylglycerol receptors per cell (O'Flaherty *et al.*, 1985b). These receptors are localized principally to the cytosol in resting cells but associate with membranes when bound to their ligand (Nishihira and O'Flaherty, 1985). Apparently, diacylglycerols enter or form within this hydrophobic environment. At this site, they attract and bind with the cytosolic receptor to construct a membrane-associated complex that possesses protein kinase C activity (Nishihira and O'Flaherty, 1985; Nishizuka, 1984).

Presumably, the complex phosphorylates neighboring proteins thereby promoting their ability to trigger events involved in physiological responses (Nishizuka, 1984).

Receptors for PAF (unpublished observations) and LTB_4 (O'Flaherty *et al.*, 1985a) are found principally in the membrane subfractions of resting PMN. We find approximately 11 000 LTB_4 and only 1100 PAF high affinity receptors per PMN; their respective affinities (K_d) are 0.5 and 0.2 nM. Although the precise events linking these receptors to cell function are currently unknown, the PAF receptor, when ligand-bound, may activate other membrane proteins (i.e. GTP-binding proteins) that regulate cellular calcium levels and certain metabolic events (Williams and Haslam, 1984; Lad *et al.*, 1985).

The mechanism of action for 5-L-HETE is even less well understood. PMN rapidly deposit this compound into cellular triglycerides and phospholipids (Stenson and Parker, 1979; O'Flaherty *et al.*, 1985c). This incorporation may modify the physiochemical characteristics of cellular membranes and thereby influence function (Stenson and Parker, 1979).

MECHANISMS OF INTERACTIONS

The binding of PAF, diacylglycerols and LTB_4 to their respective receptors is pivitol for the expression of function. Potentiating and synergistic interactions may be conveniently viewed within this framework. Thus, one lipid can act by increasing a second lipid's bioavailability for receptor binding, alter the number or ligand affinity of another's receptor, or influence events occurring after receptor binding. In our preliminary studies, we find evidence for the first two of these three types of interactions.

PMN rapidly convert LTB_4 to its corresponding 20-hydroxy and 20-carboxy analogs (Goldman and Goetzl, 1984; Lin *et al.*, 1984; O'Flaherty *et al.*, 1985a). These derivatives are about 20- and 400-fold, respectively, less active in binding to the LTB_4 receptor and in stimulating function. We find that this metabolic inactivation of LTB_4 is reduced by excess 5-HETE in whole PMN or in a cell-free system containing a mixture of PMN cytosol and endoplasmic reticulum. We also find that whole cells or this subfraction convert 5-HETE to its corresponding 20-hydroxy derivative (O'Flaherty *et al.*, 1985c). Thus, the effect of 5-HETE on the metabolism of LTB_4 may reflect substrate competition for a single ω-hydroxylase. It seems possible that 5-HETE enhances the actions of LTB_4 by blocking its inactivation and thereby prolonging its biological half-life. This mechanism, however, does not explain the effects of 5-HETE on PAF or diacylglycerols. Although PMN rapidly inactivate PAF (Chilton *et al.*, 1983), our preliminary studies find no alteration in this inactivation in cells incubated with 5-HETE. Obversely, PAF had little effect on the metabolic fate of 5-HETE. Finally, a structural analog of diacylglycerols, phorbol myristate acetate, is not metabolized by PMN (Nishihira and O'Flaherty, 1985). This compound activates PMN by binding with the diacylglycerol receptor and its bioactions, like those of diacylglycerols, is dramatically enhanced by 5-HETE (O'Flaherty *et al.*, 1983b).

Thus, the interactions between 5-L-HETE and diacylglycerols may reflect events closer to the diacylglycerol receptor. In preliminary studies, we find that 5-HETE increases the number of diacylglycerol receptors that are mobilized to the PMN membrane by a given concentration of diacylglycerol or phorbol myristate acetate. The 5-HETE appears to work, in part, by increasing the diacylglycerol receptors' ligand affinity about two- to three-fold. Other HETEs, as well as LTB_4, do not have this effect on the receptor.

CONCLUSIONS

It seems likely that PMN responses are ultimately triggered by key proteins, the activities of which are regulated by phosphorylation, calcium levels, cyclic nucleotides, and, possibly, their location within the cell. The lipids of interest here can impact on these proteins in at least four ways. First, they bind to specific receptors that are linked to calcium channels and nucleotide cyclases (e.g. PAF, and, possibly, LTB_4). Second, they mobilize and directly activate phosphorylating enzymes (e.g. diacylglycerols). Third, they may alter the physiochemical characteristics of cellular membranes (e.g. possibly 5-HETE). And, fourth, they enhance the number or affinity of certain receptors (e.g. 5-HETE influences on diacylglycerol receptors). Future investigations must confirm this general outline, clarify its many undefined areas, and specifically determine its relevancy to the responses of various cell types.

ACKNOWLEDGMENTS

Thanks to Mary Green for typing this manuscript.
The work reported in this chapter was supported by NIH grants HL 27799 and HL 26257.

REFERENCES

Betz, S.J., and Henson, P.M. (1980). 'Production and release of platelet-activating factor (PAF); dissociation from degranulation and superoxide production in the human neutrophil', *J. Immunol.*, **125**, 2756–2763.
Chilton, F.H., O'Flaherty, J.T., Walsh, C.E., Thomas, M.J., Wykle, R.L., DeChatelet, L.R., and Waite, B.M. (1982). 'Platelet activating factor. Stimulation of the lipoxygenase pathway in polymorphonuclear leukocytes by 1-*O*-2-*O*-acetyl-*sn*-glycero-3-phosphocholine', *J. Biol. Chem.*, **257**, 5402–5407.
Chilton, F.H., O'Flaherty, J.T., Ellis, J.M., Swendsen, C.L., and Wykle, R.L. (1983). 'Selective acylation of lyso platelet activating factor by arachidonate in human neutrophils', *J. Biol. Chem.*, **258**, 7268–7271.
Dale, M.M., and Penfield, A. (1984). 'Synergism between phorbol ester and A23187 in superoxide production by neutrophils', *FEBS*, **175**, 170–172.

Dewald, B., and Baggiolini, M. (1985). 'Activation of NADPH oxidase in human neutrophils. Synergism between FMLP and the neutrophil products PAF and LTB$_4$', *Biochem. Biophys. Res. Commun.*, **128**, 297–304.

Dewald, B., Payne, T.G., and Baggiolini, M. (1984). 'Activation of NADPH oxidase of human neutrophils. Potentiation of chemotactic peptide by a diacylglycerol', *Biochem. Biophys. Res. Commun.*, **125**, 367–373.

Ford-Hutchinson, A.W., Bray, M.A., Doig, M.V., Shipley, M.E., and Smith M.J.H. (1980). 'Leukotriene B, a potent chemokinetic and aggregating substance released from polymorphonuclear leukocytes', *Nature*, **286**, 264–265.

Fujita, I., Irita, K., Takeshige, K., and Minakami, S. (1984). 'Diacylglycerol, 1-oleoyl-2-acetyl-glycerol, stimulates superoxide-generation from human neutrophils', *Biochem. Biophys. Res. Commun.*, **120**, 318–324.

Goldman, D.W., and Goetzl, E.J. (1984). 'Heterogeneity of human polymorphonuclear leukocyte receptors for leukotriene B$_4$. Identification of a subset of high affinity receptors that transduce the chemotactic response', *J. Exp. Med.*, **159**, 1027–1041.

Hwang, S., Lee, C.C., Cheah, M.J., and Shen, T.Y. (1983). 'Specific receptor sites for 1-*O*-alkyl-2-*O*-acetyl-*sn*-glycero-3-phosphocholine (platelet activating factor) on rabbit platelet and guinea pig smooth muscle membranes', *Biochem*, **22**, 4756–4763.

Kreisle, R.A., and Parker, C.W. (1983). 'Specific binding of leukotriene B$_4$ to a receptor on human polymorphonuclear leukocytes', *J. Exp. Med.*, **157**, 628–641.

Lad, P.M., Olson, C.V., and Grewal, I.S. (1985). 'Platelet-activating factor mediated effects on human neutrophil function are inhibited by pertussis toxin', *Biochem. Biophys. Res. Commun.*, **129**, 632–638.

Lin, A.H., Ruppel, P.L., and Gorman, R.R. (1984). 'Leukotriene B$_4$ binding to human neutrophils', *Prostaglandins*, **28**, 837–849.

Mueller, H.W., O'Flaherty, J.T., and Wykle, R.L. (1984). 'The molecular species distribution of platelet-activating factor synthesized by rabbit and human neutrophils', *J. Biol. Chem.*, **259**, 14 554–14 559.

Nishihira, J., and O'Flaherty, J.T. (1985). 'Phorbol myristate acetate receptors in human polymorphonuclear neutrophils', *J. Immunol.*, **135**, 3439–3447.

Nishizuka, Y. (1984). 'The role of protein kinase C in cell surface signal transduction and tumour promotion', *Nature*, **308**, 693–697.

O'Flaherty, J.T., Wykle, R.L., Miller, C.H., Lewis, J.C., Waite, M., Bass, D.A., McCall, C.E., and DeChatelet, L.R. (1981). '1-*O*-alkyl-*sn*-glyceryl-3-phosphorylcholines. A novel class of neutrophil stimulants', *Am. J. Pathol.*, **103**, 70–79.

O'Flaherty, J.T., Thomas, M.J., Hammett, M.J., Carroll, C., McCall, C.E., and Wykle, R.L. (1983a). '5-L-hydroxy-6,8,11,14-eicosatetraenoate potentiates the human neutrophil degranulating action of platelet-activating factor', *Biochem. Biophys. Res. Commun.*, **111**, 1–7.

O'Flaherty, J.T., Thomas, M.J., McCall, C.E., and Wykle, R.L. (1983b). 'Potentiating actions of hydroxyeicosatetraenoates on human neutrophil degranulation responses to leukotriene B$_4$ and phorbol myristate acetate', *Res. Commun. Chem. Pathol. Pharm.*, **40**, 475–487.

O'Flaherty, J.T., Schmitt, J.D., McCall, C.E., and Wykle, R.L. (1984). 'Diacylglycerols enhance human neutrophil degranulation responses: Relevancy to a multiple mediator hypothesis of cell function', *Biochem. Biophys. Res. Commun.*, **123**, 64–70.

O'Flaherty, J.T., Kosfeld, S., and Nishihira, J. (1985a). 'Binding and metabolism of leukotriene B$_4$ by neutrophils and their subcellular organelles', *J. Cell. Physiol.*, **126**, 359–370.

O'Flaherty, J.T., Schmitt, J.D., Wykle, R.L., Redman, J.F., and McCall, C.E. (1985b). 'Diacylglycerols and mezeren activate neutrophils by a phorbol myristate acetate-like mechanism', *J. Cell Physiol.*, **125**, 192–199.

O'Flaherty, J.T., Wykle, R.L., Redman, J., Samuels, M., and Thomas, M. (1985c).

'Metabolism of 5-L-hydroxyeicosatetraenoate by human neutrophils: Production of a novel -oxidized derivative', (submitted).

Palmblad, J., Uden, A., Fribert, I., Ringertz, B., Radmark, O., Lindgren, J., Hansson, G., and Malmsten, C.L. (1983). 'Effects of novel lipoxygenase products on neutrophil and eosinophil functions *in vitro*', *Advances in Prostaglandin, Thromboxane, and Leukotriene Research*, **12**, 25–31.

Robinson, J.M., Badwey, J.A., Karnovsky, M.L., and Karnovsky, M.J. (1984). 'Superoxide release by neutrophils: Synergistic effects of a phorbol ester and a calcium ionophore', *Biochem. Biophys. Res. Commun.*, **122**, 734–739.

Rollins, T.E., Zanolari, B., Springer, M.S., Guindon, Y., Zamboni, R., Lau, C.K., and Rokach, J. (1983). 'Synthetic leukotriene B$_4$ is a potent chemotaxin but a weak secretagogue for human PMN', *Prostaglandins*, **25**, 281–289.

Samuelsson, B. (1982). 'The leukotrienes: An introduction'. In B. Samuelsson and R. Paoletti (eds.) *Leukotrienes and Other Lipoxygenase Products*, Raven Press, New York.

Shaw, J.O., Pinckard, R.N., Ferrigni, K.S., McManus, L.M., and Hanahan, D.J. (1981). 'Activation of human neutrophils with 1-*O*-hexadecyl/octadecyl-2-acetyl-*sn*-glyceryl-3-phosphorylcholine (platelet activating factor)', *J. Immunol.*, **127**, 1250–1255.

Smith, R.J., Bowman, B.J., and Iden, S.S. (1984). 'Stimulation of the human neutrophil superoxide anion-generating system with 1-*O*-hexadecyl/octadecyl-2-acetyl-*sn*-glyceryl-3-phosphorylcholine', *Biochem. Pharm.*, **33**, 973–978.

Stenson, W., and Parker, C.W. (1979). 'Metabolism of arachidonic acid in ionophore-stimulated neutrophils', *J. Clin. Invest.*, **64**, 1457–1465.

Takenawa, T., Homma, Y., and Nagai, Y. (1983). 'Role of Ca^{2+} in phosphatidylinositol response and arachidonic acid release in formylated tripeptide- or Ca^{2+} ionophore A23187-stimulated guinea pig neutrophils', *J. Immunol.*, **130**, 2849–2855.

Walsh, C.E., Waite, B.M., Thomas, M.J., and DeChatelet, L.R. (1981). 'Release and metabolism of arachidonic acid in human neutrophils', *J. Biol. Chem.*, **256**, 7228–7234.

Williams, K.A., and Haslam, R.J. (1984). 'Effects of NaCl and GTP on the inhibition of platelet adenylate cyclase by 1-*O*-octadecyl-2-*O*-acetyl-*sn*-glyceryl-3-phosphorylcholine (synthetic platelet-activating factor)', *Biochim. Biophys. Acta*, **770**, 216–223.

New Horizons in Platelet Activating Factor Research
Edited by C. M. Winslow and M. L. Lee
© 1987 John Wiley & Sons Ltd.

14

Biochemical Behavior of AGEPC (Platelet Activating Factor) on Interaction with Cells

Donald J. Hanahan, Denis B. Buxton, Rory A. Fisher,
Ceredwyn E. Hill, Shivendra D. Shukla and Merle S. Olson

INTRODUCTION

Any study of the interaction of platelet activating factor with cells, tissues or organs poses a difficult, demanding and yet intriguing problem. Not only are these reactions, which are intimately associated with the biologic action of this potent lipid chemical mediator, very rapid—of the order of 5—15 s—but the number of receptors involved in this interaction is very few. In fact, the number of high affinity, low capacity sites, considered to be the PAF receptors, appear to be less than 1000. Thus, given, for example, that high biological activity can be elicited towards washed rabbit platelets at 1×10^{-11} to 1×10^{-12} M, this means that only a few molecules are required to initiate the response. This adds another dimension of difficulty to any study directed towards elucidation of the mechanism of action of this phosphoglyceride. Nonetheless, the field has developed at an extremely rapid rate, as indicated by the rapid rise in publications on this agonist, and this expansion in interest is expressed in the wide diversity of tissues, and cells or systems under study. One of the relatively new systems, which has great potential in investigating the multifaceted activities of platelet activating factor, is the liver. A collaborative venture has been developed with Dr. Merle S. Olson and his colleagues in San Antonio to explore various facets of the interaction of platelet activating factor with liver. The data presented here will illustrate the novel and important features of the liver as an important organ platelet activating factor metabolism.

SOME GENERAL CHARACTERISTICS OF BEHAVIOR OF AGEPC ON LIVER

In our initial experimental approach, it was decided to explore the ability of AGEPC to effect glycogenolysis in the perfused rat liver. Inasmuch as one characteristic of other agonists (such as phenylephrine, glucagon) action on the liver was to cause release of glucose, this seemed to be a logical choice for an analytical guideline. Further, since the mode of action of glycogenolytic hormones appears to require the presence of calcium ions and as AGEPC would express its biologic action on platelets, for example, only if calcium were added to the reaction mixture, the influence of calcium ions on AGEPC action on the perfused liver was followed. The initial results reported by Shukla et al., 1983 showed that indeed AGEPC had a pronounced effect on glycogenolysis in the perfused (fed) rat liver as shown in Table 1. Not only was this reaction dose-dependent but also required calcium ions and at levels comparable to that needed for platelets. Further, as is evident there is a requirement for the specific sn-3 stereochemical form of AGEPC and, the deacetylated derivative, or lyso-GEPC, was inactive, as was its enantiomer, sn-1-AGEPC. Concomitant with the above experimental protocols, it was decided to explore in a preliminary manner the effect of AGEPC on polyphosphoinositide turnover in isolated hepatocytes. The results showed quite conclusively that Ptd Ins-4,5P$_2$ underwent a rapid turnover within 5s of addition of agonist, with a slower (60 s) change in PI-4P and with little change in the PI over a 5 min period (Table 2).

Table 1.   Effects of AGEPC and Related Compounds on Glycogenolysis in Perfused (Fed) Rat Liver

Compound	Glucose release $(\mu M\ g^{-1}\ h^{-1})$
sn-3-AGEPC[1]	225
control	50
sn-1-AGEPC[2]	no significant
Lyso-GEPC[2]	increase above
	background

[1] 2×10^{-10} M
[2] 1×10^{-7} M

Table 2.   AGEPC Induced Changes in Levels of Inositol Phospholipids in Rat Hepatocytes. (AGEPC, 10^{-10} M; hepatocytes labeled previously with ^{32}Pi)

Compound	% Decrease in ^{32}Pi content	Time frame (s)
Ptd Ins-4,5 P$_2$	50	5
Ptd Ins-4P	30	60
Ptd Ins	<5	300

INFLUENCE OF Ca^{2+} LEVELS AND THE DESENSITIZATION PROCESS

It was important at this point in our research program to evaluate the importance of calcium on the glycogenolytic process induced by AGEPC. Hence, Buxton *et al.* (1984) showed the dramatic influence of lowering the Ca^{2+} level concentration in the perfusate from 1.25 mM to 50 μM. The mean maximum glucose release of glucose after infusion of 2×10^{-10} M AGEPC (into fed rat livers) was 180 percent over control at 1.25 mM compared to a value near 50 percent over control at 50 μM Ca^{2+}.

During this study, it was observed that sequential infusion (over a 7 min interval) of liver with 2×10^{-10} M AGEPC caused a demonstrable decrease in the glycogenolytic response, i.e. a desensitization. Essentially after two such stimulations, there was basically no significant glucose release on the third infusion of AGEPC. However, if this were followed by an immediate infusion of phenylephrine at 1×10^{-5} M, there was a pronounced glycogenolysis. A similar positive glycogenolytic response was seen also with glucagon after a prior desensitization of AGEPC. It was evident that the sites for phenylephrine and glucagon were not the same as that for AGEPC. Interestingly, if the period of time between infusion of AGEPC was increased, there was a partial reversal of the desensitization phenomenon.

Table 3. Glucose Release from Isolated Hepatocytes

	Glucose produced,[1] (μM g^{-1} wet weight)
Control	18
AGEPC, at 10^{-9} M	18
glucagon, at 7.5×10^{-8} M	35

[1] after 25 min incubation

LACK OF DIRECT RESPONSE OF ISOLATED HEPATOCYTES TO AGEPC

Inasmuch as most of the glycogen of the liver is found in the hepatocytes, it seemed appropriate to examine the action of AGEPC on this cell. Accordingly, hepatocytes were isolated from the livers of well fed rats and the influence of AGEPC on glycogenolysis and turnover of the inositol phospholipids was explored by Fisher *et al.*, 1984. As illustrated in Table 3, addition of AGEPC at 1×10^{-9} M caused no perceptible release of glucose. As a consequence of this unexpected result, it was considered possible that there was a transient response not detectable by examination of the glucose in the medium. Hence, the activity of AGEPC and epinephrine on the glycogen phosphorylase A level in hepatocytes was measured. Though there was a significant rise in this enzymatic activity upon treatment of the hepatocytes with epinephrine, there was no discernible change, as compared to a control sample, upon treatment of these cells with AGEPC at various concentrations. However, examination of the effect of AGEPC on the Ptd Ins-4,5P$_2$ metabolic behavior of the hepatocyte showed a very positive change.

These observations were perplexing in a sense, but certainly suggested that a mechanism(s) was operative in the intact liver other than a direct effect of AGEPC on the hepatocytes. Since the enzyme system responsible for glycogenolysis was intact in the hepatocyte, it appeared likely that other cell types or systems were intimately involved in the AGEPC induced reaction. This possibility will be discussed later.

Table 4. Maximum Glucose Output in Perfused Rat Liver Subjected to Heat Aggregated IgG and AGEPC

Agonist	Increased glucose output, in % of control
IgG aggregate 17 μg ml^{-1}	101 $\pm$ 5
AGEPC, at 2 $\times$ 10^{-10} M	102 $\pm$ 17

INFLUENCE OF AGGREGATED IgG ON THE GLYCOGENOLYTIC PROCESS IN LIVER

In an effort designed to explain the lack of AGEPC activity towards the isolated hepatocytes, other cellular components were considered as potential candidates for transmission of a signal to the hepatocytes for stimulation of glycogenolysis. Of course, an immediate consideration centered on the reticuloendothelial system, which removes soluble immune complexes from the circulation (Benacerraf *et al.*, 1959; Mannik *et al.*, 1971). The liver is well recognized as the major organ for uptake and disposal of the immune complexes from the blood (Weiser and Laxon, 1962; Haakenstad and Mannik, 1976) and suggests that the Kupffer cells, which comprise the bulk of the reticuloendothelial system, would be an important cell type for study. One avenue to possible implication of the reticuloendothelial system in the glycogenolytic response was to infuse heat aggregated immunoglobulin G into the fed rat liver. Buxton *et al.*, (1984) showed very convincingly that indeed the heat aggregated IgG did cause glucose release and in a dose dependent manner. The data in Table 4 provide a comparison of the effect of AGEPC and heat aggregated IgG. Further repeated infusions of the immune IgG preparation lead to a desensitization similar to that noted for the AGEPC. Of further interest, the heat aggregated IgG stimulated the production of platelet activating factor and this latter reaction was inhibited by co-infusion of indomethacin. This result suggested a close association of platelet activating factor formation with the production of prostaglandins, but this has not been proven to date.

AGEPC INDUCED VASOCONSTRICTION AND GLYCOGENOLYSIS IN THE PERFUSED LIVER

In a study reported by Buxton *et al.*, (1984), an unusual glucose release profile was seen at an AGEPC concentration of 1×10^{-8} M. At this level, in contradistinction to the pattern seen at 1×10^{-9} and 1×10^{-10} M, there was a very sharp rise, then drop in glucose release in the early phases of infusion followed by a long broad pattern of glucose release. This observation pointed to the possible involvement of hypoxia in the early phase of the interaction and this idea was explored further in a subsequent detailed study by Buxton *et al.* (1986a,b). These investigators found that AGEPC induced a dose-dependent transient increase (150 percent of control) in portal vein pressure and a concomitant transient increase in hepatic glucose release (approximately 160 percent of control) at an AGEPC concentration of 2×10^{-10} M. Both processes exhibited similar calcium dependency.

Verapamil inhibited the portal pressure and glucose release response to AGEPC in a dose dependent manner, giving an IC_{50} of 10 μM at an AGEPC level of 6×10^{-11} M. In addition, both parameters could be desensitized by repeated infusions of AGEPC. Of importance, measurement of the glycogen phosphorylase activity in extracts from freeze clamped livers showed a significant increase in response to AGEPC administration.

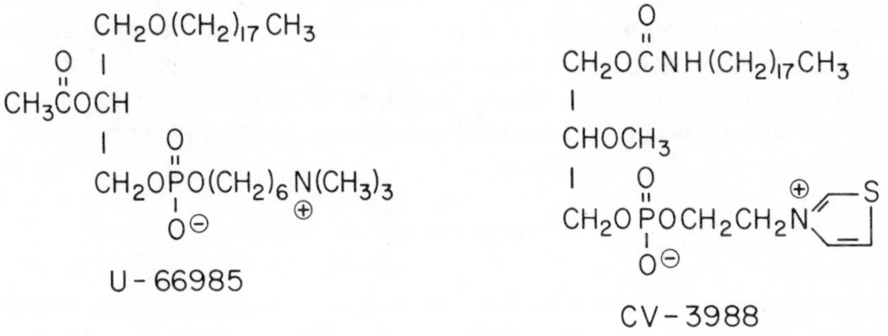

Figure 1. Structures of U−66985 and CV−3988

The availability of specific antagonists of AGEPC activity allowed our laboratory to examine their effects on the AGEPC mediated vasoconstriction and glycogenolytic process in the perfused rat liver. Two structural analogs of AGEPC, U66985 (1-*O*-octadecyl-2-*O*-acetyl-*sn*-glycero-3-phosphoric acid-6'-trimethyl ammonium hexyl ester) and CV3988 *rac*-3-(*N*-n-octadecyl carbamoyloxy)-2-methoxypropyl-2-thiazolio-ethyl phosphate) each of which were generous gifts of The Upjohn Company and the Takeda Chemical Company, respectively had the structural formulae shown in Figure 1.

These compounds proved to be very effective inhibitors of hepatic glycogenolysis and vasoconstriction of the hepatic vasculature induced by AGEPC (Buxton *et al.*, 1986a,b). These compounds were effective inhibitors if infused prior to, or simultaneously with the agonist. However, if infused subsequent to AGEPC administration, they were generally ineffective. Interestingly these inhibitors were ineffective as inhibitors of the action of the α-adrenergic agonist, phenylephrine, on the glycogenolytic process.

POSSIBLE LOCATION OF PLATELET ACTIVATING FACTOR INTERACTION SITE IN THE LIVER

An important facet of this study on AGEPC induced alterations in liver center on the location of specific binding sites. On the basis of the observations cited above it appeared likely that the reticuloendothelial system was an important loci for primary binding of AGEPC leading to development of the glycogenolytic response. In a particularly intriguing series of experiments, C. Hill and associates (unpublished observations) found that retrograde perfusion of AGEPC into the liver (via the centrolobular vein) was some 1000-fold less sensitive than infusion of the same compound via anterograde perfusion in eliciting glucose release. This was most interesting since α-adrenergic agonists, which bind and exert their activity on the hepatocyte have equal molar responses whether infused via the retrograde or anterograde pathway. On the other hand latex particles which can stimulate glucose release show a similar gradient response as does the AGEPC to antero and retrograde paths. Inasmuch as the latex particles are phagocytosable by the reticuloendothelial cells at a site(s) near to the portal vein where infusions are intimated as important in this reaction.

SUMMARY

The data presented here clearly show that the liver is an organ particularly sensitive to platelet activating factor. Essentially, liver responds to this biologically active phospholipid at molar concentrations comparable to those seen with the rabbit platelet. Furthermore, the chemical and stereochemical requirements are exactly the same and the structural analogs found to be excellent inhibitors of platelet activating factor (on platelets) are also similarly active in the liver. The finding that heat aggregated IgG can initiate glycogenolysis and also stimulate formation of platelet activating factor in the liver is indeed provocative. It suggests in a very speculative way that the reticuloendothelial system is the site of formation of this potent agonist, even though the levels of glyceryl ethers in the liver are very small. In any event, one of the major challenges in elucidating the mode of action of platelet activating factor in effecting glycogenolysis in the liver is to explain the failure of this agonist to stimulate isolated hepatocytes to release glucose from their glycogen stores. Certainly one possibility is that the reticuloendothelial system, upon stimulation by platelet activating factor, produces another, as yet unidentified, mediator which then acts on the parenchymal cells. An alternative proposal would be that the entire process is a hemodynamic one and occurs in the vasculature. These provide exciting possibilities for future research studies.

ACKNOWLEDGMENT

Supported by grants from National Institutes of Health AM33538-02 and from The Upjohn Company.

REFERENCES

Benacerraf, B., Sebestryn, M., and Cooper, N.S. (1959). 'The clearance of antigen antibody complexes from the blood by the reticuloendothelial system', *J. Immunol.*, **82**, 131–137.

Buxton, D.B., Shukla, S.D., Hanahan, D.J., and Olson, M.S. (1984). 'Stimulation of hepatic glycogenolysis by acetyl glyceryl ether phosphoryl choline', *J. Biol. Chem.*, **259**, 1468–1471.

Buxton, D.B., Hanahan, D.J., and Olson, M.S. (1984). 'Stimulation of glycogenolysis and platelet activating factor production by heat-aggregated immunoglobulin G in the perfused rat liver', *J. Biol. Chem.*, **259**, 13 568–13 761.

Buxton, D.B., Hanahan, D.J., and Olson, M.S. (1986a). 'Specific Antagonists of Platelet Activating Factor-Mediated Vasoconstriction and Glycogenolysis in the Perfused Rat Liver', *Biochem. Pharmacol.*, **35**, 893–897.

Buxton, D.B., Fisher, R.A., Hanahan, D.J., and Olson, M.S. (1986b). 'Platelet Activating Factor-Mediated Vasoconstriction and Glycogenolysis in the Perfused Rat Liver', *J. Biol. Chem.*, **261**, 644–649.

Fisher, R.A., Shukla, S.D., DeBuysere, M., Hanahan, D.J., and Olson, M.S. (1984). 'The effect of acetyl glyceryl ether phosphorylcholine on glycogenolysis and phosphatidyl inositol -4,5 bis-phosphate in rat hepatocytes', *J. Biol. Chem.*, **259**, 8685–8688.

Haakenstad, A.O., and Mannik (1976). 'The disappearance kinetics of soluble immune complexes prepared with reduced and alkylated antibodies and with intact antibodies in mice', *Lab. Invest.*, **35**, 283–292.

Mannik, M., Arend, W.P., Hall, A.P., and Gilliland, B.C. (1971). 'Studies on Antigen-Antibody Complexes I. Elimination of Soluble Complexes from Rabbit Circulation', *J. Exp. Med.*, **133**, 713–739.

Shukla, S.D., Buxton, D.B., Olson, M.S., and Hanahan, D.J. (1983). 'Acetyl glyceryl ether phosphorylcholine. A potent activator of hepatic phosphoinositide metabolism and glycogenolysis', *J. Biol. Chem.*, **258**, 10 212–10 214.

Weiser, R.S., and Laxon, C. (1962). 'The fate of fluorescein-labeled soluble antigen—antibody complex in the mouse', *J. Infect. Dis.*, **111**, 55—58.

New Horizons in Platelet Activating Factor Research
Edited by C. M. Winslow and M. L. Lee
© 1987 John Wiley & Sons Ltd.

15

Inhibition of the Bronchopulmonary Effects of Platelet Activating Factor-Acether: Relevance for Physiopathology

B. Boris Vargaftig

INTRODUCTION: SYSTEMIC EFFECTS OF PAF-ACETHER IN THE GUINEA-PIG

Collagen (Vargaftig *et al.*, 1979), ADP and ATP (reviews by Vargaftig *et al.*, 1981, 1983) or PAF-acether (Vargaftig *et al.*, 1980) induce bronchoconstriction (BC) in the guinea-pig by a platelet-dependent effect. As a consequence, BC is suppressed by platelet depletion or prostacyclin infusions. Other bronchoconstrictor agents, which act through platelet-independent mechanisms include arachidonic acid (Lefort and Vargaftig, 1978), f-met-leu-phe (Boukili *et al.*, 1986) or antigen. Sensitivity to cyclo-oxygenase (CO) inhibition does not coincide with platelet-dependency, since both AA and collagen or ATP are inhibited by aspirin, whereas ADP is platelet-dependent and aspirin-resistant. Bronchoconstrictor agents can also be classified according to their site of action: direct smooth muscle agonists, substrates for the formation of mediators (arachidonic acid, kininogen, complement cascade) and agents which stimulate cells to secrete the agonists or precursors.

Thromboxane A2 (TxA2) is not directly involved with BC induced by PAF-acether given intravenously: no circulating TxA2 is detected when BC is at its height and CO inhibitors are inactive. Hypotension by PAF-acether is also not mediated by CO deriva-tives or by platelets. Furthermore, hypotension is not due to increased vascular perme-ability, since hemoconcentration persists when the arterial blood pressure has recovered to basal levels and because hypotension can be obtained by repeated PAF-acether injections, even if the increased vascular permeability is not further accentuated.

Aerosolized PAF-acether induces a moderate BC in the guinea-pig which is hista-mine-independent (PAF-acether does not release histamine from normal guinea-pig lungs) and which is inhibited by aspirin (Vargaftig *et al.*, 1983). When alveolar macrophages are collected from animals pre-exposed to PAF-acether, they become self-desensitized and to some extent also refractory to the tripeptide f-met-leu-phe (Maridonneau-Parini *et al.*, 1985). Since only self-desensitization is observed when PAF-acether is applied to the macrophages *in vitro*, it is likely that PAF-acether triggers cell interactions within the lung, which should account for BC.

CYCLOOXYGENASE MECHANISMS

Even though CO mechanisms do not explain BC by PAF-acether, the CO inhibitor sulfinpyrazone is an effective antagonist (Chignard *et al.*, 1982). Sulfinpyrazone is not specific, since it also antagonizes the direct effects of TxA2 on human platelets (Hatmi *et al.*, 1986) and its ability to antagonize PAF-acether is short lived, whereas CO inhibition is persistent. Nevertheless, the coincidence between the ability of sulfinpyrazone to antagonize PAF-acether as well as Forssman shock in the guinea-pig (Butler *et al.*, 1979), at similar doses, suggests a participation of PAF-acether in the latter condition.

The association of indomethacin, aspirin or salicylic acid (which does not inhibit CO) to mepyramine (histamine *antagonist*) and to methysergide (serotonin *antagonist*) suppresses BC by PAF-acether (Vargaftig *et al.*, 1982), each of these antagonists alone being inactive. This drug combination is only effective *in vivo* and *ex vivo* on platelet secretion, and this led to our hypothesis that, as sulfinpyrazone, it may act by inhibiting the secretion of an as yet uncharacterized platelet-derived smooth muscle stimulant (Chignard *et al.*, 1982; Vargaftig *et al.*, 1981).

SELECTIVE ANTAGONISTS OF PAF-ACETHER

The increasing number of PAF-acether antagonists is reviewed by Braquet *et al.*, (1986). Roughly, they can be classified into PAF-related structures, such as compounds CV 3988 [rac-3-(*N*-n-octadecyl carbamoyloxy)-2-methoxypropyl-2-thiazolioethyl phosphate; Terashita *et al.*, 1982] or Ro-19-3704 [3-(4-(R)-2-(Methoxycarbonyl)oxy)-3-((octadecylcarbamoyl)oxy)propoxy)butyl)thiazolium iodide; Burri *et al.*, 1986]. Other antagonists include synthetic substances, such as the pyrrolo (1,2-c) thiazole derivative 48740 RP (Sédivy *et al.*, 1985a,b), triazolodibenzodiazepines, or natural substances such as ginkgolide B (BN 52021) (Braquet, 1984), neolignanes (Shen *et al.*, 1984) or lignanes, which inhibit different effects of PAF-acether, particularly platelet aggregation and, for those which were tested, thrombocytopenia, BC and pulmonary accumulation of radio-labeled platelets in the guinea-pig.

PHYSIOPATHOLOGY OF PAF-ACETHER WITH RESPECT TO PULMONARY IMMEDIATE HYPERSENSITIVITY

Relevant properties of PAF-acether

The pharmacological properties of PAF-acether and the fact that sulfinpyrazone antagonizes its effects and those of Forssman shock, justifies the hypothesis that PAF-acether is involved in different shock conditions. Indeed, recently available antagonists suppress or correct hypotension following systemic adminstration of endotoxin (Doebber *et al.*, 1985; Terashita *et al.*, 1985; Adnot *et al.*, 1986), under conditions where leukopenia is unaffected. The role of PAF-acether in asthma is also based upon the analogies between its effects and those of antigen, and on the recognition that PAF-acether or its precursor lyso-PAF are released by the cells involved. A role for PAF-acether and for platelets is reinforced by the findings of Lellouch-Tubiana *et al.*, (1985, in preparation) that within 1–3 min after the i.v. injection of PAF-acether or of the antigen to the passively sensitized guinea-pigs, activated platelets are found at the vicinity of the bronchial smooth muscle (see below). This may correlate with lung inflammation during asthma, which is said to account for bronchial hyper-responsiveness, a major feature of bronchial asthma.

In short, a role for PAF-acether in asthma is suggested by its ability to induce BC, bronchial hyper-reactivity (Vargaftig *et al.*, 1983; Basran *et al.*, 1984) and lung inflammation. Other potential mediators of inflammation, particularly the peptidyl leukotrienes are also said to account for the histamine-independent component of allergic bronchoconstriction, and their role is discussed elsewhere (review by Vargaftig, 1985). Nevertheless, the peptido-leukotriene antagonist FPL 55712 failed to reduce BC due to antigen given i.v. to passively or actively sensitized guinea-pigs (Detsouli *et al.*, 1984; Carmo *et al.*, 1986), but PAF-antagonists were not homogenous in suppressing this histamine and leukotriene-independent component. Indeed, the PAF-acether antagonist BN 52021 (Braquet, 1984; Desquand *et al.*, 1986) antagonized BC of passive shock, but much less so BC that of active shock. Finally, other PAF-acether antagonists were inactive against both types of systemic shock. This may either indicate that BN 52021 is 'anti-shock' (anti-allergic) because it is anti-PAF, or irrespective from it, and of course the answer to this question is vital for further research. Indeed, at this stage it is quite possible that the non-anti-shock PAF-acether antagonists do not reach the sites where the mediator is released, and preliminary results with aerosolized antigen seem to confirm this possibility (Cirino *et al.*, 1986).

These results require a critical examination: systemic shock is a major physiopathological event, involving mediator release from the lungs (as in asthma) but, contrary to allergic asthma, from other organs as well, such as the liver, a rich source of histamine in guinea-pigs and dogs. Furthermore, the mediators account for the symptoms of shock, which involve species-specific target organs. The bronchopulmonary system is the target organ for the guinea-pig in which the dominant symptom of shock is BC, accompanied by hypotension and increased vasopermeability. This distinction between the origin of the mediators (local or systemic), and the target organs allows to understand an important limitation for the use of systemic anaphylaxis as a model for bronchial (local) allergy. Since furthermore systemic shock involves mediators other than PAF-acether, one may understand that failure of the PAF-acether antagonists as a group to suppress antigen-induced BC does not indicate, at this stage, that PAF-acether is not important for asthma. We presently favor the use of aerosolized antigen on passively sensitized animals, particularly if a model were raised in which clearly determined antigens would be transfered to the recipient animals, in place of crude serum as usually done.

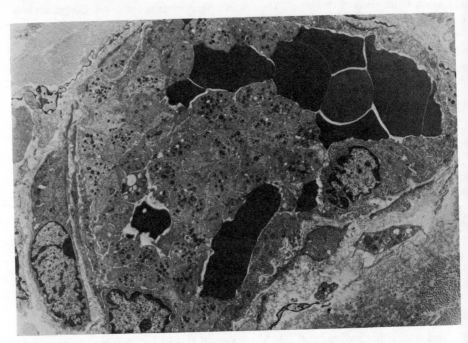

Figure 1.　Massive platelet aggregate in a peribronchial capillary 1 min after antigen injection to a passively sensitized guinea-pig. (Photograph kindly provided by Dr A. Lellouch-Tubiana, Departement d'Hystologie et d'Embryologie, Gaculté de Médecine Necker-Enfants Malades, Paris)

Morphological analogies between PAF-acether and the antigen

PAF-acether or antigen given i.v. to guinea-pigs induced bronchial and arterial constriction, formation of platelet thrombi in microvessels, leukocytosis and diapedesis, endothelium disruption, alterations of type II pneumocytes, epithelial denudation, massive infiltration of eosinophils accompanied by free eosinophilic granules scattered within the bronchial sub-mucosa. Alveolar macrophages are not activated. In contrast, activation and clumping of alveolar macrophages are noted when antigen or PAF-acether are aerosolized, platelet activation or endothelial disruption not being observed. Mast cells are rare after systemic passive shock, possibly because of early depletion during shock, but a large number of activated cells is observed after antigen aerosolization.

In analogy with findings in human skin in which PAF-acether induces marked eosinophilic infiltration selective to allergic ('atopic') individuals (Henocq and

Vargaftig, 1986), PAF-acether and antigen are major attractants for lung eosinophils (Lellouch-Tubiana *et al.*, 1985, in preparation).

Intravascular platelet aggregates are found immediately after the i.v. injections of PAF-acether (Lellouch-Tubiana *et al.*, 1985) as well as after systemic passive anaphylaxis (Lellouch-Tubiana *et al.*, 1986), even though only a mild thrombocytopenia accompanies this type of shock. In contrast, active systemic anaphylaxis is accompanied by intense thrombocytopenia, and indeed intravascular aggregation is massive under those conditions. These morphological observations are compatible with the platelet participation in anaphylactic shock and, by extension, in asthma, but the reservations discussed above, concerning the abusive parallelism between anaphylaxis and asthma should here also be kept in mind. Furthermore, the intravascular distribution of platelet aggregates in passive systemic shock and in PAF-acether-injected animals differs, because in the former case aggregates are mostly located in small arteries and arterioles and in bronchial venules, whereas the aggregates were mostly found in capillaries when PAF-acether was used. Accordingly, one possible explanation for the differences between systemic passive shock and PAF-acether, is that in the latter's case the platelets are a very early target and aggregates form intra-vascularly as soon as PAF-acether is injected, whereas in systemic passive shock, thrombocytopenia is less pronounced and takes a few minutes to develop; furthermore, since platelets from the sensitized animals do not aggregate to antigen *in vitro*, a primary platelet target is unlikely, and intra-pulmonary aggregation may result from a secondary effect, initiated by the disturbed pulmonary endothelium and/or leukocytes.

CONCLUSIONS

Alveolar macrophages appear to be an early target for aerosolized antigen and PAF-acether, leading to further cell recruitment and histamine release from mast cells (Schulman *et al.*, 1985), as also described for neutrophils (Fantozzi *et al.*, 1986). Eosinophils should be very important, since they are found at all levels of the bronchial wall of challenged guinea-pigs as markedly degranulated cells.

REFERENCES

Adnot, S., Lefort, J., Lagente, V., Braquet, P., and Vargaftig, B.B. (1986). 'Interference of BN 52021; a PAF-acether antagonist, with endotoxin-induced hypotension in the guinea-pig', *Pharmac. Res. Comm.*, (in press).

Basran, G.S., Page, C.P., Paul, W., and Morley, J. (1984). 'Platelet activating factor: a possible mediator of the dual response to allergen?', *Clin. Allergy*, **14**, 75.

Boukili, M.A., Bureau, M., Lagente, V., Lefort, J. Lellouch-Tubiana, A., Malanchère, E., and Vargaftig, B.B. (1986). 'Pharmacological modulation of the effects of N-formyl-l-methionyl-l-leucyl-l-phenylalanine in guinea-pigs: involvement of the arachidonic acid cascade', *Brit. J. Pharmacol.*, (in press).

Braquet, P.G. (1984), 'Treatment and Prevention of PAF-acether induced sickness by a new series of highly specific inhibitors', *GB Patent*, **8**, 418, 424.

Braquet, P.G., Touqui, L., Vargaftig, B.B., and Shen, T.Y. (1986). 'Perspectives in Platelet-activating Factor research', (submitted).

Burri, K., Cassal, J.-M., Hadvary, P., Weller, T., and Baumgartner, H.R. (1986). 'Effect of novel PAF antagonists on platelet function and thrombosis'. In *6th International Conference on Prostaglandins*, Florence, 1986.

Butler, K.D., and White, A.M. (1979).'Inhibition of platelet involvement in the sublethal Forssman reaction by sulfinpyrazone'. In M. McGregor, J.F. Mustard, M.F. Oliver and S. Sherry, (eds.) *Cardiovascular Actions of Sulphinpyrazone: Basic and Clinical Research*, Symposia Specialists, Miami, p.3.

Chignard, M., Wal, F., Lefort, J., and Vargaftig, B.B. (1982). 'Inhibition by sulfinpyrazone of the platelet-dependent bronchoconstriction due to Platelet-activating factor (PAF-acether) in the guinea-pig', *Eur. J. Pharmac.*, **78**, 71.

Cirino, M., Lagente, V., Lefort, J., and Vargaftig, B.B. (1986). 'A study with BN 52021 demonstrates the involvement of PAF-acether in IgE-dependent anaphylactic bronchoconstriction', *Pharmacol. Res. Comm.*, (in press).

Desquand, S., Touvay, C., Randon, J., Lagente, V., Maridonneau-Parini, I., Etienne, A., Lefort, J., Braquet, P., and Vargaftig, B.B. (1986). 'Interference of BN 52021 (ginkgolide B) with the bronchopulmonary effects of PAF-acether in the guinea-pig', *Eur. J. Pharmacol.*, (in press).

Detsouli, A., Lefort, J., and Vargaftig, B.B. (1985). 'Histamine and leukotriene-independent guinea-pig anaphylactic shock unaccounted for by PAF-acether', *Br. J. Pharmacol.*, **84**, 801.

Doebber, T.W., Wu, M.S., Robbins, J.C., Choy, B.M., Chang, M.N., and Shen, T.Y. (1985). 'Platelet-activating factor (PAF) involvement in endotoxin-induced hypotension in rats. Studies with PAF-receptor antagonist kadsurenone', *Biochem. Biophys. Res. Comm.*, **127**, 799.

Fantozzi, R. Brunelleschi, S., Rubino, A., Tarli, S., Masini, E., and Mannaioni, P.F. (1986). 'FAMLP-activated neutrophils evoke histamine release from mast cells', *Agents Actions*, **18**, 156.

Hatmi, M., Rotilio, D., Haye, B., Antonicelli, F., Joseph, D., and Vargaftig, B.B. (1986). 'Modulation by cyclic AMP of arachidonic acid-induced platelet desensitization', (submitted)

Henocq, E., and Vargaftig, B. (1986). 'Accumulation of eosinophils in response to intracutaneous PAF-acether and allergens in man', *Lancet*, **I**, (8494), ·1378−1379.

Lefort, J., and Vargaftig, B.B. (1978). 'Role of platelets in aspirin-sensitive bronchoconstriction in the guinea-pig; interactions with salicylic acid', *Br. J. Pharmacol..*, **63**, 35.

Lellouch-Tubiana A., Lefort, J., Pirotzky, E., Vargaftig, B.B., and Pfister, A. (1985). 'Ultrastructural evidence for extravascular platelet recruitment in the lung upon intravenous injection of platelet-activating factor (PAF-acether) to guinea-pigs', *Br. J. exp. Path.*, **66**, 345.

Maridonneau-Parini, I., Lagente, V., Lefort, J., Randon, J., Russo-Marie, F., and Vargaftig, B.B. (1985). 'Desensitization to PAF-induced bronchoconstriction and to activation of alveolar macrophages by repeated inhalations of PAF in the guinea-pig', *Biochem. Biophys. Res. Com.*, **131**, 42.

Schulman, E.S., Liu, M.C., Proud, D., Macglashan, D.W., Jr., Lichtenstein, L.M., and Plaut, M. (1985). 'Human lung macrophages induce histamine release from basophils and mast cells', *Amer. J. resp. Dis.*, **131**, 230.

Sédivy, P., Caillard, C.G., Floch, A., Folliard, F., Mondot, S., Robaut, C., and Terlain, B. (1985a). '48740 RP: a specific PAF-acether antagonist', *Prostaglandins*, **30**, 688.

Sédivy, P., Caillar, C.G., Carruette, A., Derégnaucourt, J., and Mondot, S. (1985b). '48740 RP: selective anti-PAF agent'. In F., Russo-Marie, J.M. Mencia-Huerta, and M. Chignard, (eds.) *Adv. Infl. Res.* Raven Press, New York, pp.171−173.

Shen, T.Y., Hwang, S.B., Chang, N.M., Doebber, W.T., Lam, M.H.T., Wu, M.S., Xui, A., Han G.D., and Li, R.Z. (1984). 'Characterization of a platelet-activating factor receptor antagonist isolated from haifenteng (*Piper futokadsura*): specific inhibition of *in vitro* and *in vivo* platelet-activating factor-induced effects', *Proc. Natl. Acad. Sci., USA*, **82**, 670.

Nishikawa, K. (1982). 'CV 3988—a specific antagonist of platelet-activating factor (PAF)', *Life, Sci.*, **32**, 1975.

Terashita, Z., Imura, Y., Nishikawa, K., and Sumida, S. (1985). 'Is platelet-activating factor (PAF) a mediator of endotoxin shock?', *Eur. J. Pharmac.*, **109**, 257.

Vargaftig, B.B. (1985). 'Do leukotrienes account for antigen-induced bronchoconstriction in the guinea-pig?', *Ann. Inst. Pasteur/Immunol.*, **136D**, 180.

Vargaftig, B.B., Lefort, J., and Rotilio, D. (1983). 'Route-dependent interactions between PAF-acether and guinea-pig bronchopulmonary smooth muscle: relevance of cyclooxygenase mechanisms'. In J. Benveniste, and B. Arnoux, (eds.), *Platelet-activating factor, INSERM Symposium No 23, 1983*, Elsevier Science Publishers, Amsterdam, P.307.

Vargaftig, B.B., Lefort, J., Chignard, M., and Benveniste, J.(1980). 'Platelet-activating factor induces a platelet-dependent bronchoconstriction unrelated to the formation of prostaglandin derivatives', *Europ. J. Pharmacol.*, **65**, 185–192.

Vargaftig, B.B., Lefort, J., Joseph, D., and Fouque, F. (1979). 'Mechanisms of bronchoconstriction and of thrombocytopenia induced by collagen in the guinea-pig', *European J. Pharmacol.*, **58**, 273.

Vargaftig, B.B., Lefort, J., Wal, F., and Chignard, M. (1981). 'Role of the metabolites of arachidonate in platelet-dependent and independent experimetal bronchoconstriction', *Bull. Europ. Physiopath. Resp.*, **17**, 723.

Vargaftig, B.B., Lefort, J., Wal, F., Chignard, M., and Medeiros, M. (1982). 'Non-steroidal anti-inflammatory drugs if combined with anti-histamine and anti-serotonin agents interfere with the bronchial and platelet effects of platelet-activating factor (PAF-acether)', *European J. Pharmacol.*, **82**, 121.

New Horizons in Platelet Activating Factor Research
Edited by C. M. Winslow and M. L. Lee
© 1987 John Wiley & Sons Ltd.

16

Toward Understanding the Mechanism of Action of Platelet Activating Factor Receptor Antagonists

Christine M. Winslow, Robert C. Anderson, Frank J. D'Aries, Glenn E. Frisch, Andrea K. DeLillo, Mark L. Lee and Robert N. Saunders

INTRODUCTION

Since the elucidation of the structure of PAF in 1979 (Benveniste *et al.*, 1979; Blank *et al.*, 1979; Demopoulos *et al.*, 1979), attempts have been made by investigators to better understand the mechanism of action of this potent ether phospholipid. One approach has been to prepare analogs of PAF with alterations in the substituents on the glycerol backbone. These approaches have yielded PAF analogs with agonist properties, enantiomers with weak agonist activity, compounds with desensitizing activity (for a recent review see Venuti, 1985), and inhibitors of PAF activity (cf. Miyamoto *et al.*, 1984; Terashita *et al.*, 1983).The most well-characterised inhibitor of PAF is the compound CV 3988, which has the structure shown in Figure 1 (Terashita *et al.*, 1983). Since that time several PAF inhibitors have been described (Hwang *et al.*, 1985; Kornecki *et al.*, 1984; Nunez *et al.*, 1986; Shen *et al.*, 1985), but they are not derivatives of the glycerol backbone of PAF.

This paper describes two novel compounds, SRI 63-072 and SRI 63-119, which are specific and potent PAF receptor antagonists (Figure 1).

MATERIALS AND METHODS

Materials

PGI$_2$ was obtained from Chinoin, Hungary. PAF, SRI 63-119, and SRI 63-072 were prepared by Sandoz Research Institute, East Hanover, New Jersey.

CV-3988

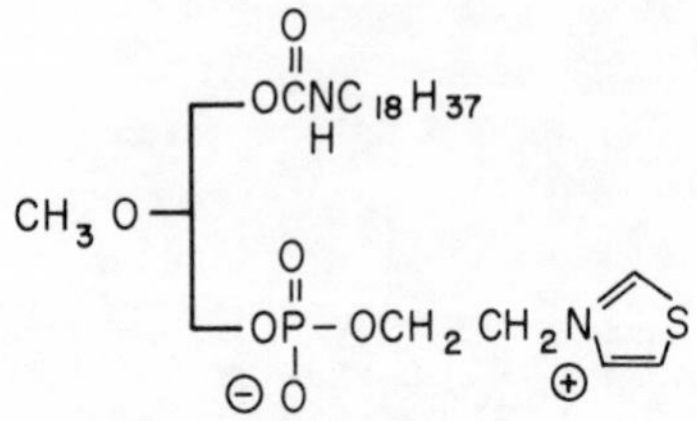

$$\text{CH}_3\text{O} \left\langle \begin{array}{l} \text{—OCNC}_{18}\text{H}_{37} \\ \quad\ \ \overset{\text{O}}{\overset{\|}{}}\ \ \overset{|}{\text{H}} \\ \\ \text{—OP—OCH}_2\text{CH}_2\overset{+}{\text{N}}{\Large\langle}\!\!\!{}_{\text{S}} \\ \quad\ \ \underset{\ominus\ \text{O}}{\overset{\|}{\text{O}}} \end{array} \right.$$

(R,S)-3-(N-n-Octadecylcarbamoyloxy)-2-methoxypropyl-2-
thiazolioethyl phosphate

SRI 63-072   •2H$_2$O

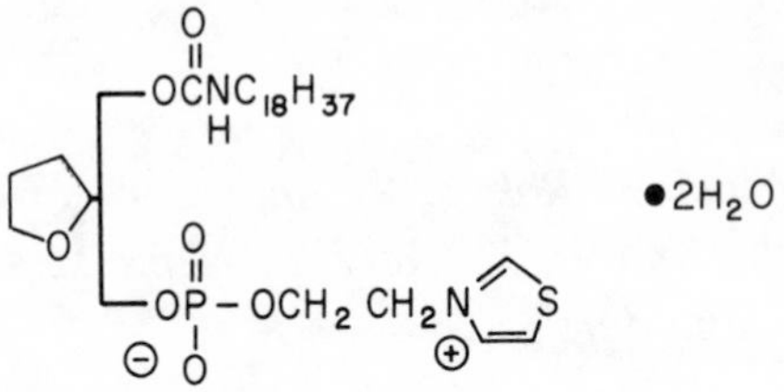

(R,S)-3-[2-[(2-Octadecylaminocarbonyloxymethyltetra-
hydro-2-furanylmethoxy)-hydroxyphosphinyloxy]-ethyl]-
thiazolium hydroxide inner salt-4-oxide

SRI 63-119   CH$_3$O   Br$^{\ominus}$

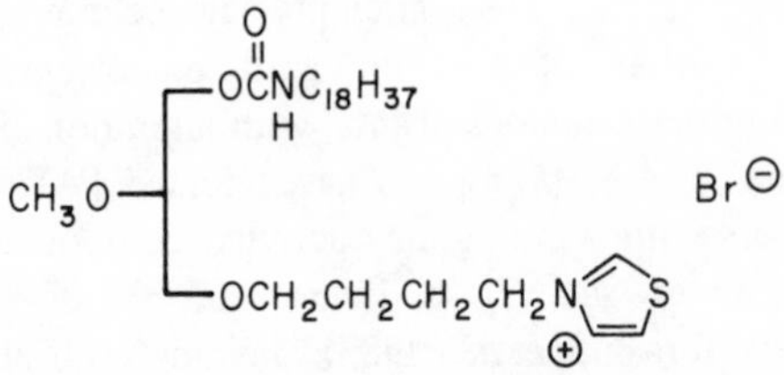

(R,S,)-3-[4-[(3-Octadecylaminocarbonyloxy-2-methoxy)-
propoxy]butyl]-thiazolium bromide

Figure 1.   Chemical structures of active PAF receptor antagonists

Platelet aggregation inhibition

Human subjects were kept aspirin free for one week and fasted overnight. Platelet rich plasma (PRP) was prepared by centrifugation (250 × g, 10 min, 24 °C) of freshly drawn blood anticoagulated with 0.38 percent sodium citrate (final concentration). Platelet count was adjusted to 2.5 × 10^5 per μl using platelet poor plasma (PPP) obtained by a second centrifugation (900 × g, 15 min, 24 °C) of the blood sample. An aliquot (0.38 ml) of the PRP was dispensed into cuvettes, incubated at 37 °C, and stirred at 900 rpm within a Payton Aggregometer which recorded the light transmission pattern of the platelet suspension. The test compound was then added at final concentrations in the range of $0.1-100$ μM. One minute after the addition of the test compound, PAF was added to the cuvette in an amount predetermined to give a consistent increase in light transmission (4.8×10^{-7} M). All aggregations were allowed to proceed for 5 min from the addition of the PAF. The aggregation response was quantitated by determining the area under the curve (AUC) using a plane polari-meter. The percent inhibition of the aggregation response was determined by dividing the AUC generated in the presence of the compound by the AUC of the PAF alone, multiplying by 100 and the subtracting from 100. Alternatively, other aggregation-inducing agents were used instead of PAF. These included ADP (5 μM), epinephrine (10 μM) and collagen (85 μg ml^{-1}).

Isolation of platelets from different species

Platelets were obtained from the whole blood of guinea pigs, rabbits, dogs and baboons using the same anticoagulant as described for humans. All platelets were suspended at 2.5×10^5 platelets μl^{-1}, except for the baboon and guinea pig platelets, which were suspended at concentrations of 4.25×10^5 and 5.0×10^5 platelets μl^{-1}, respectively.

Inhibition of [^{3}H]PAF binding to the human platelet PAF receptor

Concentration-response curve

Whole human platelets were used for the PAF receptor binding assays (Kloprogge and Akkerman, 1984; Valone *et al.*, 1982). A radioligand with high specific activity [9, 10-1-0-alkyl-^{3}H]-PAF, 49 Ci mM^{-1} was prepared (Morgat *et al.*, 1982). For the preparation of platelets a modification of the method of Radomski and Moncada (1983) was employed. Freshly drawn human blood was anticoagulated with 0.38 per-cent sodium citrate and 2.0 μg ml^{-1} PGI$_2$. Platelet rich plasma (PRP) was prepared by centrifugation of the blood at $250 \times$ g for 10 min at 24 °C. The platelets were sedimented by centrifugation at $900 \times$ g for 15 min, 24 °C, and then washed twice with a solution of tris-Tyrode's buffer, pH 7.4, containing 0.25 percent bovine serum albumin (TT/BSA) and 0.3 μg ml^{-1} PGI$_2$. The washed platelets were resuspended to 3.5×10^5 per μl in TT/BSA. Aliquots of platelets (500 μl) were mixed 1.5 nM [^{3}H] PAF (40 000 CPM). Non-specific binding was estimated in duplicate tubes contain-ing excess cold PAF (3.7×10^{-7}M final concentration).

After incubation at 24 °C for 1 hr, the reaction was stopped by the addition of 500 μl ice-cold TT/BSA. The [^{3}H]PAF bound to platelets was separated from the free radioligand by centrifugation at 900 × g for 10 min, 4 °C. Pellets were washed with TT/BSA and centrifuged at 900 × g for 15 min, 4 °C. The pellets were resuspended in 2.5ml liquid scintillation fluid. The tubes were mixed and counted for 1 min in a liquid scintillation spectrometer. The amount of specific binding was calculated as the difference in cpm between the total bound [^{3}H]PAF and non-specifically bound [^{3}H]PAF (bound in the presence of 3.7 × 10^{-7} M cold PAF). The percent inhibition of specific binding was determined by dividing the cpm specifically bound in the presence of the test compound by the cpm specifically bound in the vehicle control, multiplying by 100 and then subtracting from 100. An IC$_{50}$ (50 percent inhibitor concentration) value was generated by evaluating the test compound over the concentration range of 0.1–100 μM.

Parallel dose–response curves

[^{3}H]PAF at concentrations ranging from 0.09–9 nM was incubated with washed human platelets with and without either PAF at 3.7 × 10^{-7} M or compound at 0.05, 0.1 and 1.0 μM. Incubations and washing procedures were as described above.

Table 1. Effect of PAF Antagonists on Human Platelet Aggregation: Specificity

| | Human Platelet Aggregation IC$_{50}$ (μM) | | | |
	PAF (4.8 × 10^{-7} M)	ADP (5 μM)	Epinephrine (10 μM)	Collagen (85 μg ml^{-1})
CV 3988	6.4	>100	>100	>100
SRI 63-072	22.3 (n = 15)	>100	>100	69.1
SRI 63-119	3.8 (n = 18)	>100 (n = 3)	19.5 (n = 4)	>100

The compounds were preincubated with human platelet rich plasma for one minute prior to the addition of agonist.
CV 3988 is included for comparison.

RESULTS AND DISCUSSION

Compound SRI 63-072 was found to be a potent inhibitor of PAF-induced human platelet aggregation, with an IC$_{50}$ of 22.3 μM (n=15 determinations). It did not cross-react with ADP nor epinephrine and was a weak inhibitor of collagen-induced human platelet aggregation (Table 1). SRI 63-072 compared favorably with the Takeda compound CV 3988 (IC$_{50}$ = 6.4 μM). Compound SRI 63-119 was found to be the most potent inhibitor of PAF-induced human platelet aggregation with an IC$_{50}$ of 3.8 μM (n=18 determinations). SRI 63-119 did not cross-react with ADP nor collagen, but it was a moderate inhibitor of epinephrine-induced human platelet aggregation.

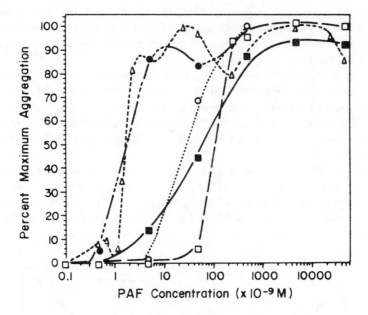

Figure 2. Comparison of responses of platelets from different species to PAF; 100 percent aggregation is defined as the maximal increase in light transmission following the addition of PAF. Symbols: □, baboon; ■, human; ○, dog; ●, rabbit; △, guinea-pig

Table 2. Effect of PAF Antagonists on Platelet Aggregation: Activity in Platelets from Different Species

	Platelet Aggregation IC_{50} (μM)				
[PAF] =	Human 0.48 μM	Guinea Pig 2.4nM	Rabbit 4.8 nM	Dog 0.48 μM	Baboon 0.48 μM
CV 3988	6.4	2.2	4.8	ND	28.8
SRI 63-072	22.3	1.4	4.7	34.1%I/ 100 μM	19.0
SRI 63-119	3.8	0.05	0.4	5.9	4.3

The compounds were preincubated with platelet rich plasma from the different species for one minute prior to the addition of PAF at the optimal concentration for each species.
CV 3988 is included for comparison

Guinea pig, rabbit, dog and baboon platelets demonstrated varying degrees of sensitivity to PAF, with guinea pig and rabbit showing the most sensitivity, followed by dog, human and baboon (Figure 2). Compound SRI 63-072 was a potent inhibitor of PAF-induced platelet aggregation in guinea pig and rabbit platelets, with IC_{50}

values of 1.4 and 4.7 μM, respectively (Table 2). SRI 63-072 did not inhibit dog plate-let aggregation (34 percent inhibition at 100 μM) and inhibited baboon platelet aggregation with a similar IC_{50} value (19 μM) as that obtained with human platelets (IC_{50} = 22.3 μM).

Compound SRI 63-119 potently inhibited PAF-induced platelet aggregation in guinea pig and rabbit platelets, with IC_{50} values of 0.05 and 0.4 μM, respectively (Table 2). SRI 63-119 inhibited dog and baboon platelet aggregation with similar IC_{50} values (5.9 μM and 4.3 μM, respectively) as that obtained with human platelets (IC_{50} = 3.8 μM). However, at 100 μM, SRI 63-119 displayed weak agonist properties in dog platelets.

Compound SRI 63-072 competed for PAF receptor binding in a concentration-dependent manner, with an IC_{50} of 1.4 μM (n = 4 determinations). Similarly, SRI 63-119 competed for PAF receptor binding with an IC_{50} of 1.3 μM (n = 8 determinations). However, both compounds were 1000 fold less potent than PAF itself (IC_{50} = 1.2 nM) (Figure 3).

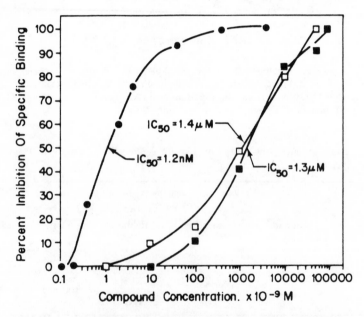

Figure 3.   Competition by SRI 63-072 and SRI 63-119 for [³H]PAF binding. Compounds were assayed as described in the text. Symbols: ●, PAF; ■, SRI 63-072; □, SRI 63-119

Parallel specific binding curves for concentrations of [³H]PAF ranging from 0.09–9 nM were analyzed in the presence and absence of either compound SRI 63-072 or SRI 63-119. The ratio of fmoles specifically bound to fM maximally bound was plotted as a function of fM of PAF added to each tube. The dose−response curves to PAF were found to be shifted in parallel to the right for each increasing concentration of either compound (not shown). The reciprocals of the data were then plotted as 1/(fmoles bound/maximal bound) v. 1/fmole added (Lineweaver-Burk analysis). The Y-axis intercept gives an approximation of 1/maximal binding. The shift in K_D from 3.67×10^{-10} M to 1.32×10^{-9} M with 1 μM SRI 63-072, with little change in the maximal binding, suggests that with increasing concentrations of PAF the binding of SRI 63-072 to the receptor can be overcome and that maximal binding of PAF can be achieved. This is the relationship that one would expect for a competitive inhibitor (Figure 4).

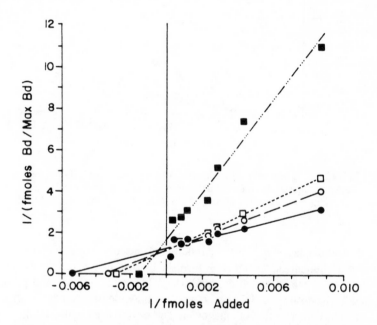

Figure 4.   Lineweaver−Burk analysis of PAF and SRI 63-072 binding to human platelets. Concentrations of SRI 63-072 in the range 0.05−1.0 μM were incubated with increasing concentrations of PAF, in the range 0.09−9 mM. The competition by PAF for the receptor in the absence and presence of the compound was analyzed as described in the text. Symbols used to represent concentrations of SRI 63-072 were: ●, Control; ○, 0.05 μM; □, 0.10 μM; ■, 1.00 μM

Similarly, the shift in K_D for the binding of PAF to the human platelet receptor from 4.86×10^{-10} M to 4.80×10^{-9} M with 1 μM SRI 63-119, with little change in the maximal binding, suggests competitive inhibition by this compound as well (Figure 5).

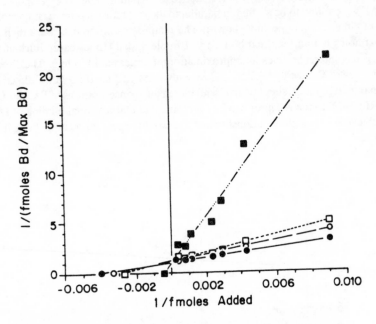

Figure 5.   Lineweaver–Burk analysis of PAF and SRI 63-119 binding to human platelets. Assays were as described in Figure 4. Symbols used to represent concentrations of SRI 63-119 were: ●, Control; ○, 0.05 μM; □, 0.10 μM; ■, 1.00 μM

The dextral displacements of the parallel concentration–response curves of PAF binding to the human platelet receptor furnished an estimate of the number of fmoles of PAF required for half-maximal binding (EC_{50}) in the absence and presence of compound. The dose-ratio (DR) was defined as the ratio between the EC_{50}s for PAF after and before the addition of antagonist. These were used in the Schild equation:

$$\log (DR-1) = N \log [B] - \log K_{B.}$$

where B was the molar concentration of compound and K_B was the equilibrium dissociation constant of the antagonist for the receptor. If the Schild regression was linear with a slope not significantly different from unity, the intercept was taken as an estimate of the K_B for the compound tested (Arunlakshana and Schild, 1959). SRI 63-072 and SRI 63-119 met these criteria with slopes of 1.21 (r=0.998) and 1.13 (r=0.997), respectively. An estimated K_B for SRI 63-072 for the human platelet receptor is 1.97×10^{-7} M. The estimated K_B for SRI 63-119 for the human platelet PAF receptor is 1.24×10^{-7} M (Figure 6).

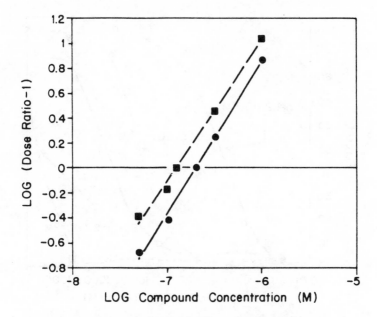

Figure 6. Schild regression of SRI 63-072 and SRI 63-119 inhibition of PAF receptor binding. Analysis was performed as described in the text. SRI 63-072, ■, gave a calculated K_B value of 1.97×10^{-7} M (slope = 1.21, n = 0.998). SRI 63-119, ●, had a K_B of 1.24×10^{-7} M (slope = 1.13, n = 0.997)

PAF has a chiral center at carbon-2 and can exist as the R or S-enantiomer. In nature, the R-enantiomer prevails. The human platelet PAF receptor recognizes both enantiomers. The R-enantiomer of PAF is 500 × more active than the S-enantiomer at the receptor level and is 230 × more active than the S-enantiomer in human platelet aggregation (Figure 7).

The PAF receptor antagonists which have been analyzed to date which approach the K_D of PAF for the receptor take on agonist properties as opposed to antagonist properties. The chiral SRI 63-072 and SRI 63-119 compounds do not show enantiomeric specificity for the receptor nor for platelet aggregation (Table 3). This may be a result of the size or polarity of the substituents at carbon-2, allowing the compounds to fit into the receptor in either configuration. It may also be that the compounds are weak antagonists (active in the concentration range of S-PAF) and that a more potent antagonist might show enantiomeric specificity.

These compounds are at the frontier of the discovery of newer and more potent PAF antagonists. As these become more widely available, they will be useful in better understanding whether PAF is acting via receptor mechanisms in anaphylaxis (McManus *et al.*, 1980), inflammation (Wykle *et al.*, 1981), and cardiovascular disease (cf. Halonen *et al.*, 1980).

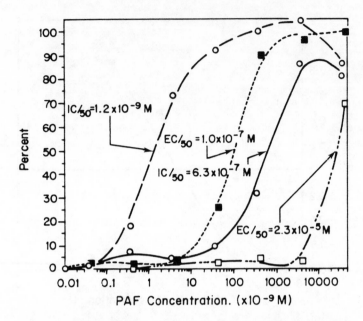

Figure 7.　Comparison of receptor binding to platelet aggregation: enantiomeric specificity. In receptor competition experiments, 50 percent inhibition of specific binding (IC_{50}) was calculated for *R*-PAF, ●, and *S*-PAF, ○. In platelet aggregation experiments, the concentration of PAF required for 50 percent aggregation (EC_{50}) was calculated for *R*-PAF, ■, and *S*-PAF, □

Table 3.　Effect of Enantiomeric Configuration on Activity of PAF Antagonists

	IC_{50} (μM)	
	Human Platelet Agg.	Human Platelet Receptor
Rac-63-119	3.80	1.33
L-63-119	4.07	1.72
D-63-119	4.96	1.66
Rac-63-072	22.30	1.44
63-072/1[1]	23.96	0.86
63-072/2[1]	45.45	0.42

[1]　The absolute stereochemistry of these chiral congeners of 63-072 is unknown, however, they are of opposite relative configuration

ACKNOWLEDGMENTS

The authors would like to thank Ms Sonya Beasley for typing this manuscript.

REFERENCES

Arunlakshana, O., and Schild, H.O. (1959). 'Some quantitative uses of drug antagonists', *Br. J. Pharmacol. Chemother.*, **14**, 48−58.

Benveniste, J., Tencé, M., Varenne, P., Bidault, J., Boullet, C., and Polonsky, J. (1979). 'Semi-synthése et structure proposée du facteur activant les plaquettes (P.A.F.): PAF-acether, un alkyl ether analogue de la lysophosphatidylcholine', *C.R. Acad. Sci. Paris D*, **289**, 1037−1040.

Blank, M.L., Snyder, F., Byer, L.W., Brooks, B., and Muirhead, E.E. (1979). 'Antihypertensive activity of an alkyl ether analogue of phosphatidylcholine', *Biochem. Biophys. Res. Commun.*, **90**, 1194−1200.

Demopoulos, C.A., Pinckard, R.N., and Hanahan, D.J. (1979). 'Platelet-activating factor. Evidence for 1-0-alkyl-2-acetyl-*sn*-glyceryl-3-phosphorylcholine as the active component (A new class of lipid chemical mediators)', *J. Biochem.*, **254**, 9355−9358.

Halonen, M., Palmer, J.D., Lohman, I.C., McManus, L.M., and Pinckard, R.N. (1980).'Respiratory and circulatory alterations induced by acetyl glyceryl ether phosphorylcholine, a mediator of IgE anaphylxis in the rabbit', *Amer. Rev. Resp. Dis.*, **122**, 915−924.

Hwang, S.-B., Lam, M.-H., Biftu, T., Beattie, T.R., and Shen, T.Y. (1985). 'Trans-2,5-bis-(3,4,5-trimethoxyphenyl) tetrahydrofuran, an orally active specific and competitive receptor antagonist of platelet activating factor', *J. Biol. Chem.*, **260**, 15639−15645.

Kloprogge, E., and Akkerman, J.W.N. (1984). 'Binding kinetics of PAF-acether (1-0-alkyl-2-acetyl-*sn*-glycero-3-phosphocholine) to intact human platelets', *Biochem. J.*, **223**, 901−909.

Kornecki, E., Ehrlich, Y.H., and Lenox, R.H. (1984).'Platelet activating factor-induced aggregation of human platelets specifically inhibited by triazolobenzodiazepines', *Science*, **226**, 1454−1456.

McManus, L.M., Hanahan, D.J. Demopoulos, C.A., and Pinckard, R.N. (1980). 'Pathobiology of the intravenous infusion of acetyl glyceryl ether phosphorylcholine (AGEPC), a synthetic platelet-activating factor (PAF), in the rabbit', *J. Immunol.*, **124**, 2919−2924.

Miyamoto, T., Ohno, H., Yano, T., Okada, T., Hamanaka, N., and Kawasaki, A. (1984). 'A new potent antagonist of platelet-activating factor', *Kyoto Conference on Prostaglandins*. Nov. 25−28, 1984, Kyoto, Japan (Abstr. S13-9).

Morgat, J.L., Roy, J., Wichrowski, B., Michel, E., Heymans, F., and Godfroid, J.J. (1982). 'Radio-labeling of 1-0-alkyl-2-0-acetyl-*sn*-glycero-3-phosphorylcholine, 1-0-(9,10-di³H)-octadecyl PAF-acether', *Agents and Actions*, **12**, 705−706.

Nunez, D., Chignard, M., Korth, R., LeCouedic, J.P., Norel, X., Spinnewyn, B., Braquet, P., and Benveniste, J. (1986). 'Specific inhibition of PAF-acether induced platelet activation by BN52021 and comparison with the PaF-acether inhibitors kadsurenone and CV 3988', *Eur. J. Pharmacol.*, **123**, 197−205.

Radomski, M., and Moncada, S. (1983). 'An improved method for washing of human platelets with prostacyclin', *Thromb. Res.*, **30**, 383−389.

Shen, T.Y., Hwang, S.B., Chang, M.N., Doebber, T.W., Lam, M.H., Wu, M.S., and Wang, X. (1985). 'The isolation and characterization of kadsurenone from haifenteng (Piper futo-kadsura) as an orally active specific receptor antagonist of platelet-activating factor', *Int. J. Tiss. Reac.*, **7**, 339−343.

Terashita, Z., Tsushima, S., Yoshioka, Y., Nomura, H., Inada, Y., and Nishikawa, K. (1983). 'CV-3988 - A specific antagonist of platelet-activating factor (PAF)', *Life Sciences*, **32**, 1975−1982.

Valone, F.H., Coles, E., Reinhold, V.R., and Goetzl, E.J. (1982). 'Specific binding of phospholipid platelet-activating factor by human platelets', *J. Immunol.*, **139**, 1637−1641.

Venuti, M.C. (1985). 'Platelet-activating factor: multifaceted biochemical and physiological mediator', *Ann. Rep. Med. Chem.*, **20**, 193–202.

Wykle, R.C., Miller, C.H., Lewis, J.C., Schmitt, J.D., Smith, J.A., Surles, J.R., Piantadosi, C., and O'Flaherty, J.T. (1981). 'Stereospecific activity of 1-*O*-alkyl-2-*O*-acetyl-*sn*-glycero-3-phosphocholine and comparison of analogues in the degranulation of platelets and neutrophils', *Biochem. Biophys. Res. Commun.*, **100**, 1651–1658.

New Horizons in Platelet Activating Factor Research
Edited by C. M. Winslow and M. L. Lee
© 1987 John Wiley & Sons Ltd.

17

Regulation of [³H]Platelet Activating Factor Binding to its Receptors by Ions and GTP and PAF-Induced Activation of GTPase in Rabbit Platelet Membranes

San-Bao Hwang and My-Hanh Lam

INTRODUCTION

Platelet activating factor (PAF) has been suggested to be a potent mediator involved in various inflammatory, respiratory and cardiovascular disorders (Page *et al.*, 1984; Vargaftig and Benveniste, 1984; Levi *et al.*, 1984). Due to its high potency to activate platelets and its specific molecular structure requirements, a receptor mediated process for the PAF function has been proposed. Indeed, specific receptor sites for PAF have been found in a variety of cell membranes (Valone *et al.*, 1982; Hwang *et al.*, 1983; Valone and Goetzl, 1983; Kloprogge and Akkerman, 1984; Hwang *et al.*, 1985a). However, the exact mechanism by which PAF-receptor binding regulates biological function is not known. Based on the observations by Haslam and Vanderwil (1982), Lad *et al.*, (1985) and our data, in this communication, we propose a signal transduction mechanism for PAF actions following the receptor activation.

MATERIALS AND METHODS

Materials

The tritium labeled PAF(1-0-[1,2-³H₂]-alkyl-2-0-acetyl-*sn*-glycero-3-phosphocholine) was purchased from New England Nuclear (Boston, MA) with a specific activity of 45 Ci mmole⁻¹. Unlabled C₁₆-PAF (1-0-hexadecyl-2-0-acetyl-*sn*-glycero-3-phosphocholine) was obtained from Bachem (Torrance, CA). The purity of C₁₆-PAF has been shown to be higher than 99 percent, and it was used without further purification. Calmodulin from bovine brain was purchased from Sigma Chemical Co. (St Louis, MO). All other reagents used were either analytical or reagent grade.

Methods

Preparations of rabbit platelet membranes

Rabbit platelets were prepared as previously described (Hwang *et al.*, 1983). The rabbit platelet membranes were prepared by the modified procedure (Hwang *et al.*, 1985c,1986). The prepared rabbit platelets were lysed by at least three cycles of repeatedly freezing with liquid N_2 and thawing at room temperature in a Na^+ free medium containing 5 mM $MgCl_2$, 10 mM Tris and 2 mM EDTA pH 7.5 at a concentration of $2-5 \times 10^{-9}$ platelets ml^{-1}. The cytoplasmic proteins were removed and the membranes were further fractionated through the sucrose density gradient (Hwang *et al.*, 1983). The fractionated membranes were stored at -80 °C and thawed before use.

[^{3}H]PAF receptor binding assay

Specific [^{3}H]PAF receptor binding to rabbit platelet membranes was performed as previously described (Hwang *et al.*, 1983,1984,1985a,b,1986). The specific [^{3}H]PAF binding was defined as the difference between total binding and non-specific binding, whereas non-specific binding was defined as the total binding in the presence of 1000-fold excess unlabeled C_{16}-PAF.

Preparation of rabbit platelets and monitoring the platelet aggregation

Rabbit platelets were prepared following the procedure of Pinckard *et al.*, (1979) and the aggregation of washed rabbit platelets was performed as described (Hwang *et al.*, 1983).

RESULTS AND DISCUSSION

The binding of specific [^{3}H]PAF to isolated rabbit platelet membranes was found to be regulated by monovalent and divalent ions and GTP (Hwang *et al.*, 1986). Na^+ and Li^+ inhibited the specific [^{3}H]PAF binding with ED_{50} of approximately 6 and 150 nM respectively. In contrast, K^+, Cs^+ and Rb^+ and divalent cations Mg^{2+}, Mn^{2+} and Ca^{2+} potentiated the specific [^{3}H]PAF binding. K^+ showed 50 percent of the maximal effect at 30 mM and a maximal effect at 150 mM with 80 percent potentiation of the specific binding of the control. Mg^{2+} ions were slightly more effective than the other two cations in potentiating the specific binding. Half-maximal stimulation was achieved at approximately 0.5 mM and the maximal stimulation at 10 mM (Hwang *et al.*, 1986). From a detailed Scatchard analysis, the Na^+ inhibitory effect was apparently due to an increase in the equilibrium dissociation constant (K_d) of the PAF receptor binding, but not in the number of receptor sites (B_{max}), whereas the increase in specific [³H]PAF binding by K^+ or divalent cations was partially attributed to the increase in the PAF affinity for its receptor and partially to the increase in the total number of detectable receptor sites (Table 1). Potentiation effects of Mg^{2+} and K^+ seemed to be identical. Both the binding affinity and the maximal receptor sites doubled in the presence of Mg^{2+} or K^+. This confirmed our previous observation that no further increment of specific binding was observed when both K^+ and Mg^{2+} were present in the assay (Hwang *et al.*, 1986).

Table 1. Effects of Monovalent and Divalent Cations on the Equilibrium Dissociation Constant (K_d) of [³H]PAF Binding to Rabbit Platelet Membranes and the Maximal Number of Receptor Sites (B_{max})

Conditions	K_d (nM) (mean ± S.D.)	B_{max} (mean ± S.D.) (10^{-13} mole mg^{-1} protein)
1. 10 mM MgCl$_2$	0.53 (±0.063)[1] (n=3)	23.0[1] (± 4.0)
2. 10 mM CaCl$_2$ 0.2 mM MgCl$_2$ without NaCl	0.84	34.8
3. 0.2 mM MgCl$_2$ without NaCl	0.99 (±0.018)[1] (n=2)	9.6[1] (±0.9)
4. 0.2 mM MgCl$_2$ with 150 mM NaCl	4.2 (±0.21)[1] (n=4)	12.0[1] (±2.9)
5. 150 mM KCl 0.2 mM MgCl$_2$ without NaCl	0.56	24.8

[1] From Hwang *et al.*, 1986.

In contrast to the above, Ca^{2+} seemed to potentiate the specific [³H]PAF binding by increasing the maximal detectable receptor sites rather than the affinity to the receptors. In the presence of 10 mM CaCl$_2$, the B_{max} increased more than threefold, whereas the K_d remained almost identical to that found in the assay with the ionic conditions of 0.2 mM MgCl$_2$, 10 mM Tris and 0.25 percent BSA pH 7.0 (Table 1). Therefore the binding sites for Ca^{2+} and Mg^{2+} seemed to be different since Mg^{2+} and Ca^{2+} are very different cations. The differences may stem mainly from the difference in ion size: Mg^{2+}, 0.60 Å; Ca^{2+}, 0.95 Å (Levine and Williams, 1982). La^{3+} and Mn^{2+} cations usually replaced Ca^{2+} ions almost exactly. Therefore, they also potentiated the specific [³H]PAF binding. In fact, lanthanide ions were more effective in the potentiation of the specific PAF binding (Figure 1). They showed a maximal effect at a lower concentration (0.3 mM). Ba^{2+} also potentiated the binding; however, Ni^{2+} showed no effect. The effectiveness of the cations on the potentiation of the specific [³H]PAF binding is quite different from the selectivity of the cations on the PAF-induced platelet aggregation (Figure 2). As shown in Figure 2, the extracellular Ca^{2+} played an important role on the aggregation of the washed rabbit platelets even though it was not absolutely required. Mn^{2+}, Co^{2+} and

Sr^{2+} also enhanced the PAF-induced platelet aggregation but not Ba^{2+} and La^{3+}. In fact, La^{3+} inhibited the Ca^{2+} potentiation effect. These results suggest that the divalent ions, similar to Na^+ ions (Motulsky and Insel, 1983) must also bind to the intracellular site(s) of the cell membrane to affect the specific [^{3}H]PAF binding. Also, the Ca^{2+} potentiation effect seemed to be independent of calmodulin. With 10 μg calmodulin ml^{-1} in the assay, no significant difference on the binding potentiation was observed (Figure 3). Apparently, the physiological significance of this potentiation remained to be elucidated.

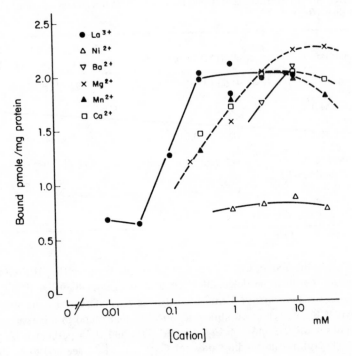

Figure 1.   Regulation of divalent cations, Mg^{2+}, Ca^{2+}, Mn^{2+}, Ba^{2+}, Ni^{2+}, La^{3+} on the specific binding of the [^{3}H]PAF (1 nM) to the isolated rabbit platelet membranes (100 μg membrane protein ml^{-1}). The divalent cation or La^{3+} was added to the reaction mixture which contains 0.2 mM $MgCl_2$ resulted from the addition of 44 μl of platelet membranes prepared in 5 mM $MgCl_2$

Similar Na^+-inhibitory and Mg^{2+}-potentiation effects have also been reported for other membrane receptors including opioids, α_2-adrenergic agents, histamine, angiotensin II, and leukotriene D_4 (Chang and Snyder, 1980; Crane et al., 1982; Blume et al., 1979; Motulsky and Insel, 1983; Pong and Dehaven, 1983). Decrease in receptor affinity by Na^+ have been confined in those receptors which are related

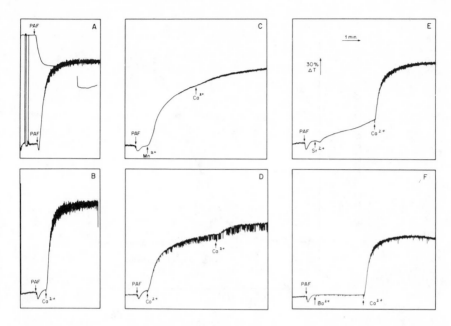

Figure 2. Divalent ionic selectivity on the enhancement of PAF-induced platelet aggregation. Washed platelets (2 × 10⁸ platelets ml⁻¹) were prepared in basic Tyrode's solution pH 6.5 and platelet aggregation and ATP release (only on A) were induced by 1.8 × 10⁻⁹ M PAF with 2 mM CaCl₂ (A) or without CaCl₂ (B—F). After 0.5 min stimulation with PAF, 2 mM CaCl₂ (B), 2 mM MnCl₂ (C), 2 mM CoCl₂ (D), 2 mM SrCl₂ (E) or 2 mM BaCl₂ (F) was added. Enhancement on platelet aggregation was observed in the order of $Ca^{2+} > > Co^{2+} \sim Mn^{2+} > Sr^{2+} > Ba^{2+}$. Further aggregation was also observed with the addition of 2 mM CaCl₂ after 3 min. PAF stimulation (C—F)

to adenylate cyclase inhibition (Motulsky and Insel, 1983; Koski *et al.*, 1982). Indeed, Haslam and Vanderwel (1982) have recently reported that PAF inhibits the basal, prostaglandin E_1-stimulated and fluoride-stimulated adenylate cyclase activities of platelets. In addition, pertussis toxin which is known to ADP-ribosylate the inhibitory guanyl nucleotide regulatory protein inhibits the PAF-mediated chemotaxis, superoxide generation, aggregation and release of lysozyme in human neutrophils (Lad *et al.*, 1985). Furthermore, a PAF-induced GTPase activity was observed in the isolated rabbit platelet membranes and appeared to be a receptor-mediated process (Hwang *et al.*, 1986). The biologically active C_{16}-PAF stimulates $[\gamma{-}^{32}P]$ GTP hydrolysis with an ED_{50} of 0.7 nM, whereas the inactive enantiomer of PAF does not stimulate GTPase activity even at a µM concentration. The PAF stimulation of GTPase activity can be fully blocked by the specific PAF antagonist, kadsurenone, but not by its inactive analog, kadsurin B. Also, Na^+ is required for the PAF-stimulated GTPase activity. Therefore, we proposed that the activated PAF receptor (R*) may interact with the adenylate cyclase system through an inhibitory guanyl

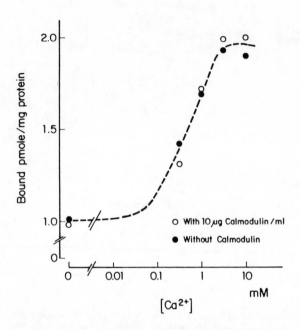

Figure 3.   Effect of calmodulin (10 μg ml^{-1}) on the Ca^{2+}-potentiated specific [^{3}H]PAF (1 nM) binding to the rabbit platelet membranes (100 μg protein ml^{-1}). The point with zero concentration of Ca^{2+} was performed without the addition of Ca^{2+} to the incubation mixture

nucleotide regulatory protein and the signal transduction mechanism for the PAF function could be due to the inhibition of the cAMP production (Figure 4). Multiple forms of the PAF receptor exist depending on the presence of Na$^+$, GTP or divalent cations and on the coupling status among PAF, receptor and effectors.

Sequential interactions among PAF, receptor and effectors have been proposed (Hwang *et al.*, 1986). Binding of PAF to the receptor may facilitate the interaction between the receptor and the inhibitory guanyl nucleotide regulatory protein, which is manifested by the increase in GTPase activity. Metal ions may be involved in this complex coupling mechanism and regulate the affinity of PAF receptor. Desensitization effects of PAF on the PAF-induced functions could be possibly due to this feedback regulation of the PAF receptor affinity.

ACKNOWLEDGMENTS

We are grateful to Mrs Joan Kiliyanski for excellent secretarial assistance.

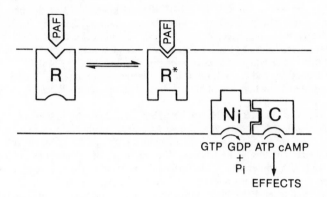

Figure 4.

REFERENCES

Blume, A.J., Lichtshtein, D., and Boone, G. (1979). 'Coupling of opiate receptors to adenylate cyclase: Requirement for Na⁺ and GTP', *Proc. Natl. Acad. Sci. USA*, **76**, 5626–5630.

Chang, R.S.L., and Snyder, S.H. (1980). 'Histamine H_1-receptor binding sites in guinea pig brain membranes: Regulation of agonist interactions by guanine nucleotides and cations', *J. Neurochem.*, **34**, 916–922.

Crane, J.K., Campanile, C.P., and Garrison, J.C. (1982).'The hepatic angiotensin II receptor. II. Effect of guanyl nucleotides and interaction with cyclic AMP-production', *J. Biol. Chem.*, **257**, 4959–4965.

Haslam, R.J., and Vanderwel, M. (1982). 'Inhibition of platelet adenylate cyclase by 1-0-alkyl-2-O-acetyl-*sn*-glyceryl-3-phosphorylcholine (platelet activating factor)', *J. Biol. Chem.*, **257**, 6879–6885.

Hwang, S-B., Lee, C.-S.C., Cheah, M.J., and Shen, T.Y. (1983).'Specific receptor sites for 1-0-alkyl-2-0-acetyl-*sn*-glycero-3-phosphocholine (platelet activating factor) on rabbit platelet and guinea pig smooth muscle membranes', *Biochemistry*, **22**, 4756–4763.

Hwang, S-B., Cheah, M.J., Lee, S.-S.C., and Shen,T.Y. (1984). 'Effects of nonsteroid anti-inflammatory drugs on the specific binding of platelet activating factor to membrane preparations of rabbit platelets', *Thromb. Res.*, **34**, 519–530.

Hwang, S.-B., Lam, M.-H., and Shen, T.Y. (1985a).'Specific binding sites for platelet activating factor in human lung tissues', *Biochem. Biophys. Res. Commun.*, **128**, 972–979.

Hwang, S.-B., Li, C.L., Lam, M.-H.T., and Shen, T.Y. (1985b). 'Characterization of cutaneous vascular permeability induced by platelet activating factor [PAF] in guinea pigs and rats and its inhibition by a PAF receptor antagonist', *Lab. Invest.*, **52**, 617–630.

Hwang, S.-B., Lam, M.-H., Biftu, T., Beattie, T.R., and Shen, T.Y. (1985c). 'Trans-2,5-bis-(3,4,5-trimethoxyphenyl) tetrahydrofuran, an orally active specific and competitive receptor antagonist of platelet activating factor ', *J. Biol. Chem.*, **260**, 15639–15645.

Hwang, S.-B., Lam, M.-H, and Pong, S.-S. (1986).'Ionic and GTP regulation of binding of platelet-activating factor to receptors and platelet-activating factor-induced activation of GTPase in rabbit platelet membranes', *J. Biol. Chem.*, **261**, 532–537.

Kloprogge, E., and Akkerman, J.W.N. (1984). 'Binding kinetics of PAF-acether (1-*O*-alkyl-2-acetyl-*sn*-glycero-3-phosphocholine) to intact human platelets', *Biochem. J.*, **223**, 901–909.

Koski, G., Streaty, R.A., and Klee, W.A. (1982). 'Modulation of sodium-sensitive GTPase by partial opiate agonists: An explanation for the dual requirement for Na$^+$ and GTP in inhibitory regulation of adenylate cyclase', *J. Biol. Chem.*, **257**, 14 035–14 040.

Lad, P.M., Olson, C.V., and Grewal, I.S. (1985). 'Platelet-activating factor mediated effects on human neutrophil function are inhibited by pertussis toxin', *Biochem. Biophys. Res. Commun.*, **129**, 632–638.

Levi, R., Burke, J.A., Guo, Z.G., Hattori, Y., Hoppens, C.M., McManus, L.M., Hanahan, D.J., and Pinckard, R.N. (1984). 'Acetyl glyceryl ether phosphorylcholine (AGEPC). A putative mediator of cardiac anaphylaxis in the guinea pig', *Cir. Res.*, **54**, 117–124.

Levine, B.A., and Williams, R.J.P. (1982). 'The chemistry of calcium ion and its biological relevance'. In L.J. Anghileri and A.M. Tuffet-Anghileri (eds.) *The Role of Calcium in Biological Systems* CRC Press, Boca Raton, Florida. Vol. I, pp. 3–26.

Motulsky, H.J., and Insel, P.A. (1983).'Influence of sodium on the α-adrenergic receptor system of human platelets. Role of intraplatelet sodium in receptor binding', *J. Biol. Chem.*, **258**, 3913–3919.

Page, C.P., Archer, C.B., Paul, W., and Morley, J. (1984). 'PAF-acether: A mediator of inflammation and asthma', *Trends Pharmacol. Sci.*, **5**, 239–241.

Pinckard, R.N., Farr, R.S., and Hanahan, D.J. (1979). 'Physicochemical and functional identity of rabbit platelet activating factor (PAF) released *in vivo* during IgE anaphylaxis with PAF released *in vitro* from IgE sensitized basophils', *J. Immunol.*, **123**, 1847–1857.

Pong, S.-S., and Dehaven, R.N. (1983). 'Characterization of a leukotriene D$_4$ receptor in guinea pig lung', *Proc. Natl. Acad. Sci. USA*, **80**, 7415–7419.

Valone, F.H., Cole, E., Reinhold, V.R., and Goetzl, E.J. (1982). 'Specific binding of phospholipid platelet activating factor by human platelets', *J. Immunol.*, **129**, 1637–1641.

Valone, F.H., and Goetzyl, E.J. (1983). 'Specific binding by human polymorphonuclear leukocyte of the immunological mediator 1-*O*-hexadecyl/octadecyl-2-acetyl-*sn*-glycero-3-phosphorycholine', *Immunology*, **48**, 141–149.

Vargaftig, B.B., and Benveniste, J. (1983). 'Platelet-activating factor today', *Trends Pharmacol. Sci.*, **4**, 341–343.

New Horizons in Platelet Activating Factor Research
Edited by C. M. Winslow and M. L. Lee
© 1987 John Wiley & Sons Ltd.

18

Platelet Activating Factor-Acether-Induced Fibrinogen Binding to Platelets

Jan Willem N. Akkerman and Ed Kloprogge

INTRODUCTION

PAF-acether induces platelet aggregation and secretion of the contents of the dense-, α- and lysosomal granules (Kloprogge *et al.*, 1983). These responses are initiated via binding to specific receptors which can be identified on isolated plasma membranes (Hwang *et al.*, 1983) and on intact platelets in incubation studies with ^{3}H-labeled PAF-acether in concentrations of 1 nM or less (Kloprogge *et al.*, 1984). At higher concentrations PAF-acether is taken up and metabolized but these events appear unimportant for the induction of platelet responses (Pieroni and Hanahan, 1983; Kloprogge and Akkerman, 1984). Platelets contain about 240 PAF-acether receptors cell^{-1}. Formation of a PAF-acether–receptor complex initiates alterations in the metabolism of polyphosphoinositides, Ca^{2+} translocation and phosphorylation of specific proteins resulting in three types of secretion responses and exposure of fibrinogen binding sites located on the glycoprotein IIb–IIIa complex. Binding of fibrinogen to the exposed sites results in platelet-platelet bridges and aggregate formation.

PAF-acether induces two types of fibrinogen binding, a high affinity type with about 2 400 sites per platelet, and a low affinity type with about 27 000 sites per platelet. High affinity binding is specifically inhibited by indomethacin and thromboxane synthetase inhibitors indicating that this type of binding is mediated via thromboxane A_2. On the other hand, low affinity binding is specifically abolished by ADP-scavengers such as phosphoenolpyruvate-pyruvate kinase (PEP-PK) indicating that it is mediated via ADP secreted from the dense granules (Kloprogge and Akkerman, 1985). The fact that one type of fibrinogen binding can be abolished while leaving the other type unchanged opens the possibility to compare the relative contribution of high and low affinity fibrinogen binding in platelet aggregation.

MATERIALS AND METHODS

Fibrinogen, purchased from KABI (Grade L, Stockholm, Sweden) was further purified and radiolabeled with ^{125}I (iodine-125, Amersham, International, Buckinghamshire, England) as described (Kloprogge et. al., 1984) and stored at -70 °C (spec.act. 200 Ci mM $^{-1}$). PAF-acether, 1-O-alkyl-2-acetyl-sn-glycero-3-phosphocholine, from Calbiochem Behring Corp. (La Jolla, Ca, USA) was dissolved in bovine albumin saline solution and stored at -20 °C. The cyclo-oxygenase inhibitor indomethacin was from Merck, Sharp & Dohm (Rahway, N.J., USA); phosphoenolpyruvate and pyruvate kinase (PEP/PK) were from Boehringer, Mannheim, Germany.

Platelet isolation

Freshly drawn venous blood was collected from healthy human volunteers (with informed consent) into 0.1 volume of 13 mM sodium citrate. The donors claimed not to have taken any medicines during the previous ten days and had been fasting for at least 10 h, a precaution that proved to be essential for the preservation of platelet responsiveness towards PAF-acether (Kloprogge et. al., 1983).

After centrifugation (200 $\times$ g, 10 min, room temperature) the supernatant, platelet-rich plasma, was placed on a Sepharose 2B column (Pharmacia, Uppsala, Sweden) (Walsh, 1972) equilibrated in Ca^{2+} −free Tyrode's solution (pH 7.25) containing 0.2 percent of bovine serum albumin (Organon Teknika) and 5 mM glucose (BDH chemicals Ltd, Poole, England). The final concentration of the gel-filtered platelets was adjusted to 2.0 $\times$ 10^8 cells ml^{-1} by dilution in Ca $^{2+}$ −free Tyrode's buffer.

Analysis of platelet aggregation

Aggregation of gel-filtered platelets induced by PAF-acether was measured by counting the disappearance of single platelets (Frojmovic et. al., 1983). For the latter technique the incubation was stopped by fixing the platelets in nine volumes of cold (0 °C) 0.5 percent glutaraldehyde (Fluka, Buchs, Switzerland) in 0.15 M NaCl. The platelets were counted in a Platelet Analyzer 810 (Baker Instruments, Allentown, PA, USA) with apertures set at 3.2 and 16 μm^3. In unstimulated platelet suspensions 94.5 $\pm$ 1.1 percent (mean $\pm$ S.D., $n = 11$) of total platelets were counted within these settings.

Binding studies with [^{125}I] fibrinogen

[^{125}I]fibrinogen binding was measured after incubation of the platelets with 500 nM PAF-acether in the presence of 50 or 500 nM [^{125}I]fibrinogen. Triplicate samples of cell suspensions (200 μl each) were collected and placed on 100 μl 20 percent (w/v) sucrose in Tyrode's solution, in polypropylene tubes (0.4 ml tubes for microsedimentation, Sarstedt, Wien, Austria). Immediately thereafter, the samples were centrifuged in a Beckman microfuge (Beckman Instruments, Mijdrecht, The Netherlands, 12 000 × g, 22 °C) for 2 min. The tips of the tubes were cut off just above the pellet and the radioactivity was counted. Non-specific binding was measured by incubating the platelets with [^{125}I]fibrinogen in the absence of PAF-acether. Control studies have shown that those cells bound as much [^{125}I]fibrinogen as platelets incubated with PAF-acether and [^{125}I]fibrinogen in the presence of a 100-fold molar excess of non-radiolabeled fibrinogen.

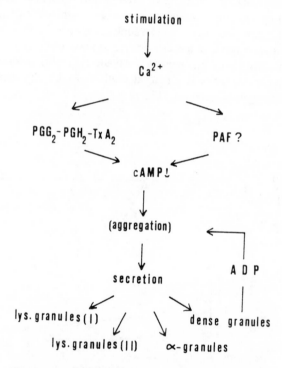

Figure 1. Stimulus–response coupling in platelets. Platelet activation is mediated via binding of an agonist to its receptor, signal processing in which Ca^{2+} translocation plays a central role and the initiation of two pathways that induce aggregation probably via lowering cyclic AMP. One pathway is mediated via prostaglandins G$_2$, H$_2$ and thromboxane A$_2$. The other pathway remains unresolved although PAF-acether may take part in it. Aggregation leads to secretion of two types of lysosomal granules, α-granules and dense granules which liberate ADP that enhances the aggregation response

RESULTS AND DISCUSSION

Most platelet stimulating agents activate the cell via binding to a specific receptor. Receptor occupancy initiates second messenger generation in which the liberation of Ca^{2+} ions from intracellular storage sites plays a central role. Elevation of cytosolic Ca^{2+} initiates two pathways that lead to aggregation and secretion. One mechanism involves the liberation of arachidonate from membrane phospholipids leading to endoperoxide formation and synthesis of thromboxane A_2. Each of these metabolites is a potent platelet activator, and probably acts via lowering the cyclic AMP content. The second pathway is largely obscure although it has been postulated that endogenous synthesis of PAF-acether would be involved. With sufficient stimulation aggregation is followed by secretion. Strong agonists such as thrombin, trigger secretion whether the cells aggregate or not. Weak agonists, however, such as ADP and PAF-acether induce little secretion unless aggregation can take place. Among the different secretory granules the dense granules are particularly important since they contain ADP, which can activate the cells via an extracellular feed back mechanism thereby enhancing the aggregation response. (Figure 1).

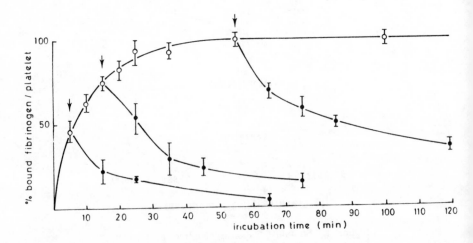

Figure 2. PAF-acether-induced fibrinogen binding. Incubation of platelets with 500 nM PAF-acether in the presence of 50 nM [^{125}I]fibrinogen induces binding, which shifts from a reversible to an irreversible pattern as demonstrated by addition of a 100-fold molar excess of unlabelled fibrinogen (arrows)

Figure 2 illustrates the binding of [^{125}I]-labeled fibrinogen to platelets stimulated with PAF-acether. Fibrinogen binding reaches saturation between 30 to 60 min (depending on fibrinogen concentration). During the first 10 min the binding is completely reversible but during longer incubation more fibrinogen becomes irreversibly linked to the cells. PAF-acether-induced fibrinogen binding occurs at binding sites located on the glycoprotein IIb–IIIa complex which is similar to the binding induced by other agonists. This is illustrated in Figure 3 which shows that platelets from two patients with Glanzmann thrombasthenia, who have a deficiency in these glycoproteins, fail to bind fibrinogen following stimulation with PAF-acether.

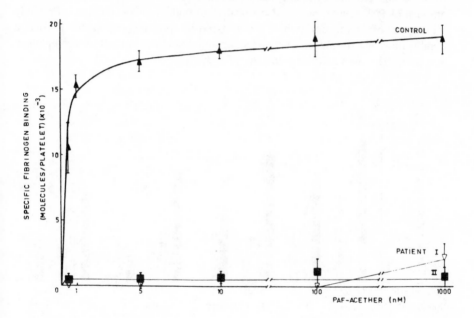

Figure 3.   Failure of Glanzmann platelets to bind fibrinogen. Platelets from patients with Glanzmann thrombasthenia lack the glycoproteins IIb-IIIa and fail to bind fibrinogen (500 nM) upon stimulation with 500 nM PAF-acether

PAF-acether induces two types of fibrinogen binding, a high affinity type and a low affinity type. Preincubation with inhibitors of thromboxane A_2 formation specifically abolishes high affinity binding leaving the low affinity binding unaltered. On the other hand, when secreted ADP is removed with ADP scavengers such as PEP-PK low affinity binding disappears while high affinity binding remains unchanged. Hence, PAF-acether induces two types of fibrinogen binding via two, mutually independent mechanisms (Kloprogge and Akkerman, 1985). This property opens the possibility to investigate the contribution of each type of fibrinogen binding in the formation of platelet aggregates. Gel-filtered platelets were stimulated with 500 or 0.5 nM PAF-acether in the presence of a high dose of fibrinogen (enabling binding via high and low affinity systems) or a low fibrinogen concentration (enabling binding primarily via high affinity binding). Platelets were left untreated, or incubated with indomethacin (to prevent high affinity binding) and/or PEP-PK (to prevent low affinity binding). Figure 4 illustrates that both types of binding support the aggregation response. However, the contribution of low affinity binding is much greater than that of the high affinity system especially at low concentrations of PAF-acether. Interestingly, two additional types of aggregation become apparent. One type is evident in the absence of fibrinogen when PAF-acether triggers aggregation via both thromboxane A_2- and ADP-mediated pathways. The other type is evident in the absence of PAF-acether and is also sensitive to both types of inhibitors. Probably these types of aggregation (which are not seen in optical aggregometers) reflect a combination of a fibrinogen - dependent agglutination plus contact-induced platelet activation (Holmsen and Dangelmaier, 1977, 1981).

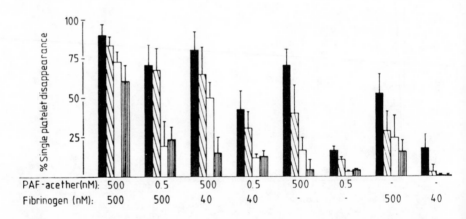

Figure 4. Effect of indomethacin and PEP/PK on single platelet disappearance. Gel-filtered platelets were stirred (900 rpm) at 22 °C in the presence and absence of PAF-acether and fibrinogen in the concentrations indicated in the figure. Each group of four columns illustrate, from left to right: untreated platelets, platelets pretreatment with indomethacin (30 μM), platelets pretreated with PEP/PK (0.28 mM and 3 U ml^{-1}, respectively) and platelets pretreated with both inhibitors. Single platelet disappearance is expressed as a percent of total free platelets following 5 min incubation with PAF-acether and /or fibrinogen (means $\pm$ S.D., n = 6). Data of suspensions treated with inhibitors differed significantly from controls ($p < 0.05$) except for indomethacin-treated cells at 500 nM fibrinogen. The combination of the two inhibitors had the same effect as PEP/PK alone ($p > 0.05$)

ACKNOWLEDGMENTS

These investigations were supported in part by the Netherlands Foundation for Medical Research FUNGO (grant 13-30-60) and the Dutch Heart Foundation (grant 82.055)

REFERENCES

Frojmovic, M.M., Milton, J.G., and Duchastel, A. (1983). 'Microscopic measurements of platelet aggregation reveal a low ADP-dependent process distinct from turbidometrically measured aggregation', *J. Lab. Clin. Med.*, **86**, 964-976.

Holmsen, H., and Setkowsky-Dangelmaier, C.A. (1977). 'Adenine nucleotide metabolism of blood platelets X. Formaldehyde stops centrifugation induced secretion after A23187-stimulation and causes breakdown of metabolic ATP'. *Biochim. Biophys. Acta*, **497**, 46−61.

Holmsen, H., and Dangelmaier, C.A.(1981). 'Evidence that the platelet plasma membrane is impermeable to calcium and magnesium complexes of A23187', *J. Biol. Chem.*, **256**, 10 449-10 452.

Hwang, S.-B., Lee, C.S.B., Cheah, M.J., and Shen, T.Y. (1983). 'Specific receptor sites for 1-*O*-alkyl-2-acetyl-*sn*-glycero-3-phosphocholine (platelet activating factor) on rabbit platelet and guinea pig smooth muscle membranes', *Biochemistry*, **22**, 4756−4763.

Kloprogge, E., de Haas, G.H., Gorter, G., and Akkerman, J.W.N. (1983). 'Properties of PAF-acether-induced platelet aggregation and secretion studies in gel-filtered human platelets', *Thromb. Res.*, **29**, 595−608.

Kloprogge, E., and Akkerman, J.W.N. (1984). 'Binding kinetics of PAF-acether (1-*O*-alkyl-2-acetyl-*sn*-glycero-3-phosphocholine) to intact human platelets', *Biochem. J.*, **223**, 901−909.

Kloprogge, E., and Akkerman, J.W.N. (1985). 'PAF-acether induces high−and low-affinity fibrinogen binding to platelets via independent mechanisms', *Thromb. Haemost.*, **54**, 220.

Pieroni, G., and Hanahan, D.J. (1983). 'Metabolic behavior of acetyl glyceryl ether phosphorylcholine on interaction with rabbit platelets', *Arch. Biochem. Biophys.*, **224**, 485−493.

Walsh, P.N. (1972). 'Albumin density separation and washing of platelets and the study of platelet coagulant activities', *Br. J. Haematol.*, **22**, 205−217.

19

Detection of Receptor and Synthesis Antagonists of Platelet Activating Factor in Human Whole Blood and Neutrophils using Luminol-Dependent Chemiluminescence

Knox Van Dyke and Vincent Castranova

INTRODUCTION

A soluble mediator has been described which is released from activated rabbit leukocytes and induces histamine secretion from rabbit platelets (Barbaro and Zvaifler, 1966; Siraganian and Osler, 1971). This factor has been isolated, characterized and named platelet activating factor, PAF (Benveniste *et. al.*, 1972). PAF has since been chemically identified as 1-0-alkyl-2-acetyl-*sn*-glyceryl-3-phosphocholine (Benveniste *et. al.*, 1979; Demopoulous *et. al.*, 1979).

PAF is a lipid mediator of broad biological activity. It causes smooth muscle contraction, contraction of lung tissue and decreased FEV_1; while enhancing capillary permeability thus causing edema (Pinkard, 1983). In addition, PAF is a chemo-attractant and can lead to inflammation.

PAF has been reported to stimulate the release of lysosomal enzymes, leukotriene B_4, and lipid metabolites from neutrophils (Smith *et. al.*, 1983; Shaw *et. al.*, 1981; Lin *et. al.*, 1982; O'Flaherty *et. al.*, 1984). The objective of the present investigation was to further characterize PAF-induced stimulation of granulocytes and to develop a bioassay, i.e. chemiluminescence, for screening PAF receptor antagonists and inhibitors of PAF-induced activation of granulocytes. The possible use of the chemiluminescence assay to monitor PAF synthesis by human granulocytes is also described.

METHODS

Blood was drawn from healthy volunteers into a blood storage bag containing CPD anticoagulant. Granulocytes were partially purified by dextran sedimentation and

181

further purified by centrifugal elutriation as described previously (Jones *et. al.*, 1980). Granulocytes obtained by this procedure were approximately 95 percent pure. The number of granulocytes in this preparation was determined using an electronic cell counter (Coulter Model Z_B, Coulter Instrument Co., Hialeah, FL). Isolated granulocytes were used to monitor membrane potential, hydrogen peroxide and superoxide release, oxygen consumption, calcium uptake and, in some cases, chemiluminescence. Studies of PAF receptor antagonists were conducted using neutrophils isolated by density centrifugation. Briefly, blood was layered onto Mono-Poly-Resolving Medium (Flow Laboratories, McLean, VA) and centrifuged at 22 °C and 300 g for 30 min. Neutrophils collected from the second band of this gradient were at least 90 percent pure.

Transmembrane potential (E_m) of human granulocytes was measured fluorometrically at 37 °C at an excitation wavelength of 622 nm and an emission wavelength of 665 nm using the fluorescent probe, Di-S-C_3(5) (Jones *et. al.*, 1980). Samples contained 0.66 μg ml^{-1}Di-S-C_3(5) and 2.3 $\times$ 10^7 cells in 3 ml of HEPES-buffered medium (145 mM NaCl, 5 mM KCl, 10 mM Na HEPES, 5 mM glucose, and 1 mM CaCl$_2$; pH-7.4).

Hydrogen peroxide release was measured by monitoring the fluorescence of scopoletin at 37 °C at an excitation wavelength of 350 nm and an emission wavelength of 460 nm (Root *et. al.*, 1975). Samples contained 1 $\times$ 10^7 cells in 2.5 ml of HEPES-buffered medium containing 2.5 μM scopoletin and 40 μg ml^{-1} horseradish peroxidase (165 units mg^{-1}).

Superoxide anion release was measured by monitoring cytochrome C reduction spectrophotometrically at 550 nm at 37 °C (Babior *et. al.*, 1973). Samples contained 1 $\times$ 10^7 cells suspended in 2.5 ml of a HEPES-buffered medium containing 1.2 $\times$ 10^{-4} M cytochrome C.

Oxygen consumption was measured at 37 °C using a Clark electrode (Castranova *et. al.*, 1980). Samples contained 6.5 $\times$ 10^5 cells suspended in 1.7 ml of HEPES-buffered medium.

Calcium transport was monitored at 37 °C by measuring the uptake of ^{45}Ca by granulocytes. Briefly, cells (2.5 x 10^7) were suspended in 1.5 ml of HEPES-buffered medium. At zero time, 7.5 μCi of ^{45}Ca was added and a 200 μl sample of this suspension placed immediately over a 100 μl cushion (dibutyl phthalate-mineral oil, density = 1.025 g ml^{-1}). This sample was centrifuged in an air-fuge (Eppendorf Model 5412, Brinkman Instrument, Westbury, NY) and the supernatant and cushion removed by suction. The cell pellet was dissolved in 100 μl of 0.1 percent Triton X-100, mixed with 10 ml of Aquasol (New England Nuclear,Boston, MA) and counted in a liquid scintillation counter. In this manner, uptake was monitored by taking cell samples at various time intervals.

Chemiluminescence generated from purified granulocytes was measured at 37 °C using a liquid scintillation counter operated in the out-of-coincidence mode (Trush *et. al.*, 1978). Briefly, granulocytes (1 $\times$ 10^6 cells) were suspended in 5 ml of HEPES-buffered medium containing 1 $\times$ 10^{-8} M luminol.

Whole blood chemiluminescence was monitored at 37 °C using a luminometer (Berthold Model LB 9500T, Berthold Instrument Inc., Wildbad, W. Germany) linked to a computer data handling system (Edinboro *et. al.*, 1985). Briefly, whole blood was diluted 1:50 in HEPES-buffered medium (500 μl) containing 1.12×10^{-4} M luminol.

PAF was obtained from Bachem (Torrance, CA). This PAF was used as a mixture containing 60 percent C_{16} and 40 percent C_{18}. PAF was dissolved in 1 percent bovine serum albumin diluting with HEPES-buffered medium.

RESULTS AND DISCUSSION

The present study characterizes the effects of PAF on the membrane potential, ionic permeability, and respiratory burst activity of human granulocytes. Furthermore, these responses to PAF are compared to those for a known stimulant of phagocytes, i.e. the chemotactic agent FMLP. These results are summarized in Table 1.

Table 1.   Characteristics of PAF Stimulation of Human Neutrophils: Comparison to Stimulation with FMLP[1]

Response	PAF	FMLP
Chemiluminescence	+	+++
Superoxide release	+	+++++
Oxygen consumption	0	+++
H_2O_2	++	++++
Depolarization	+++	+++
Increased P_{Ca}	0	++
Increased P_{Na}	+++	+++

[1] Responses to maximal doses of stimulant, i.e., 1×10^{-5} M PAF and 1×10^{-7} M FMLP. The relative magnitude of enhancement is signified by +. No response is signified by 0.

PAF induces a rapid but transient depolarization of the granulocyte plasma membrane. This depolarization peaks within 15 s in response to a maximal dose of PAF (1×10^{-5} M). This response is short-lived with the membrane potential repolarizing to the resting level within 90 s. PAF fails to alter membrane potential in the absence of extracellular sodium. However, PAF-induced depolarization is unaffected by removal of extracellular calcium. These results suggest that the PAF-induced change in membrane potential is the result of a transient increase in sodium permeability but not calcium permeability. Indeed, measurement of ^{45}Ca uptake indicates that calcium transport of granulocytes is not enhanced by PAF. The effect of PAF on the membrane potential of human granulocytes is dose-dependent. Responses can be measured between doses of 10^{-7} to 10^{-5} M with an ED_{50} of 2.5×10^{-6} M. At doses of PAF above 2.5×10^{-5}M, the magnitude of the response declines. This PAF-induced depolarization is similar in magnitude and time course to that produced by FMLP. However, unlike FMLP, PAF does not produce a delayed fall in fluorescence signal below the resting level. It has been shown that this fall is the result of myeloperoxidase-H_2O_2 dependent oxidation of the fluorescent probe (Castranova and Van Dyke, 1984; Whitin *et al.*, 1981). Thus, in contract to FMLP, PAF may not stimulate the release of myeloperoxidase from granulocytes. Furthermore, while PAF enhances only sodium permeability, FMLP increased both sodium and calcium permeability of granulocytes.

FMLP is a known stimulant of respiratory burst activity in human granulocytes, i.e. FMLP stimulates large changes in oxygen consumption, secretion of superoxide anion and H_2O_2, and chemiluminescence. In comparision, stimulation by PAF is smaller and less complete. PAF-induced secretion of superoxide anion is only 20 percent of that induced by FMLP and H_2O_2 release in response to PAF is only 50 percent of the FMLP level. In further contrast to FMLP, PAF does not enhance oxygen consumption of granulocytes and PAF-induced chemiluminescence is only 30 percent of that seen with FMLP stimulation. It is interesting that as with stimulant-induced depolarization, PAF- and FMLP-induced chemiluminescence is dependent on the presence of extracellular sodium, i.e. little chemiluminescence is seen if external sodium is replaced by potassium.

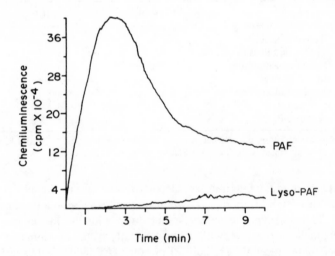

Figure 1. Chemiluminescence generated from human whole blood in response to 1×10^{-5} M PAF or lyso-PAF

Chemiluminescence has proven to be a simple and rapid method to monitor the effects of PAF on granulocytes. In contrast to other parameters studied, chemiluminescence can be monitored with whole blood. This eliminates the time involved in cell purification. An example of PAF-induced chemiluminescence in whole blood is given in Figure 1. PAF-stimulated chemiluminescence generated from purified granulocytes exhibits a time course which is similar to that of the whole blood response. However, the magnitude of the response is somewhat larger with purified cells because of quenching of light by red blood cells in the whole blood assay. In addition, the ED_{50} for PAF is higher, i.e. 9×10^{-5} M in the whole blood system because of non-specific binding to cells other than granulocytes.

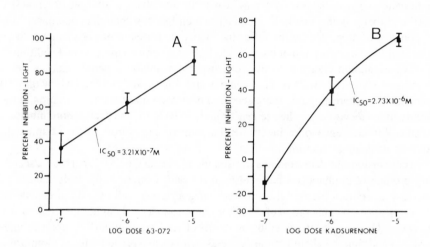

Figure 2. Dose—response curves for inhibition of PAF-induced chemiluminescence from purified granulocytes by 63-072 (A) or kadsurenone (B). Granulocytes were stimulated with 1×10^{-5} M PAF

Table 2. Effect of Inhibitors on PAF-Induced Chemiluminescence in Human Neutrophils

Inhibitor	Maximal inhibition[1]	IC_{50}[2]
63-072	88%	3.2×10^{-7} M
Kadsurenone	70%	2.7×10^{-6} M
NDGA	62%	–
Indomethacin	20%	–

[1] Maximal inhibition was measured at an inhibitor dose of 1×10^{-5} M
[2] IC_{50} is the inhibitor concentration which results in 50 percent of maximal inhibition.

The effects of PAF-receptor antagonists on PAF-induced chemiluminescence are shown in Figure 2. 63-072, an inhibitor synthesized by Sandoz Research Institute, is a potent inhibitor of PAF causing an 88 percent decrease in PAF-induced chemiluminescence at 1×10^{-5} M with an IC_{50} of 3.2×10^{-7} M. Kadsurenone, a Merck compound, is less potent causing 70 percent inhibition at 1×10^{-5} M with an IC_{50} of 2.7×10^{-6} M. The lipoxygenase pathway seems to be much more important in the generation of PAF-induced chemiluminescence than the cyclo-oxygenase pathway, since nordihydroguaiaretic acid (NDGA) is an effective inhibitor of PAF-stimulated chemiluminescence while indomethacin is not very effective (Table 2).

The effect of lyso-PAF on chemiluminescence is shown in Figure 1. Note that lyso-PAF, the inactive metabolite of PAF, does induce chemiluminescence in leukocytes. Compared to PAF, the response to lyso-PAF is delayed and of decreased magnitude. This delay suggests that lyso-PAF may be used by the cells as a substrate to synthesize PAF and that it is this newly formed PAF which induces chemiluminescence. This hypothesis is supported by the following evidence. Calcium has been shown to be essential for the conversion of lyso-PAF to PAF and our data indicate that addition of EDTA, a calcium chelator, to the cell suspension inhibits chemiluminescence in response to lyso-PAF by 75 percent while decreasing the response to PAF by only 50 percent. It is interesting that there seems to be a wide interpersonal variation in the ability of leukocytes to synthesize PAF from lyso-PAF, i.e. the delay before initiation of chemiluminescence following lyso-PAF treatment ranges from 15 s to 4.5 min with an average delay of 1.5 min (n=75).

In conclusion, the data from this investigation indicate the PAF is not only a secretory product of granulocytes but is also an activator of these cells. PAF induces an increase in sodium permeability in these phagocytes as well as sodium dependent depolarization and generation of chemiluminescence. The chemiluminescence assay has proved to be useful in screening inhibitors of activation and PAF-receptor antagonists. In addition the chemiluminescence assay may also prove useful in monitoring synthesis of PAF from lyso-PAF.

REFERENCES

Babior, B.M., Kipnes, R.S., and Curnette, J.T. (1973). 'Biological defense mechanisms: The production by leukocytes of superoxide, a potential bactericidal agent', *J. Clin. Invest.*, **52**, 741−744.

Barbaro, J.F., and Zvaifler, G.F. (1966). 'Antigen induced histamine release from platelets of rabbits producing homologous PCA antibody, (3137)', *Proc. Soc. Exp. Biol. Med.*, **122**, 1245−1247.

Benveniste, J., Henson, P.M., and Cochrane, C.G. (1972). 'Leukocyte-dependent histamine release from rabbit platelets', *J.Exp. Med.*, **136**, 1356−1377.

Beneveniste, J., Tence, M., Varenne, P., Bidault, J., Boullet, C., and Polonsky, J. (1979). 'Platelet activating factor', *Comptes Rendus hebd. S'eanc Acad Sci Paris*, **289D**, 1037−1040.

Castranova, V., Bowman, L., Reasor,M.J., and Miles, P.R. (1980). 'Effects of heavy metal ions on selected oxidative metabolic processes in rat alveolar macrophages', *Tox. Appl. Pharmacol.*, **53**, 14−24.

Castranova, V., and Van Dyke, K. (1984). 'Analysis of oxidation of the membrane potential probe Di-S-C$_3$(5) during activation', *Microchem. J.*, **29**, 151−161.

Demopoulous, C.A., Pinckard, R.N., and Hanahan, D.J. (1979). 'Platelet activating factor', *J. Biol. Chem.*, **254**, 9355-9358.

Edinboro, L.E., Van Dyke, K., Peden, D., Castranova, V., and Wierda, D. (1985). 'Studies of luminol-dependent whole-blood chemiluminescence induced by platelet-activating factor (PAF)', *Microchem. J.*, **31**, 261−271.

Jones, G.S., Van Dyke, K., and Castranova, V. (1980). 'Purification of human granulocytes by centrifugal elutriation and measurement of transmembrane potential'. *J. Cell Physiol.*, **104**, 425-432.

Lin, A.H. Morton, D.R., and Gorman,R.R. (1982). 'Acetylglyceryl ether phosphorylcholine stimulates leukotriene B_4 synthesis in human polymorphonuclear leukocytes', *J. Clin. Invest.*, **70**, 1058−1063.

O'Flaherty, J.T., Wykle, P.L., Thomas, M.J., and McCale, C.E. (1984). 'Neutrophil degranulation responses to combinations of aradidonate and platelet activating factor', *Res. Comm. Chem. Path. Pharmacol.*, **43**, 3−23.

Pinckard, R.N. (1983). 'Platelet activating factor', *Hosp. Prac.*, **19**, 67−76.

Root, R.K., Metcalf, J., Oshino, N., and Chance, B. (1975). 'H_2O_2 release from human granulocytes during phagocytosis. I. Documentation, quantitation, and some regulating factors', *J. Clin. Invest.*, **55**, 945−955.

Shaw, J.O., Pinckard, R.N., Ferrigni, K.S., McManus, L.M., and Hanahan, D.J. (1981). 'Activation of hyman neutrophils with 1-0-hexadecyl/octadecyl-2-acetyl-glyceryl-3-phosphorylcholine (platelet activating factor)', *J. Immunol.*, **127**, 1250−1255.

Siraganian, R.P. and Osler, A.G. (1971). 'Destruction of rabbit platelets in the allergic response of sensitized leukocytes', *J. Immunol.*, **106**, 1244−1251.

Smith, R.J., Bowman, B.J., and Iden. S.S. (1983). 'Characteristics of 1-0-hexadeyl and 1-octadecyl-2-0-acetyl-*sn*-glyceryl-3 phosphorylcholine stimulated granule enzyme release from human neutrophils', *Clin. Immunol.*, **28**, 13−28.

Trush, M.A., Wilson, M.E., and Van Dyke, K. (1978). 'The generation of chemiluminescence (CL) by phagocytic cells'. In M. Deluca (ed.) *Methods in Enzymology*, Academic Press, New York, Vol.57, pp. 462−494.

Whitin, J.C., Clark, E.R., Simons, E.R., and Cohen, H.J. (1981). 'Effects of the myeloproxidase system on the fluorescent probes of granulocyte membrane potential', *J. Biol. Chem.*, **256**, 8904−8906.

New Horizons in Platelet Activating Factor Research
Edited by C. M. Winslow and M. L. Lee
© 1987 John Wiley & Sons Ltd.

20

Inhibition of Edema in Allergic Inflammatory Reactions by Receptor Antagonists of Platelet Activating Factor

P.G. Hellewell and T.J. Williams

INTRODUCTION

Intradermal injection of platelet-activating factor (PAF) induces local edema formation in the rabbit and marked synergism with a vasodilator prostaglandin, PGE_2, has been observed (Wedmore and Williams, 1981a). PAF appears to act directly on venular endothelial cells to increase microvascular permeability. Depletion of circulating PMN leukocytes abolishes edema responses to intradermal injection of the leukocyte chemo-attractants, C5a des Arg, N-formyl-methionyl-leucyl-phenylalanine (FMLP) and leuko-triene $B_4(LTB_4)$, whilst responses induced by PAF (like those to histamine and bradykinin) are not affected by the depletion (Wedmore and Williams, 1981a,b).

It has been suggested that following intradermal injection of C5a des Arg, FMLP and LTB_4, PMNs are stimulated to release PAF which then induces edema forma-tion. Using two putative PAF receptor antagonists, we have investigated this proposal and the possibility that PAF is involved in mediating the microvascular changes observed in animal models of allergic inflammation. Edema responses were induced both by exogenous inflammatory mediators and by endogenous mediators generated in the passive cutaneous anaphylactic reaction (PCA) and the reversed passive Arthus reaction (RPA) in rabbit skin.

METHODS

We measured local edema formation in rabbit skin following intradermal injection of agents under test. Rabbits were anaesthetized, the dorsal skin shaved and ^{125}I-human serum albumin with Evans blue dye was injected intravenously (i.v.). Agents were injected intradermally in 0.1 ml volumes in six replicates and 30 min later the animal was killed. Injection sites were punched out (17 mm diameter) and counted together with plasma samples in a γ-counter. Plasma protein accumulation at each site was expressed in terms of μl plasma.

For a PCA reaction, anti-bovine gamma globulin (BGG) antiserum containing tissue-fixing IgE (raised according to Kravis and Zvaifler, 1974) was injected intradermally followed 48 h later by intradermal antigen challenge (BGG, 10μ g /site $^{-1}$). Local edema formation was measured for 30 min.

For a RPA reaction, anti-BGG antiserum (raised according to Jose et al., 1983) was injected intradermally followed 5 min later by an i.v. injection of BGG (5 mg kg^{-1}). Local edema formation was measured for 2 h.

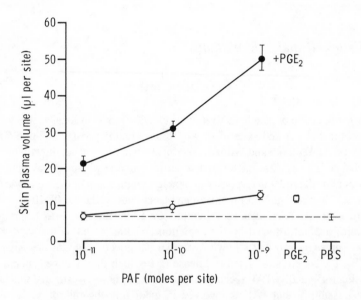

Figure 1. Local edema formation in rabbit skin induced by intradermal injection of PAF alone (○), PAF + PGE$_2$ (3 × 10^{-10} moles site^{-1}, ●), or PGE$_2$ alone. The dashed line is the control value obtained following injection of PBS. The values shown are mean ± S.E.M. of six replicate injections

RESULTS

Intradermal injection of PAF alone into rabbit skin induced little edema formation (Figure 1), however, when the vasodilator PGE$_2$, which itself does not induce leakage, was injected with PAF there was marked accumulation of labeled albumin demonstrating synergism between these two mediators.

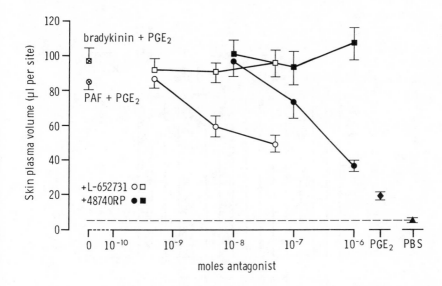

Figure 2. The effect of local L-652731 and 48740 RP administration of edema formation induced by intradermal PAF (10^{-9} M) + PGE_2 (3×10^{-10} moles) and bradykinin (5×10^{-11} M) + PGE. Antagonists, at the doses shown, were mixed with agonists prior to injection. The values shown are mean ± S.E.M. of six replicate injections

We tested the ability of two putative PAF receptor antagonists, L-652731 (Hwang *et al.*, 1985) and 48740 RP (Desquand *et al.*, 1985), to inhibit edema responses induced by intradermal injection of PAF (10^{-9} moles) + PGE_2 (3×10^{-10} moles) and bradykinin (5×10^{-11} moles) + PGE_2 in rabbit skin. Figure 2 shows that when the antagonists were mixed with the agonists prior to intradermal injection there was a dose−dependent inhibition of the edema response to PAF + PGE_2. L-652731 was approximately 20 times more potent than 48740 RP. In contrast, the edema response induced by intradermal injection of bradykinin + PGE_2 was not affected by either antagonist.

To investigate the possibility that PAF was involved in mediating the effects of the PMN-leukocyte dependent agents, C5a des Arg, FMLP and LTB_4 were injected intradermally mixed with PGE_2 in the absence or presence of antagonists. The results obtained with L-652731 (5×10^{-8} moles site^{-1}) are shown in Figure 3. Similar results (not shown here) were obtained with 48740 RP (10^{-6} moles site^{-1}). It is apparent that the only response to be suppressed by the antagonist was that obtained following intradermal injection of PAF + PGE_2 suggesting that the antagonist is selective for PAF and that a release of endogenous PAF is not responsible for the edema responses induced by the PMN-leukocyte dependent mediators.

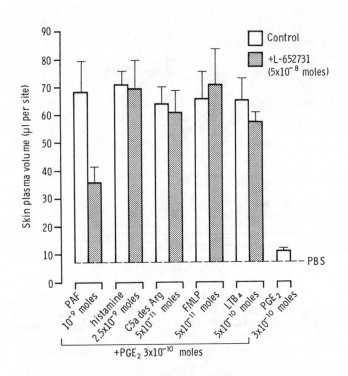

Figure 3.   The effect of local L-652731 administration of edema formation induced by a range of mediators (at the dose shown) when mixed with PGE$_2$ (3 $\times$ 10^{-10} moles site^{-1}). The results are the mean $\pm$ S.E.M. of six replicate injections

In a PCA reaction, local edema formation in response to intradermal injection of antigen (BGG) was dependent on antiserum dilution (Figure 4). Local administration of L-652731 (5 $\times$ 10^{-8} moles site^{-1}) with antigen produced no suppression of the reaction suggesting that PAF is not an important mediator in this type of allergic inflammation. Shown for comparison is a dose−response curve to PAF + PGE$_2$ performed in the same animal showing effective suppression of PAF-induced edema formation by local administration of L-652731.

In contrast, in a RPA reaction, intradermal injection of L-652731 and 48740 RP mixed with antiserum resulted in an effective (approximately 50 percent) suppression of edema formation measured for 2 h after antigen challenge (Figure 5). Again, shown for comparison are responses to injection of PAF (10^{-9} moles) + PGE$_2$ demonstrating suppression of edema formation by local administration of both antagonists.

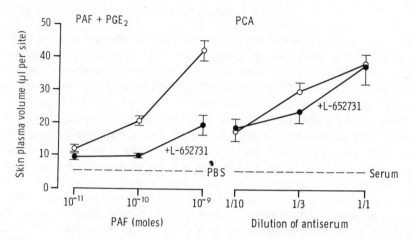

Figure 4. The effect of local administration of L-652731 (5×10^{-8} moles site^{-1}) on edema formation induced by PAF + PGE$_2$ (3×10^{-10} moles site^{-1}) and the PCA reaction. The results are the mean ± S.E.M. of six replicate injections

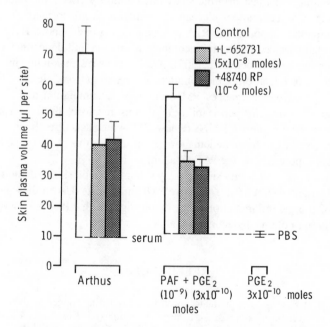

Figure 5. The effect of local administration of L-652731 and 48740 RP (at the doses shown) on edema formation in the RPA and following injection of PAF (10^{-9} moles) + PGE$_2$ (3×10^{-10} moles). The results are the mean ± S.E.M. of six replicate injections

DISCUSSION

In this study we have shown that two proposed PAF antagonists are selective for PAF-induced edema responses in rabbit skin. The observation that neither compound affects edema responses induced by the PMN leukocyte-dependent mediators suggests that the release of PAF from stimulated PMNs is not the mechanism whereby these agents increase vascular permeability.

We have also shown that both antagonists are effective in suppressing edema formation in a RPA reaction, but interestingly not edema associated with a PCA reaction. This latter observation is somewhat surprising because there is much evidence suggesting a causal link between endogenous PAF production and the progression of other anaphylactic reactions in the rabbit; for example, administration of PAF systemically to rabbits produces symptoms similar to those observed in rabbits during systemic anaphylaxis and furthermore, during such allergic reactions, circulating platelets are refractory to stimulation with PAF ex vivo (Pinckard et al., 1982). However, it would appear from our studies that PAF is not involved in mediating the microvascular changes in a cutaneous anaphylactic reaction.

Using a variety of in vivo and in vitro tests (not presented here) we have shown that neither PAF antagonist tested in the study has inhibitory effects on other mediator pathways (e.g. C5a generation, eicosanoid formation, kinin formation) suggesting that the compounds suppress the RPA by antagonizing endogenous PAF. The RPA reaction is characterized by immune complex formation and deposition within the walls of microvessels (Cochrane, 1963). We hypothesize that following complex formation there is activation of the complement system in tissue fluid leading to the generation of C5a which induces PMN-leukocyte accumulation and as a consequence, increased vascular permeability (Williams and Jose, 1981). During phagocytosis of immune complexes, PMNs release PAF which acts directly on the venular endothelium, leading to further edema formation and it is this phase of the RPA reaction which is suppressed by the PAF antagonists.

In conclusion, we have used a simple assay system in rabbit skin to demonstrate that both L-652731 and 48740 RP are selective PAF antagonists. Use of these antagonists in models of allergic inflammation in the rabbit suggests that PAF may have a role in Arthus-type, but not anaphylactic-type, allergic reactions.

REFERENCES

Cochrane C.G. (1963). 'Studies on the localization of circulating antigen-antibody complexes and other macromolecules in vessels. I. Structural studies', *J. Exp. Med.*, **118**, 489–501.

Desquand, S., Lefort, J., Deregnaucourt, J., Sedivy, P., Lagente, V., Randon, J., and Vargaftig, B.B. (1985). 'Inhibition by the PAF acether antagonist 48740 RP of the bronchopulmonary effects of PAF-acether', *Int. J. Immunopharmacol.*, **3**, 383

Hwang, S-B., Lam, M-H., Biftu, T., and Shen, T-Y. (1985). 'A synthetic competitive and specific antagonist of platelet activating factor', *Fed. Proc.*, **44**, 1435.

Jose, P.J., Forrest, M.J., and Williams, T.J. (1983). 'Detection of the complement fragment C5a in inflammatory exudates from the rabbit peritoneal cavity using radioimmunoassay', *J. Exp. Med.*, **158**, 2177–2182

Kravis, T.C., and Zvaifler, N.J.(1974). 'Characterization of a rabbit homocytotropic antibody responsible for passive cutaneous anaphylactic reactions with a short (4-hour) latent period', *Int. Arch Allergy. appl. Immunol.*, **46**, 60–67

Pinckard, R.N., McManus, L.M., and Hanahan, D.J. (1982). 'Chemistry and biology of acetylglyceryl ether phosphorylcholine (platelet-activating factor)'. In: G. Weissman (ed.) *Advances in Inflammation Research*, Raven Press, New York, Vol.4. pp. 147–180.

Wedmore, C.V., and Williams, T.J. (1981a). 'Platelet-activating factor (PAF), a secretory product of polymorphonuclear leukocytes, increases vascular permeability in rabbit skin', *Br. J. Pharmac.*, **74**, 916–917P.

Wedmore, C.V., and Williams, T.J.(1981b). 'Control of vascular permeability by polymorphonuclear leukocytes in inflammation', *Nature*, **289**, 646–650.

Williams, T.J., and Jose, P.J. (1981). 'Mediation of increased vascular permeability after complement activation. Histamine-independent action of rabbit C5a', *J. Exp. Med.*, **153**, 136–153.

New Horizons in Platelet Activating Factor Research
Edited by C. M. Winslow and M. L. Lee
© 1987 John Wiley & Sons Ltd.

21

Phorbol Ester-Induced Desensitization of Platelet Activating Factor Effects on Calcium Flux in Vascular Endothelial Cells

Tommy A. Brock, Kathy K. Griendling
and Michael A. Gimbrone, Jr.

SUMMARY

Platelet activating factor(PAF), but not its deacetylated derivatives, acts in an agonist-specific manner on cultured bovine aortic endothelial cells (BAEC) to induce a rapid increase in $^{45}Ca^{2+}$ efflux, in part, by mobilizing intracellular Ca^{2+} stores. We report herein that brief incubation (5 min) with protein kinase C activators inhibits PAF-induced calcium mobilization, as measured by $^{45}Ca^{2+}$ efflux, in cultured BAEC. Pretreatment with 4β-phorbol 12-myristate 13-acetate (PMA) induced a concentration-dependent ($IC_{50} = 3 \times 10^{-9}$ M) inhibition of subsequent PAF (10^{-8} M)-induced $^{45}Ca^{2+}$ efflux. Phorbol 12,13-dibutyrate (10^{-7}M) and 1-oleoyl-2-acetylglycerol (OAG) (7.5×10^{-5} M), but not 4-0-methyl PMA (a weak activator of protein kinase C), also inhibit PAF action on BAEC. $^{45}Ca^{2+}$ efflux was not directly affected by either phorbol ester or OAG. These data suggest that activation of protein kinase C by endogenous sn-1,2-diacylglycerol in agonist-stimulated cells may modulate the responsiveness of vascular endothelium to platelet activating factor.

The endothelial lining of blood vessels is a target for the action of diverse mediators which promote permeability changes, inflammation and coagulation. Platelet activating factor (PAF), a potent *in vivo* mediator of immune–inflammatory reactions (reviewed in Benveniste, and Vargaftig, 1983; Pinckard *et al.*, 1982), is known to influence a broad range of important cardiovascular events including: platelet and leukocyte aggregation and secretion, leukocyte chemotaxis, smooth muscle contraction, cardiac contractility, peripheral vasodilatation and vascular permeability (Archer *et al.*, 1984; Beneveniste and Vargaftig, 1983; Kamatani *et al.*, 1984; Pinckard *et al.*, 1982). Recent studies indicate that PAF increases microvascular permeability and induces vasodilatation without involvement of platelets, neutrophils and mast cells (Humphery et al., 1984; Sanchez Crespo et al., 1982), thus suggesting a direct action of PAF on blood vessels. Utilizing cultured vascular endothelial cells (EC), we (Brock et al., 1984, 1986b) and others (Bussolini et al., 1985) have provided evidence that PAF acts directly on vascular endothelium causing a rapid increase in $^{45}Ca^{2+}$ flux. More recently, we have found that PAF acts in a concentration-dependent, stereo-selective manner to increase cytosolic ionized calcium (Brock et al., 1986b). Thus, certain of the biological actions of PAF in this cell type may involve calcium-dependent intracellular mechanisms.

Cytosolic free calcium concentration ($[Ca^{2+}]_i$) is believed to play an important role in stimulus−response coupling in vascular endothelium (Jaffe, 1983). In other cell types, hormonally-induced elevation in $[Ca^{2+}]_i$ has been linked to activation of phosphoinositide metabolism. Calcium-mobilizing hormones stimulate the selective phospholipase C-mediated hydrolysis of phosphatidylinositol 4,5-bisphosphate (PIP_2) to yield two distinct intracellular messengers—inositol trisphosphate (IP_3) and sn-1,2 diacylglycerol (DG), which have been implicated in Ca^{2+} mobilization and protein kinase C activation, respectively (Berridge and Irvine,1984). Previous studies utilizing platelets have demonstrated that 4β-phorbol 12-myristate 13-acetate (PMA) inhibits both PAF-induced phosphoinositide breakdown and calcium flux (MacIntyre et al., 1985). Since tumor-promoting phorbol esters are able to substitute for DAG and cause a persistent stimulation of protein kinase C (Nishizuka, 1984), these data suggest a possible physiologic role of DG−protein kinase C in the inhibition of PAF activation of phospholipase C and subsequent calcium mobilization. At the present time, however, little is known about the interactions between protein kinase C activation and calcium flux during agonist stimulation of vascular endothelium. Therefore, to gain insights into potential mechnisms modulating endothelial responsiveness to PAF, we have examined the effects of activators of protein kinase C, such as phorbol esters and the synthetic diglyceride, 1-oleoyl-2-acetylglycerol, on PAF-stimulated calcium flux in cultured bovine aortic EC.

MATERIALS AND METHODS

Cell Culture

Bovine aortic endothelial cells (BAEC) were isolated from calf thoracic aorta as previously described (Gimbrone, 1976). BAEC from a single strain (65-BAEC, passages 8−35) were cultured in DME supplemented with 10 percent heat-inactivated calf-serum. Passaged cells were routinely harvested twice a week using trypsin-versene and passaged at a 1:4 ratio in 75 cm^2 flasks. For experimental use, cells were replicate-plated into 35 mm culture dishes ($2-4 \times 10^4$ cells cm^{-2}), fed every other day and used after 4−6 days as confluent monolayers.

Alkylphosphoglycerides

Synthetic 1-O-hexadecyl-2-acetyl-sn-glyceryl-3-phosphorylcholine (C_{16}PAF), 1-O-hexadecyl-sn-glyceryl-3-phosphorylcholine (lyso-C_{16}PAF), 1-O-octadecyl-2-sn-acetyl-glyceryl-3-phosphorylcholine (C_{18}PAF), 1-O-octadecyl-sn-glyceryl-3-phosphorylcholine (lyso-C_{18}PAF), 3-O-hexadecyl-2-acetyl-sn-glyceryl-1-phosphorycholine (PAF-inv), 3-O-hexadecyl-sn-glyceryl-1-phosphorylcholine (lyso-PAF-inv), 1-O-hexadecyl-2-benzyl-sn-glyceryl-3-phosphorylcholine (benzyl-PAF), and 1-O-octadecyl-2-methyl-sn-glyceryl-3-phosphorycholine (methyl-PAF) were obtained from Bachem, Bubendorf, Switzerland. CV-3988 (rac-3-(N-n-octadecylcarbamoyloxy)-2-methoxypropyl-2-thiazolioethyl phosphate) was a generous gift from Dr M. Nishikawa, Takeda Chemical Industries, L, Osaka, Japan.

Measurement of Unidirectional $^{45}Ca^{2+}$ Efflux

$^{45}Ca^{2+}$ efflux was determined as described previously (Brock *et al.*, 1986b). In brief, replicate-plated cultures which had been preloaded with $^{45}Ca^{2+}$ (2 μCi ml^{-1}) were washed three times with warm balanced salt solution (BSS) (130 mM NaCl, 5 mM KCl, 1 mM MgCl$_2$, 1.5 mM CaCl$_2$, and 20 mM HEPES, buffered to pH 7.4 with Tris base); 1 ml of BSS containing 10 mM glucose with and without PAF or a related compound was then added to each dish. Lipid compounds were dissolved in methanol and stored at -20 °C. The PAF antagonist, CV-3988 (Terashita, 1983), was dissolved in ethanol. Stock solutions were made daily in BSS containing 2.5 mg ml^{-1} bovine serum albumin, and diluted so that its final concentration in the BSS was 0.05 mg ml^{-1}. Spontaneous $^{45}Ca^{2+}$ efflux refers to the unstimulated loss of cellular isotope into buffer containing 1.5 mM non-radioactive calcium.

$^{45}Ca^{2+}$ flux reactions were rapidly terminated by washing culture dishes four times with ice-cold calcium-free BSS containing 10 mM LaCl$_3$, followed by an additional 5 min incubation in this same solution. Cell-associated $^{45}Ca^{2+}$ was extracted from the cultures with 1 ml of 0.1 N HNO$_3$ and quantitated by liquid scintillation spectrophotometry. PAF-stimulated $^{45}Ca^{2+}$ efflux was calculated as the difference in cell-associated $^{45}Ca^{2+}$ in the presence and absence of the agonist. Data are expressed as mean $\pm$ standard error of the mean (S.E.M.) and analyzed using the unpaired Student's t-test.

RESULTS

Effect of PAF on $^{45}Ca^{2+}$ Efflux

We have previously demonstrated that PAF stimulates a rapid ($<$ 15 s), concentration-dependent(EC$_{50}$ = 10^{-10} M) mobilization of intracellular calcium in cultured

BAEC (Brock *et al.*, 1984, 1986b). Spontaneous $^{45}Ca^{2+}$ efflux from preloaded, unstimulated cells into medium containing 1.5 mM non-radioactive calcium exhibits biphasic kinetics, and PAF increases the $^{45}Ca^{2+}$ efflux rate only during the early rapid phase. The effects of hexadecyl and octadecyl species and related derivatives on $^{45}Ca^{2+}$ efflux under these conditions are compared in Figure 1. At 10^{-7} M, $C_{16}PAF$ and $C_{18}PAF$ stimulated a comparable amount of $^{45}Ca^{2+}$ efflux (approximately 70 percent increase) during a 5 min assay. PAF-treated cells contained significantly less $^{45}Ca^{2+}$ than untreated cells (twenty expts., $p < 0.001$), the difference representing approximately 25 ± 2 percent of the initial cell-associated $^{45}Ca^{2+}$. In contrast, lyso-$C_{16}PAF$ and lyso-$C_{18}PAF$ (inactive deacetylated derivatives) did not significantly alter $^{45}Ca^{2+}$ efflux. Increased $^{45}Ca^{2+}$ efflux was also observed with $C_{16}PAF$-inverse and methyl-$C_{18}PAF$, at relatively high concentrations (10^{-7} M), whereas lyso-$C_{16}PAF$-inverse and benzyl-$C_{16}PAF$ did not increase $^{45}Ca^{2+}$ efflux. However, at concentrations less than or equal to 10^{-8} M, $C_{16}PAF$-inverse and methyl-$C_{18}PAF$ were ineffective, whereas $C_{16}PAF$ at this concentration caused a near-maximal increase in $^{45}Ca^{2+}$ efflux (Brock *et al.*, 1986b).

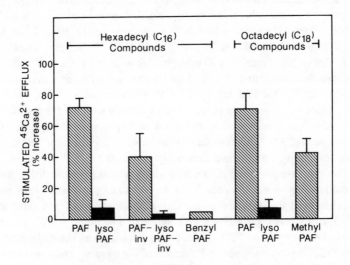

Figure 1. Effect of hexadecyl and octadecyl PAF derivatives on $^{45}Ca^{2+}$ efflux. Data (mean $\pm$ S.E.M.) from three or more experiments are expressed as percentage increases above spontaneous $^{45}Ca^{2+}$ efflux from untreated cells (1.2 ± 0.3 nM mg^{-1} protein) during a 5 min period. Initial $^{45}Ca^{2+}$ content equaled 4.8 ± 0.3 nM mg^{-1} protein. Adapted in part from Brock and Gimbrone (1986b)

CV-3988, a drug which specifically inhibits PAF-induced hypotension *in vivo* and platelet aggregation *in vitro* (Terashita *et al.*, 1983), inhibited $C_{16}PAF$ (10^{-8} M, 5 min)-stimulated $^{45}Ca^{2+}$ efflux in a concentration-dependent manner (Figure 2).

Addition of CV-3988 (3×10^{-5} M) alone to the efflux buffer had no effect on spontaneous $^{45}Ca^{2+}$ efflux.

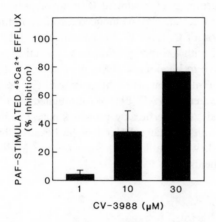

Figure 2. Effect of CV-3988 on PAF (10^{-8} M)-stimulated $^{45}Ca^{2+}$ efflux. EC cultures were preincubated with the indicated concentrations of CV-3988 for 15 min prior to PAF exposure (5 min). Each bar represents the mean of three to five experiments. Adapted from Brock and Gimbrone (1986b)

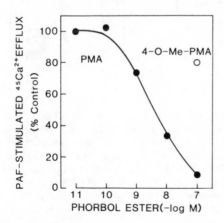

Figure 3. Concentration–response relationship of PMA and 4-0-methyl PMA inhibition of PAF-stimulated $^{45}Ca^{2+}$ efflux. Each phorbol ester was added directly to the loading media containing $^{45}Ca^{2+}$ for 5 min prior to the efflux assay. Cells were then exposed to $C_{16}PAF$ (10^{-8} M) for 5 min during an efflux assay. Each data point represents the mean of triplicate determinations

Effect of Phorbol Ester and OAG on PAF-induced $^{45}Ca^{2+}$ Efflux

As illustrated in Figure 3, brief treatment (5 min) of preloaded BAEC with 4β-phorbol 12-myristate 13-acetate (PMA) induced a concentration-dependent ($IC_{50} = 3 \times 10^{-9}$ M) inhibition of $C_{16}PAF$ (10^{-8} M)-stimulated $^{45}Ca^{2+}$ efflux. In contrast, pretreatment of BAEC with 4-O-methyl PMA, a weak activator of protein kinase C, was much less effective in blocking $C_{16}PAF$-induced $^{45}Ca^{2+}$ flux. As illustrated in Figure 4, phorbol 12,13-dibutyrate (10^{-7} M) and OAG (7.5×10^{-5} M) also significantly inhibited subsequent $C_{16}PAF$ (10^{-8} M)-stimulated $^{45}Ca^{2+}$ efflux. The inhibition of PAF-stimulated $^{45}Ca^{2+}$ efflux by protein kinase C activators could not be explained by a depletion of total cellular isotope because the $^{45}Ca^{2+}$ contents of control and treated cells were similar after 5 min ($+ 10^{-7}$ M PMA, 101 $\pm$ 4 percent control, three experiments).

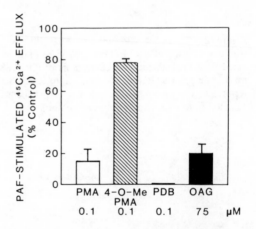

Figure 4.   Effect of different phorbol esters and 1-oleoyl-2-acetylglycerol (OAG) on PAF-stimulated $^{45}Ca^{2+}$ efflux. Cultured BAEC were preincubated for 5 min with each compound and then exposed to $C_{16}PAF$ (10^{-8} M, 5 min) during an efflux assay. Each bar represents the mean of duplicate or triplicate experiments. PMA = 4β-phorbol 12-myristate 13-acetate; PDB = phorbol 12,13-dibutyrate

DISCUSSION

Recent studies have identified specific [^{3}H]PAF binding sites in several non-endothelial cell types, thus suggesting that PAF may interact with a specific receptor to exert its biological actions (Hwang et al., 1983; Valone and Goetzl, 1983). PAF has been documented to stimulate $^{45}Ca^{2+}$ influx and to increase cytosolic free calcium in platelets (Hallam *et al.*, 1984; Lee *et al.*, 1981). Utilizing cultured endothelial cells, we (Brock *et al.*, 1984, 1986b) and Bussolini *et al.* (1985) have shown that PAF causes a specific increase in $^{45}Ca^{2+}$ flux. We have also demonstrated that PAF induces a rapid increase in $[Ca^{2+}]_i$ in cultured BAEC, as measured with the calcium-sensitive fluorescent dye, Quin 2 (Brock *et al.*, 1986b). The observations summarized in this report provide further evidence for receptor-mediated action of PAF on vascular endothelial cells and also identify possible mechanisms involved in regulating PAF responsiveness.

Other pathophysiological mediators, such as bradykinin and thrombin (Brock *et al.*, 1984, 1986a, unpublished observations) also appear to mobilize intracellular calcium stores in cultured vascular endothelial cells. Although several potential sites for intracellular calcium storage (mitochondria, endoplasmic reticulum, plasma membrane) exist in endothelial cells, the endoplasmic reticulum is the most likely source of calcium which is mobilized by these agents (Berridge and Irvine, 1984). Inositol trisphosphate (IP$_3$), a water soluble product of receptor-mediated PIP$_2$ hydrolysis, has been shown to be an extremely potent stimulus for Ca^{2+} mobilization from an intracellular non-mitochondrial compartment (presumably the endoplasmic reticulum) in numerous cell types (Berridge and Irvine, 1984). Interestingly, calcium deposits have been localized within the endoplasmic reticulum of endothelial cells (Somlyo and Somlyo, 1971). Thus, it seems likely that PAF, as well as other mediators, mobilize calcium from endoplasmic reticulum in EC.

The mechanism by which phorbol esters and OAG inhibit PAF-induced Ca^{2+} flux in endothelial cells is not known at this time. These compounds appear to attenuate PAF-induced calcium flux in platelets by inhibiting phospholipase C activation and subsequent IP$_3$ formation and Ca^{2+} mobilization (MacIntyre *et al.*, 1985). Tumor-promoting phorbol esters and synthetic diglycerides are believed to exert their physiological actions by substituting for naturally occurring *sn*-1,2-diacylglycerol in intact cells and stimulating protein kinase C (Nishizuka, 1984). Diacylglycerols and inositol phosphates are generated during phospholipase C-mediated hydrolysis of PIP$_2$ and other phosphoinositides (Berridge and Irvine, 1984; Nishizuka, 1984). We have observed that PAF and bradykinin, as well as thrombin, increase IP$_3$ levels in [^{3}H]-myoinositol-labeled cultured bovine and human EC, respectively (Brock *et al.*, 1986a, unpublished observations). In a previous study, we demonstrated that prior exposure of endothelial cells to PAF (but not to PAF analogs or bradykinin) induced an agonist-specific desensitization of subsequent PAF-induced $^{45}Ca^{2+}$ efflux (Brock *et al.*, 1986b). Based on these observations and the known mechanisms of phorbol ester and OAG action, the results of the present study suggest that DG formation during PAF activation of EC may feedback via protein kinase C activation to inhibit prolonged phospholipase C-mediated IP$_3$ formation and calcium mobilization in EC.

In summary, our observations indicate that vascular endothelium may be a target for platelet activating factor, a potent lipid mediator of inflammation, and suggest that

PAF-induced alterations in endothelial calcium flux may be relevant to its *in vivo* inflammatory actions. Furthermore, it appears that this pathophysiological mediator may be capable of initiating at least two signaling pathways following receptor activation in EC (IP_3 −calcium and DAG−protein kinase C). Our observations indicate that protein kinase C may play an important role in modulating the 'activation' of vascular endothelium by PAF.

ACKNOWLEDGMENTS

The authors thank Kay Case and Anne Brock for their excellent assistance in cell culture. This research was supported by grants HL-36028, HL 36561 from the National Heart, Lung and Blood Institute and by a grant from the American Heart Association, Massachusetts Affiliate, Inc.

REFERENCES

Archer, C.B., Page C. P., Paul W., Morley J., and Macdonald, D.M. (1984). 'Inflammatory characteristics of platelet activating factor (PAF-acether) in human skin', *Brit. J. Dermatol.*, **110**, 45−50.

Benveniste, J., and Vargaftig, B.B. (1983). 'Platelet activating factor: an ether lipid with biological activity'. In H.K. Mangold and F. Paltauf, (eds.) *Ether Lipids: Biochemical and Biomedical Aspects* Academic Press, New York, pp. 356−376.

Berridge, M.J., and Irvine, R.F.(1984). 'Inositol trisphosphate, a novel second messenger in cellular signal transduction', *Nature*, **312**, 315−321.

Brock, T.A., Alexander, R.W., and Gimbrone, M.A., Jr. (1984). 'Bradykinin and platelet activating factor stimulate calcium fluxes in cultured endothelial cells', *Fed. Proc.*, **43**, 460.

Brock T.A., Capasso, E.L., and Gimbrone, M.A., Jr.(1986a). 'Cellular signaling events involved in thrombin activation of vascular endothelium', *Fed. Proc.*, **45**, 1072.

Brock, T.A., and Gimbrone, M.A., Jr. (1986b). 'Platelet activating factor alters calcium homeostasis in cultured endothelial cells', *Am. J. Physiol.*, **250**, H1086−H1092.

Bussolini, F., Aglietta, M., Sanavio, F., Stacchini, A., Lauri, D., and Camussi, G. (1985). 'Alkyl-ether phosphoglycerides influence calcium fluxes into human endothelial cells', *J. Immunol.*, **135**, 2748−2753.

Gimbrone, M.A., Jr. (1976). 'Culture of vascular endothelium', *Prog. Hemost. Thromb.*, **3**, 1−28.

Hallam, T.J., Sanchez, A., and Rink, T.J. (1984). 'Stimulus−response coupling in human platelets: changes evoked by platelet activating factor in cytosolic free calcium monitored with the fluorescent calcium indicator quin 2'. *Biochem. J.*, **218**, 819−827.

Humphery, D.M., McManus, L.M., Hanahan, D.J., and Pinckard, R.N. (1984). 'Morphological basis of increased vascular permeability induced by acetyl glyceryl ether phosphorylcholine', *Lab. Invest.*, **50**, 16−25.

Hwang, S.-B., Lee C.-S.C., Cheah, M.J., and Shen, T.Y. (1983). 'Specific receptor sites for 1-0-alkyl-2-acetyl-*sn*-3-phosphocholine (platelet activating factor) on rabbit platelet and guinea pig smooth muscle membranes', *Biochemistry*, **22**, 4756−4763.

Jaffe, E.A., (ed.) (1983). *Biology of Endothelial Cells*, Martinus Nijhoff, Boston.

Kamatani, T., Katamoto, M., Tatsumi, M., Katsuta, K., Ono, T., Kikuchi, H., and Kamada, S. (1984). 'Mechanisms of the hypotensive effect of synthetic 1-0-octadecyl-2-0-acetyl-glycero-3-phosphorylcholine', *Eur. J. Pharmacol.*, **98**, 357–366

Lee, T.-C., Malone, B., Blank, M.L., and Snyder, F. (1981). '1-Alkyl-2-acetyl-*sn*-glycero-3-phosphocholine (platelet activating factor) stimulates calcium influx in rabbit platelets', *Biochem. Biophys. Res. Commun.*, **102**, 1262–1268

MacIntyre, D.E., McNichol, A., and Drummond, A.H.(1985). 'Tumour-promoting phorbol esters inhibit agonist-induced phosphatide formation and Ca^{2+} flux in human platelets', *FEBS Letters*, **180**, 160-164.

Nishizuka, Y. (1984). 'The role of protein kinase C in cell surface signal transduction and tumour promotion', *Nature*, **308**, 693–698.

Pinckard, R.N., McManus, L.M., and Hanahan. D.J. (1982) 'Chemistry and biology of acetyl glyceryl ether phosphorylcholine (platelet activating factor)', *Adv. Inflammation Res.*, **4**, 147–180.

Sanchez Crespo, M., Alonso, F., Inarrea, P., Alvarez, V., and Egido, J. (1982). 'Vascular actions of synthetic PAF-acether (a synthetic platelet activating factor) in the rat: evidence for a platelet independent mechanism', *Immunopharm.*, **4**, 173–185.

Somlyo, A.V., and Somlyo, A.P. (1971). 'Strontium accumulation by sarcoplasmic reticulum and mitochondria in vascular smooth muscle', *Science*, **174**, 955–958.

Terashita, Z., Tsushima, S., Yoshioka, Y., Nomura, H., Inada, Y., and Nishikawa, K. (1983). 'CV-3988—a specific antagonist of platelet activating factor (PAF)', *Life Sciences*, **32**, 1975–1982

Valone, F.H., and Goetzel, E.J. (1983). 'Specific binding by human polymorphonuclear leukocytes of the immunologic mediator 1-0-hexadecyl/octadecyl-2-acetyl-*sn*-3-phosphorylcholine', *Immunology*, **48**, 141–149.

New Horizons in Platelet Activating Factor Research
Edited by C. M. Winslow and M. L. Lee
© 1987 John Wiley & Sons Ltd.

22

AGEPC-Mediated Platelet Dependent Coronary Artery Vasodilation

Charles V. Jackson, Jonathon Homeister, Edward M. Driscoll and Benedict R. Lucchesi

INTRODUCTION

Activated basophils, leukocytes and platelets have been shown to release a unique phosphoglyceride, platelet activating factor (AGEPC). AGEPC has been shown to cause platelet (Henson, 1970; Vargaftig *et al.*, 1981) and neutrophil aggregation (Ford-Hutchinson, 1983). This phosphoglyceride produces hypotension in spontaneously hypertensive and normotensive rats (Blank *et al.*, 1979; Tokumura *et al.*, 1979; Feurstein *et al.*, 1982; Lai *et al.*, 1983). In addition, AGEPC produces pulmonary (Stimler and O'Flaherty, 1983, Kenzora *et al.*, 1984) and coronary vascular constriction in porcine (Feurstein *et al.*, 1984), guinea pig (Benveniste *et al.*, 1983; Levi *et al.*, 1984) and canine (Sybertz *et al.*, 1985) hearts, and enhancement of vascular permeability in rabbits and guinea pigs (Humphrey *et al.*, 1982).

The present study describes the coronary vascular effects of the direct intracoronary administration of AGEPC in anesthetized dogs. Since AGEPC could result in the release of vasoactive substances (histamine, serotonin, adenine nucleotides) from platelets during aggregation and degranulation, the influence of platelet depletion upon the AGEPC-induced coronary vasomotor responses was examined after the induction of thrombocytopenia. Experiments were also conducted employing washed-platelet preparations to aid in the characterization of the AGEPC-induced coronary vasodilator response.

METHODS

Surgical Preparation and Instrumentation

Male, mongrel dogs (16−22 kg) were anesthetized with sodium pentobarbital (30 mg kg^{-1}, i.v.) and ventilated with positive pressure (Harvard respirator) using room air. A left thoracotomy was performed at the fifth intercostal space and the heart was suspended in a pericardial cradle. A 1–2cm segment of the left circumflex (LCX) coronary artery was isolated proximal to its first descending branch. An electromagnetic flow probe (Carolina Medical Electronics) was positioned around the LCX artery for continuous measurement of circumflex coronary blood flow (CBF). A 27 gauge needle catheter was inserted through the wall of the LCX artery distal to the electromagnetic flow probe for drug administration. Patency of the intracoronary catheter was maintained during the experiments by infusing 0.9 percent sodium chloride solution at a rate of 3.0 ml h^{-1}. Polyethylene catheters (PE-160) were placed in the carotid and jugular veins for the measurement of arterial blood pressure and the intravenous administration of drugs, respectively. Continuous recordings of regional or LCX coronary artery blood flow, mean arterial blood pressure, heart rate and the Lead II electrocardiogram were made on a Grass Model 7 polygraph. A period of 30 min was allowed for equilibration of all hemodynamic parameters before intiation of the study.

Method of Producing Thrombocytopenia

In all experiments platelet counts ranged from 200,000 to 400,000 μl^{-1} of whole blood. Platelet depletion was produced by the intravenous administration of a sheep-derived platelet antiserum specific for the dog platelet. The administration of the anti-serum resulted in a 95 ± 3 percent reduction in the circulating platelet count; determined before and 30 min after the administration of the antiserum.

Preparation of Washed-Platelets

Venous blood (9.0 ml) was drawn in to 3.8 percent sodium citrate solution (1.0 ml) and centrifuged at 150 × g for 5 min to obtain platelet rich plasma (PRP). PRP was centrifuged at 550 × g for 7 min and the supernate was removed. The platelets were resuspended in calcium-free Tyrode's solution containing EDTA (0.3 mM) and bovine serum albumin (0.35 percent) at a pH of 6.5. The cells were agitated gently for 2 min and the centrifugation and wash procedure were repeated two more times. The final washed-platelet pellet was resuspended in a calcium-free Tyrode's solution, pH 7.35. The washed-platelet suspensions were diluted with Tyrode's solution to adjust the platelet count to 250,000–350,000 μl^{-1}. Calcium chloride was added to the washed-platelet suspensions to a final concentration of 2 mM and followed by the addition of lyso-GEPC (2 nM) or AGEPC (2 nM) and allowed to incubate for 10 min after which the preparations were centrifuged at 1325 × g for 10 min to remove all cellular constituents. Aliquots (0.2 ml) of the supernate from the activated, washed-platelet suspensions were administered by intracoronary injection to dogs made thrombocytopenic. Injections of supernates from non-activated washed-platelet suspensions were used as controls.

Preparation of Drug Solutions

AGEPC, 1-*O*-hexadecyl-2-*O*-acetyl-*sn*-glycero-3-phosphorylcholine and the biologically inactive phosphoglyceride, Lyso-GEPC (1-*O*-hexadecyl-2-*O*-lyso-*sn*-glycero-3-phosphorylcholine, both obtained from Bachem, Torrence, CA) were dissolved in phased-chloroform and stored at −20 °C. Phosphorus analysis was performed to determine the concentration of each phosphoglyceride (Bartlett, 1959; Ames, 1966). Aliquots were taken from the stock solutions and dried under nitrogen gas. The phosphoglycerides were then dissolved in a 0.9 percent sodium chloride solution containing 0.25 percent bovine serum albumin (Fraction V, Sigma). The concentration of AGEPC and lyso-GEPC was adjusted so that the injected volume was 0.2 ml.

Statistical Analysis

Differences between groups were determined by Student's t-test (paired analysis). Multiple group comparisons were made by a one-way analysis of variance followed by Student−Neuman−Keuls multiple range test. A value of $p < 0.05$ was considered as significant. All values in the text are given as the mean ± S.E.M.

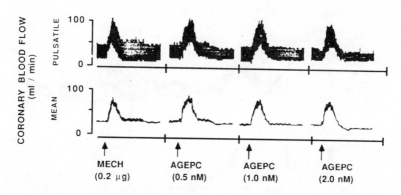

Figure 1. A typical recording illustrating the coronary blood flow response observed after the intracoronary administration of AGEPC into the canine LCX coronary artery. MECH (methacholine)

RESULTS

Effects of the Intracoronary Administration of AGEPC on Coronary Artery Blood Flow

Figure 1 illustrates a respresentative example of the LCX coronary artery blood flow response to AGEPC. LCX coronary blood flow was observed to increase immediately after the injection of AGEPC (0.5, 1.0, 2.0 nM) by 53 ± 7, 51 ± 8 and 55 ± 7ml min^{-1} (n = 7). The injection of methacholine (0.2 μg) produced a similar increase in CBF as did AGEPC. Methacholine was used in these studies to insure vascular reactivity, and as an indirect indication of endothelial cell integrity. The inactive phosphoglyceride, lyso-GEPC, failed to cause any change in CBF (not illustrated).

Effects of Platelet Depletion on the Coronary Blood Flow Response to AGEPC

Platelet depletion produced by the administration of sheep-derived dog platelet anti-serum resulted in a mean decrease in the circulating platelet count of 95 ± 3 percent without producing any immediate observable effects upon the recorded basal hemo-dynamic parameters. LCX coronary blood flow before the administration of platelet antiserum averaged 31 ± 2 ml min^{-1} and was 29 ± 3 ml min^{-1} (n = 7) 30 min after platelet depletion. The increases in CBF caused by the direct administration of AGEPC (0.5–2.0 nM) were reduced significantly in the presence of thrombo-cytopenia. A representative recording of the administration of 2.0 nM of AGEPC is illustrated in Figure 2. The induction of thrombocytopenia produced a 77 ± 5 per-cent inhibition of the increase in CBF produced by the intracoronary injection of AGEPC. Methacholine (0.2 μg)-induced increases in CBF (27 ± 2 ml min^{-1}) were not altered by platelet depletion (26 ± 3 ml min^{-1}).

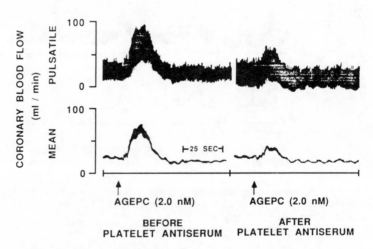

Figure 2.   A representative recording of the coronary vascular response to AGEPC before and after the induction of thrombocytopenia

Effects of Supernates from AGEPC-activated Washed-Platelets on Coronary Blood Flow

Figure 3 illustrates a representative recording of the intracoronary administration of cell-free supernates (CFS), which have been activated with either AGEPC or lyso-GEPC, into the LCX of thrombocytopenic dogs. CFS from washed-platelet suspensions activated with AGEPC (2.0 nM) produced an increase in CBF of 46 ± 5 ml min^{-1} (n = 4) when injected into the LCX coronary artery. The injection of CFS obtained from washed-platelets activated with lyso-GEPC (2.0 nM) failed to cause a significant increase in CBF (2.0 ± 2 ml min^{-1}). CFS from preparations of washed-platelet suspensions did not produce a significant increase in CBF when injected into the LCX coronary artery.

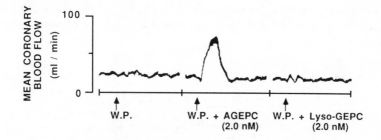

Figure 3. A representative recording of the coronary vascular response to the administration of cell-free supernates obtained from washed-platelet (W.P.) suspensions activated with AGEPC or Lyso-GEPC. Injections of the supernates were made in thrombocytopenic dogs

DISCUSSION

In the experiments presented in this study, the major effect of the direct administration of platelet activating factor, AGEPC, into the LCX coronary artery was vasodilation. AGEPC-induced coronary artery vasodilation was observed to be dependent upon the presence of circulating platelets. The injection of cell-free supernates prepared from washed-platelet suspensions activated with AGEPC were observed to produce coronary artery vasodilation. These data indicate that AGEPC activates platelets, resulting in the release of a substance into the coronary circulation which is capable of mediating coronary artery vasodilation.

Since AGEPC is one of the most potent activators of platelet aggregation and degranulation, it is possible to postulate that the increase in CBF in response to AGEPC is due to the release from the platelet of some known mediator(s) of vascular reactivity (e.g. serotonin, ADP, ATP). Coronary artery vasoconstriction has been attributed to the release of the secondary mediators, serotonin and thromboxane A_2 (Vargaftig *et al.*, 1982; Feurstein *et al.*, 1982, 1984). The AGEPC-induced vasodilator response has been shown to be inhibited by 35−40 percent in the presence of the H_1-receptor antagonist, diphenhydramine or the non specific serotonin antagonist, methysergide, indicating the presence of the two autacoids (Jackson *et al.*, 1986). In these experiments, the vasodilator response to exogenously administered histamine or serotonin, however, was inhibited by 80 percent. Jackson *et al.*, (1986) also have shown that the adenine nucleotides, ADP and ATP, and products of cyclooxygenase do not appear to play a role in the AGEPC-induced vasodilator response. The major portion, therefore, appears to be due to some other platelet-derived vasodilator substance.

The induction of thrombocytopenia eliminated the increase in CBF in response to the direct coronary administration of AGEPC. Cell-free supernates taken from washed-platelet suspensions activated with AGEPC and given to the thrombocytopenic dog retained the ability to induce an identical coronary vasodilator response. Supernates from washed-platelets or washed-platelets activated with lyso-GEPC failed to produce a change in coronary artery blood flow. These data illustrate the dependency upon the platelet for the release of a mediator of coronary artery vasodilation.

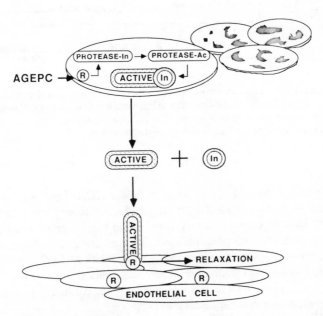

Figure 4.   Illustrates a proposed working model of the activation of platelets by AGEPC at its receptor (R) to produce the subsequent release of the vasodilator substance. In=inhibited, Ac=active

In summary, Figure 4 illustrates that AGEPC by interacting through its cell surface receptor may activate a precursor serine protease which then initiates the secretory process within the platelet (Henson and Oades, 1976). The data from the present investigation would suggest that during the secretory process the platelet in response to AGEPC releases an unidentified mediator of coronary artery vasodilation.

REFERENCES

Ames, B.N. (1966). 'Assay of inorganic phosphate, total phosphate and phosphatases', *Methods in Enzymology*, **8**, 115–118.

Bartlet, G.R. (1959). 'Phosphorus assay in column chromatography', *J. Biol. Chem.*, **234**, 466–468.

Benveniste, J., Boullet, C., Brink, C., and Labat, C. (1983). 'The actions of PAF-acether (platelet-activating factor) on guinea-pig isolated heart preparations', *Br. J. Pharmacol.*, **80**, 81–83.

Blank, M.L., Synder, F., Byers, L.W., Brooks, B., and Muirhead, E. (1979). 'Antihypertensive activity of an alkyl ether analog of phosphatidylcholine', *Biochem. Biophys. Res. Commun.*, **90**, 1194–1200.

Feuerstein, G., Boyd, L.M., Ezra, D., and Goldstein, R.E. (1984). 'Effect of platelet-activating factor on coronary circulation of the domestic pig', *Am. J. Physiol.*, **146**, H466–H471.

Feuerstein, G., Zukowska-Grojec, Z., Krausz, M.M., Blank, M.L., Snyder, F., and Kopin, I.J. (1982). 'Cardiovascular and sympathetic effects of 1-0-hexadecyl-2-acetyl-*sn*-glycero-3-phosphocholine in conscious SHR and WKY rats', *Clin. Exp. Hyperten.*, **A4**, 1335–1350.

Ford-Hutchinson, A.W. (1983). 'Neutrophil aggregating properties of PAF-acether and leukotriene B_4', *Int. J. Immunopharmacol.*, **5**, 17–21.

Henson, P.M. (1970). 'Release of vasoactive amines from rabbit platelets induced by sensitized mononuclear leukocytes and antigen', *J. Exp. Med.*, **131**, 287–304.

Henson, P.M., and Oades, Z.G. (1976). 'Activation of platelets by platelet-activating factor (PAF) derived from IgE-sensitized basophils. II. The role of serine proteases, cyclic nucleotides, and contractile elements in PAF-induced secretion', *J. Exp. Med.*, **143**, 953–968.

Jackson, C.V., Schumacher, W.A., Kunkel, S.L., Driscoll, E.M. and Lucchesi, B.R. (1986). 'Platelet activating factor and the release of a platelet-derived coronary artery vasodilator substance in the canine', *Circ. Res.* **58**, 218–229.

Lai, F.M., Shepard, C.A., Cervoni, P., and Wissner, H. (1983). 'Hypotensive and vasodilatory activity of ($\pm$) 1-0-octadecyl-2-acetyl-glyceryl-3-phosphorylcholine in the normotensive rat', *Life Sci.*, **32**, 1159–1166.

Levi, R., Burke, J.A., Guo, Z.G., Hattori, Y., Hoppens, C.M., McManus, L.M., Hanahan, D.J., and Pinckard, R.N. (1984). 'Acetyl glyceryl ether phosphorylcholine (AGEPC): A putative mediator of cardiac anaphylaxis in the guinea pig', *Circ. Res.*, **54**, 117–124.

Stimler, N.P., and O'Flaherty, J.T. (1983). 'Spasmogenic properties of platelet-activating factor: Evidence for a direct mechanism in contractile response of pulmonary tissues', *Am. J. Pathol.*, **113**, 75–84

Sybertz, E.J., Watkins, R.W., Baum, T., Pula, K., and Rivelli, M. (1985). 'Cardiac, coronary and peripheral vascular effects of acetyl glyceryl ether phosphoryl choline in the anesthetized dog', *J. Pharmacol. Exp. Ther.*, **232**, 156–162.

Vargaftig, B.B., Chignard, M., Benveniste, J., Lefort, J., and Wal, F. (1981). 'Background and present status of research on platelet-activating factor (PAF-acether)', *Ann. NY. Acad. Sci.*, **370**,119–137.

Vargaftig, B.B., Lefort, J., Wall, F., Chignard, M., and Medeiros, M.C. (1982). 'Non-steroidal anti-inflammatory drugs if combined with anti-histamine and anti-serotonin agents interfere with bronchial and platelet effects of 'platelet-activating factor' (PAF-acether)', *Eur. J. Pharmacol.*, **82**, 121–130.

New Horizons in Platelet Activating Factor Research
Edited by C. M. Winslow and M. L. Lee
© 1987 John Wiley & Sons Ltd.

23

Inhibition of Platelet Activating Factor Binding to Human Platelets by Calcium Channel Blockers

Frank H. Valone

ROLE OF CALCIUM IN PAF-INDUCED PLATELET ACTIVATION

Calcium has long been recognized as playing a critical role in platelet activation by platelet activating factor (PAF) and by other agonists (Benveniste *et al.*, 1972; Henson, 1976). Platelet activation by PAF absolutely requires extracellular calcium. In the absence of extracellular calcium platelet exposure to PAF selectively desensitizes platelets to PAF (Henson, 1976; Valone *et al.*, 1982). Desensitization may occur through the mechanism of receptor down regulation (Valone *et al.*, 1982; Chesney *et al.*, 1983; Kloprogge and Akkerman, 1984). That PAF-stimulated calcium influx into platelets is essential to platelet activation is suggested by the observation that PAF induces ^{45}Ca uptake by platelets (Lee *et al.*, 1983). These studies could not distinguish between a direct ionophore action of PAF and calcium influx through a receptor-linked channel. Furthermore, analyses of ^{45}Ca uptake do not quantify the mobilization of intracellular calcium stores which can be substantial (Hallam *et al.*, 1984) and cannot easily distinguish between calcium influx into cytoplasmic pools and calcium binding to newly exposed plasma membrane proteins (Brass and Shattil, 1984).

The free platelet cytoplasmic calcium concentration ($[Ca^{2+}]_i$) can be quantified using probes such as Quin 2 (Rink *et al.*, 1982; Feinstein *et al.*, 1983: Hallam *et al.*, 1984; Valone and Johnson, 1985a, b and Aequorin (Johnson *et al.*, 1985). These probes have demonstrated that the $[Ca^{2+}]_i$ of resting platelets is 90−100 nM. $[CA^{2+}]_i$ increases to 1−5 μM when platelets are exposed to agonist concentrations which are substantially greater than those required for maximal platelet activation such as 500 nM PAF (Hallam *et al.*, 1984). In contrast, dose−response studies of platelet aggregation and changes in $[Ca^{2+}]_i$ reveal that 2−5 nM PAF elicit 100 percent aggregation of Quin 2-loaded human platelets and that these concentrations of PAF increase

$[Ca^{2+}]_I$ only one- to two-fold (Valone and Johnson, 1985a). Thus, PAF and other agonists can increase $[Ca^{2+}]_i$ to levels substantially greater than those required to support maximal platelet activation.

EVIDENCE FOR A PAF RECEPTOR-LINKED CALCIUM CHANNEL

Probes such as the calcium-sensitive fluorescent indicator Quin 2 have provided substantial evidence that PAF stimulates calcium influx into platelets through a receptor-linked calcium channel. The exact nature of the linkage—whether it is direct or mediated by products of a second pathway such as the phosphoinositol pathway—is unknown. When platelets are stimulated by low concentrations of PAF in calcium-free medium $[Ca^{2+}]_i$ rises by less than 20 percent. This minimal rise apparently results from the release of intracellular calcium from dense granule stores as extracellular calcium chelators such as EDTA cannot block the increase in $[Ca^{2+}]_i$ (Hallam *et al.*, 1984). Products of phosphoinositol metabolism may mediate calcium release from these intracellular stores (O'Rourke *et al.*, 1985). Insights into the nature of the calcium channel can be obtained from 'add-back' experiments in which platelets in calcium-poor buffer are first stimulated by PAF and calcium is then added back to the buffer at different times. Such studies demonstrate that increased $[Ca^{2+}]_i$ resulting from intracellular calcium release is maximal within 15 s. Restoration of extracellular calcium to physiological concentrations (1.8 mM) at that time induces a substantial further increase in $[Ca^{2+}]_i$ to levels comparable to those observed when calcium is present throughout the study. This suggests that PAF opens a calcium channel which allows calcium influx and that calcium influx accounts for 80–90 percent of the increased $[Ca^{2+}]_i$ induced by low concentrations of PAF (Valone and Johnson, 1985b). PAF-induced calcium influx is only transient, however, so that no influx is noted 3–5 min after PAF stimulation. Thus, the PAF-induced calcium channel closes with an apparent half-life of 45 s. This contrasts with thrombin whose inducible calcium channel remains open for 5–10 min. The rate of closure of the PAF-induced calcium channel closely parallels the rate of development of specific platelet desensitization to PAF (Valone *et al.*, 1982; Valone and Johnson , 1985a). PAF may remain reversibly associated with its receptor for up to 1 h after binding (Kloprogge, 1984; Valone, 1985). Thus, dissociation of the link between the PAF receptor and the calcium channel may account initially for the development of specific desensitization.

More direct evidence for a PAF receptor-linked calcium channel comes from studies of Mn^{2+} influx into Quin 2-loaded platelets (Hallam and Rink, 1985). Mn^{2+} has greater avidity for Quin 2 than does Ca^{2+} and Mn^{2+} binding quenches calcium-stimulated Quin 2 fluorescence. PAF stimulation of platelets in the presence of extracellular Mn^{2+} causes a rapid quenching of intracellular Quin 2 fluorescence indicating that PAF opens a calcium channel which also admits Mn^{2+}. That the channel is selective is suggested by the observation that Li^+ does not enter the cell. The initial phase of increased $[Ca^{2+}]_i$ which has been attributed to release of calcium from membrane stores is not affected by Mn^{2+} in the extracellular fluid. Thus, PAF appears to increase $[Ca^{2+}]_i$ by both intracellular release and by calcium influx.

Calcium channel blockers such as diltiazem, verapamil and nifedipine inhibit platelet activation by PAF (Shaw *et al.*, 1983) and block PAF-induced ^{45}Ca influx (Lee *et al.*, 1983). These studies suggest the existence of a PAF-induced calcium channel. However, platelets lack the voltage-dependent calcium channels which are blocked by these agents (Doyle and Ruegg, 1985) and the concentrations used are much greater than those which inhibit calcium influx through voltage-dependent channels in other cells. Calcium channel blockers are also known to inhibit binding of epinephrine, serotonin and other ligands to their specific cell receptors (Barnathan *et al.*, 1982; Motulsky *et al.*, 1983). These observations suggest that calcium channel blockers may inhibit PAF-induced platelet activation by inhibiting PAF binding rather than by inhibiting calcium influx directly.

Table 1. Inhibition of PAF-Induced Platelet Aggregation and of PAF Binding by the Calcium Channel Blockers Diltiazem and Verapamil

| | Calcium Channel Blocker | |
	Diltiazem	Verapamil
IC_{50} Aggregation[1]	28 ± 19 μM^2	42 ± 20 μM
IC_{50} Binding	47 ± 25 μM	63 ± 12 μM

[1] Concentration of diltiazen or verapamil which inhibits aggregation or binding by 50 percent.
[2] Mean ± S.D.; $n = 5$ for diltiazem and $n = 6$ for verapamil.

Inhibition of PAF Binding by Calcium Channel Blockers

The capacity of the calcium channel blockers diltiazem and verapamil to inhibit platelet activation and PAF binding to the same preparations of human platelets was examined (Table 1). Both agents inhibited platelet aggregation and PAF binding in a dose-related manner. Fifty percent inhibition of aggregation and binding was observed at 28 μM and 47 μM diltiazem respectively. Similarly, verapamil inhibited aggregation and PAF binding with 50 percent inhibition at 42 μM and 63 μM respectively. These studies suggest that inhibition of PAF binding accounts for at least 25−50 percent of the capacity of these agents to inhibit platelet activation by PAF.

The high concentrations of diltiazem and verapamil which were required to inhibit PAF binding suggest that inhibition may be non-specific rather than the result of competition for receptor binding. A series of experiments were undertaken to distinguish between these two possible mechanisms. If one assumes that diltiazem and verapamil bind to the PAF receptor then the dose−response data used to calculate the IC_{50}s can be used to construct Scatchard plots (Figures 1 and 2). Based on these plots, the K_d are 3.2 ± 1.7 x $10^{-5}M$ for diltiazem ($n = 5$) and 5.6 ± 2.4 x 10^{-5} M for verapamil ($n = 6$). In contrast the K_d for PAF itself was $4.0 \pm 1.2 \times 10^{-10}$ M in the same studies indicating that the receptor has substantially greater affinity for PAF.

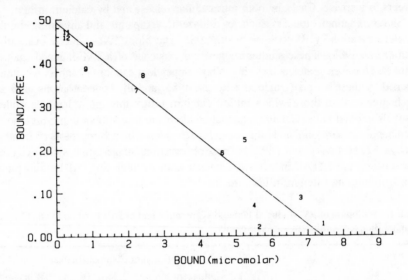

Figure 1.   Scatchard plot of diltiazem binding to platelets. The data are derived from competition between diltiazem and [^{3}H]PAF for platelet binding. Each number represents an individual data point

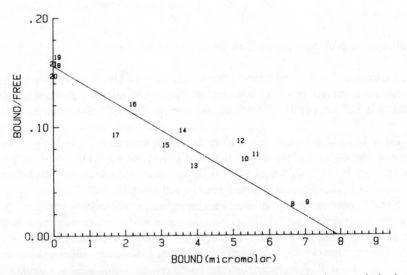

Figure 2.   Scatchard plot of verapamil binding to platelets. The data are derived from competition between diltiazem and [^{3}H]PAF for platelet binding. Each number represents an individual data point

The capacity to develop saturation isotherms and Scatchard plots does not guarantee that diltiazem and verapamil compete for PAF binding to its receptor as changes in receptor affinity for PAF could yield similar data and plots. To examine the effect of the channel blockers on the PAF receptor in greater detail, saturation isotherms were made of PAF binding in the presence of different, fixed concentrations of either diltiazem or verapamil. Double reciprocal plots of the data (1 bound^{-1} v 1 free^{-1}) revealed families of lines which intersect slightly to the right of the ordinate in five studies. These data suggest that diltiazem and verapamil inhibit PAF binding largely by competition but that these agents have other more complex effects on PAF binding. Perhaps the PAF receptor exists in two distinct states, a low density, high affinity state and a high density, low affinity state and the channel blockers modulate transition between these two states. Alternatively, the channel blockers may interact differently with the receptor depending on whether it has bound PAF or they may bind to only a portion of the PAF binding site.

If the channel blockers compete with PAF for binding to platelets then the reciprocal should also occur. That is PAF should compete for binding of the channel blockers to platelets. Preliminary studies have examined the binding of [^{3}H]diltiazem to washed human platelets using the methods and conditions employed to quantify PAF binding (Valone, 1985). Under those conditions, minimal but definite diltiazem binding is observed (Table 2). Binding is rapid and reaches saturation within 20 min at room temperature. Initial studies of binding competition between PAF and diltiazem reveal that PAF inhibits diltiazem binding to platelets (Table 2) providing further evidence that PAF and diltiazem share platelet binding sites.

Table 2. Inhibition of [^{3}H]Diltiazem Binding to Human Platelets by Platelet Activating Factor

| Binding Inhibitor | [^{3}H]Diltiazem Binding | |
	CPM	Percent
None	2967[2]	6.1
Diltiazem (100 μM)	1774	3.8
PAF (10 μM)	1816	3.9

[1] The indicated inhibitor and approximately 50 000 CPM of [^{3}H]diltiazem were placed in microfuge tubes. 0.5 ml of platelets (1×10^8) in phosphate-buffered saline, pH 7.4, containing 0.1 percent human serum albumin were added to the tubes. The mixture was incubated for 30 min at room temperature after which the platelets were sedimented using a microfuge. The unbound diltiazem in the supernatants and the bound diltiazem in the platelet pellets were then quantified.
[2] Mean of two determinations.

REFERENCES

Barnathan, E.S., Addonizio, V.P., and Shattil, S.J. (1982). 'Interaction of verapamil with human platelet alpha-adrenergic receptors', *Am. J. Physiol.*, **242**, H19–H23.

Benveniste, J., Henson, P.M., and Cochrane, C.G. (1972). 'Leukocyte-dependent histamine release from rabbit platelets. The role of IgE, basophils and a platelet-activating factor', *J. Exp. Med.*, **136**, 1356-1377.

Brass, L.F., and Shattil, S.J. (1984). 'Identification and function of the high affinity binding sites for Ca²⁺ on the surface of platelets', *J. Clin. Invest.*, **73**, 626-632.

Chesney, C.M., Pifer, D.D., and Huch, K.M. (1983). 'Alpha-adrenergic antagonists inhibit binding of platelet-activating factor (PAF) to gel-filtered platelets'. In J. Benveniste and B. Arnoux (eds.) *Platelet Activating Factor*, Elsevier Science Publishers, Amsterdam, pp.177-186.

Doyle, V.M., and Ruegg, A.T. (1985). 'Lack of evidence for voltage dependent calcium channels in platelets', *Biochem. Biophys. Res. Commun.*, **113**, 598-604.

Feinstein, M.B., Egan, J.J., Sha'afi, R.I., and White, J. (1983) 'The cytoplasmic concentration of free calcium in platelets is controlled by stimulators of cyclic AMP production (PGD2, PGE1, forskolin)', *Biochem. Biophys. Res. Comm.*, **113**, 598-604.

Hallam, T.J., Sanchez, A., and Rink, T.J. (1984). 'Stimulus-response coupling in human platelets: Changes evoked by platelet-activating factor in cytoplasmic free calcium monitored with the fluorescent calcium indicator Quin 2', *Biochem. J.*, **218**, 819-827.

Hallam, T.J., and Rink, T.J. (1985).'Agonists stimulate divalent cation channels in the plasma membrane of human platelets', *Fed. Eur. Biochem. Soc.*, **186**, 175-179.

Henson, P.M. (1976). 'Activation and desensitization of platelets by platelet-activating factor (PAF) derived from IgE-sensitized basophils. 1. Characteristics of the secretory response', *J. Exp. Med.*, **143**, 937-952.

Johnson, P.C., Ware, J.A., Clivden, P.B., Smith, M., Dvorak, A.M., and Salzman, E.W. (1985). 'Measurement of ionized calcium in blood platelets with the photoprotein Aequorin. Comparison with Quin 2', *J. Biol. Chem.*, **260**, 2069-2076.

Kloprogge, E., and Akkerman, J.W.N. (1984). 'Binding knitics of PAF-acether (1-0-alkyl-2-acetyl-*sn*-glycero-3-phosphocholine) to intact human platelets'. *Biochem. J.*, **223**, 901-909.

Lee, T-C., Malone, B., and Snyder, F. (1983). 'Stimulation of calcium uptake by 1-alkyl-2-acetyl-*sn*-glycero-3-phosphocholine (platelet activating factor) in rabbit platelets: Possible involvement of the lipoygenase pathway', *Arch. Biochem. Biophys.*, **223**, 33-39.

Motulsky, H.J., Snavely, M.D., Hughes, R.J., and Insel, P.A. (1983). 'Interaction of verapamil and other calcium channel blockers with alpha-1 and alpha-2-adrenergic receptors', *Circ. Res.*, **52**, 226-231.

O'Rourke, F.A., Halenda, S.P., Zavoico, G.B., and Feinstein, M.B. (1985). 'Inositol 1,4,5-triphosphate releases Ca²⁺ from a Ca²⁺-transporting membrane vesicle fraction derived from human platelets', *J. Biol. Chem.*, **260**, 956-962.

Rink, T.J., Smith, S.W., and Tsien, R.Y. (1982). 'Cytoplasmic free Ca²⁺ in human platelets: Ca²⁺ thresholds and Ca-independent activation for shape-change and secretion', *Fed. Eur. Biochem. Soc.*, **148**, 21-26.

Shaw, A.M., Brydon, L.J., Pollock, W.M., and MacIntyre, D.E. (1983). 'The effects of class I, II and III calcium antagonists on human platelet aggregation induced by ADP, U44609, and PAF', *Thromb. Haemost.*, **50**, 45-51.

Valone, F.H., Coles, E., Reinhold, V.R., and Goetzl, E.J. (1982). 'Specific binding of phospholipid platelet activating factor by human platelets', *J. Immunol.*, **129**, 1637-1641.

Valone, F.H. (1985). 'Inhibition of binding of the platelet-activating factor AGEPC to platelets by the AGEPC analog rac-3-(*N*-n-octadecyl-carbamoyloxy)-2-methoxypropyl 2-thiazolio-ethyl phosphate (CV-3988)', *Biochem. Biophys. Res. Commun.*, **126**, 502-508.

Valone F.H., and Johnson, B.J. (1985a). 'Modulation of cytoplasmic calcium in human platelets by the phospholipid platelet-activating factor 1-0-alkyl-2-acetyl-*sn*-glycero-3-phosphocholine', *J. Immunol.*, **134**, 1120-1124.

Valone, F.H., and Johnson, B.J. (1985b). 'Decay of the activating signal after platelet stimulation with 1-0-alkyl-2-acetyl-*sn*-glycero-3-phosphocholine', *Thromb. Res.*, **40**, 385–392.

New Horizons in Platelet Activating Factor Research
Edited by C. M. Winslow and M. L. Lee
© 1987 John Wiley & Sons Ltd.

24

Effect of Platelet Activating Factor-Acether Antagonists on Human Platelets: Comparison of BN 52021 with Kadsurenone and CV 3988

M. Chignard, D. Nunez, R. Korth, X. Norel, P. Braquet and J. Benveniste

INTRODUCTION

PAF-acether (platelet activating factor) is a potent platelet agonist inducing calcium flux, arachidonate metabolism, phosphatidyl inositol turnover, protein phosphorylation, fibrinogen binding, shape change, granule content release and aggregation (see review by Chignard *et al.*, 1986). It has been shown to be formed by platelets upon activation by different agonists such as the calcium ionophore A 23187 or thrombin (Chignard *et al.*, 1979, 1980). Taking into consideration different data, it was postulated that PAF-acether could be a mediator of platelet activation like adenosine 5'-diphosphate (ADP) and arachidonic acid (AA) (Chignard *et al.*, 1979, 1986; Vargaftig *et al.*, 1980, 1981). In addition to a possible participation in thrombosis, PAF-acether has been ascribed a potential role in other pathologies including inflammation and allergy (see reviews by Vargaftig *et al.*, 1981; Pinckard *et al.*, 1981; Benveniste and Vargaftig, 1983; Roubin *et al.*, 1983). As a consequence, specific antagonists could provide powerful tools to investigate the role of PAF-acether in pathophysiological processes.

In this report we describe the activity of three PAF-acether antagonists recently developed by three different pharmaceutical companies, namely CV3988 (Terashita *et al.*, 1983), kadsurenone (Shen *et al.*, 1985) and BN 52021 (Nunez *et al.*, 1986) from Takeda Chemical Ind. (Japan), Merck Sharp and Dohme (USA) and Institut Henri Beaufour (France). CV 3988 is a structural analog of PAF-acether while the latter two compounds are natural products extracted from Chinese plants. Potency and specificity of these antagonists were studied using a standard biological model, i.e. human platelet aggregation in plasma and in Tyrode's buffer.

MATERIALS AND METHODS

Human blood was collected from a forearm vein over citric acid−trisodium citrate−dextrose (0.8−2.2−2.45 in percent; 1 vol for 9 vol of blood). Platelet-rich plasma (PRP) was obtained by centrifugation (100 g; 15 min). washed platelets were prepared according to the method of Lalau-Keraly et al., (1984) so as to render them specifically sensitive to PAF-acether by preincubation with ADP and aspirin (both used at 0.1 mM final concentration). Such platelets were refractory to ADP and AA. When ADP or AA was used as agonist, platelets were pretreated with only aspirin or ADP respectively. The platelets ($3 \times 10^8 \times ml^{-1}$) were incubated for 1 min in the presence of the inhibitors or their solvent (DMSO; 0.1 percent final concentration for BN 52021 and kadsurenone and 0.9 percent NaCl for CV 3988) before addition of the tested agonist. Each agonist was used at concentration inducing a submaximal aggregation. In some experiments dealing with PRP, different concentrations of PAF-acether were used in order to draw concentration-response curves in the presence and absence of BN 52021. Data presented are the means ± 1 S.D. of at least three distinct experiments.

For binding studies washed platelets were prepared as previously described and resuspended at $1 \times 10^8 \times ml^{-1}$ in Tyrode's buffer (pH 7.4) containing 0.25 percent fatty acid-free bovine serum albumin and 1.3 mM $CaCl_2$. Platelet suspensions (500 μl) were incubated with 0.65 nM radiolabeled [^{3}H]PAF-acether. Subsequent to incubation at 20 °C without stirring for different time intervals, platelets were separated from the medium by vacuum filtration through glass filters. The filters were then scintillation counted according to standard procedures. The counts obtained on filters without platelets were substracted from the mean duplicates. BN 52021 (60 μM) or cold PAF-acether (50 nM) was either added with [^{3}H]PAF-acether or 30 min later.

Changes in cytosolic free calcium were measured in platelets loaded with the fluorescent calcium indicator fura-2 (Tsien et al., 1985; Grynkiewicz et al., 1985). The platelet pellet obtained following PRP centrifugation (500 g; 15 min) was resuspended in one-half volume of plasma and incubated for 45 min at 37 °C with 3 μM fura-2 acetoxy methyl ester. Platelets were then pelleted (500 g; 20 min) and resuspended in Tyrode's buffer. Fluorescence measurements following platelet stimulation were performed as described by Selak and Smith (1986).

RESULTS AND DISCUSSION

Potency of BN 52021

BN 52021 inhibited PAF-acether-induced aggregation in a concentration-dependent manner. The IC_{50} (concentration inhibiting by 50 percent the control aggregation) found with washed platelets were 0.8 ± 0.4 and 9.8 ± 3.1 μM when using 2.5 and 50 nM PAF-acether, respectively. PAF-acether concentration-aggregation curves were established for PRP in the absence and presence of BN 52021. The effective concentrations (EC_{50}) of PAF-acether inducing half-maximal aggregation were 0.05 ± 0.02, 0.26 ± 0.08 and 2.33 ± 0.57 μM for 0, 1 and 5 μM of BN 52021, respectively. The concentration-aggregation curves were displaced to the right by BN 52021, suggesting a competitive inhibition.

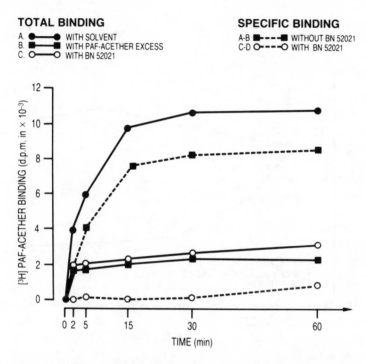

Figure 1. Inhibition by BN 52021 of the binding of [^{3}H]PAF-acether to intact washed human platelets. BN 52021 (60μM) or cold PAF-acether (50 nM) was added to the platelet suspension with 0.65 nM of radiolabeled PAF-acether. Total binding of [^{3}H]PAF-acether was measured at different time intervals in presence of an excess of cold PAF-acether, BN 52021 or its solvent. Specific binding in presence and absence of BN 52021 was calculated from these different values. Each point is the mean of duplicate determination in one experiment representative of three

BN 52021 and PAF-acether binding

Experiments were performed to analyse [^{3}H]PAF-acether binding to washed platelets in the presence of 60 μM BN52021. When the antagonist and radiolabeled PAF-acether were added concomitantly to platelets the total binding was significantly reduced when compared to the control conducted in the presence of solvent. The addition of an excess of cold PAF-acether (50 nM) in place of BN 52021 had exactly the same effect. Calculations from these data showed that BN 52021 totally suppressed the specific PAF-acether binding to platelets (Figure 1). When BN 52021 (60 μM) was added to platelets 30 min after the addition of radiolabeled PAF-acether, a displacement of the bound radiolabeled material was observed. A similar displacement was obtained with 50 nM cold PAF-acether (Figure 2).

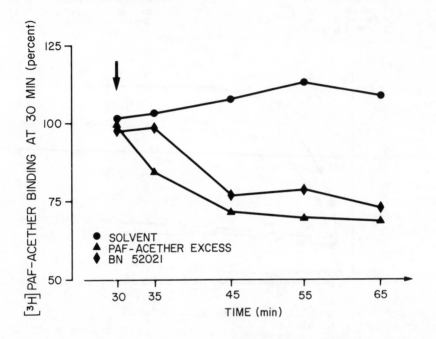

Figure 2. Displacement by BN 52021 of the binding of [³H]PAF-acether to intact washed human platelets. Experiments were conducted exactly as those described in Figure 1 except that excess cold PAF-acether (50 nM), Bn 52021 (60μM) or its solvent was added 30 min following [³H]PAF-acether addition. Each point is the mean of duplicate determination in one experiment representative of three

Specificity of BN 52021

BN 52021 used at 4.5, 22 and 220 μM was tested against concentrations of ADP and AA inducing submaximal aggregation of washed platelets. It was observed that even the highest concentration of BN 52021 had no significant effect. Similar results were obtained with PRP, i.e. no inhibition of ADP- and AA-induced aggregation by BN 52021 concentrations ranging from 0.6 to 220 μM. By contrast under the same experimental conditions, BN 52021 inhibited PAF-acether-induced aggregation with an IC_{50} of 3.3 $\pm$ 1.8 μM (Table 1).

Table 1. Inhibition by BN 52021, kadsurenone and CV 3988 of PAF-acether-induced aggregation using washed platelets and platelet-rich plasma. Comparison of the IC_{50}

| | IC_{50} (μM) | |
	Washed platelets	Platelet-rich plasma
Bn 52021	2.2 ± 0.8	3.3 ± 1.8
Kadsurenone	0.8 ± 0.4	19.6 ± 10.4
CV3988	1.0 ± 0.1	27.6 ± 9.3

Concentrations of PAF-acether inducing submaximal aggregations were 7.5 nM and 2 μM for washed platelets and platelet-rich plasma respectively.

Effects of kadsurenone and CV 3988

Kadsurenone and CV 3988, like BN 52021, inhibited PAF-acether-induced aggregation in both washed platelets and PRP (Table 1). Nevertheless as opposed to BN 52021 and kadsurenone, CV 3988 did not show a good specificity, particularly when washed platelets were used. An inhibition was thus observed against ADP and AA with IC_{50} of 10.2 ± 2.3 and 2.2 ± 0.1 μM respectively. A better specificity was obtained with PRP. Up to 30 μM no inhibition of ADP- and AA-induced aggregation could be detected. Above this concentration aggregations triggered by AA but not by ADP were affected.

PAF-acether antagonists and platelet activation

BN 52021 and kadsurenone are specific PAF-acether antagonists. Only in PRP does CV 3988 exhibit a similar property. The use of these compounds should enable one to check for a role of PAF-acether in thrombin-induced platelet activation. Thrombin concentration-aggregation curves were established in the absence and presence of 60 μM BN 52021. Although some shift to the right was observed, it was not significant even when using platelets desensitized to ADP and AA. In addition, when measuring the cytosolic free calcium in fura-2-loaded platelets, 100 μM BN 52021 did not modify the rise induced by low concentrations of thrombin (Figure 3). This data should lead one to conclude that PAF-acether plays no role in platelet activation by thrombin. Nevertheless, since the experiments were performed in presence of aspirin, it should also be concluded that the AA metabolite, thromboxane A_2, is not involved. Another possible conclusion is that the experimental models used were not adequate to unveil the participation of these mediators. A possibly more fruitful indication might be obtained by measuring the bleeding time which is prolonged upon aspirin administration *in vivo*. What is known about PAF-acether antagonist effects? The feasibility of this approach is suggested by the fact that BN 52021 is able to suppress PAF-acether-induced thrombus *in vivo* (Bourgain et al., 1985).

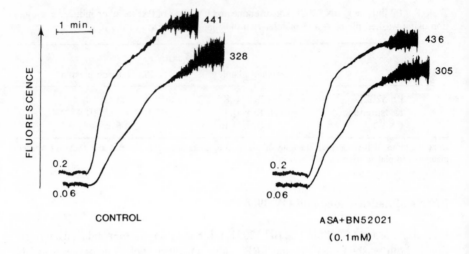

CONTROL   ASA+BN52021
                                                        (0.1mM)

Figure 3.   Effect of BN52021 on the cytosolic free calcium rise induced by thrombin in fura-2-loaded washed human platelets. Fura-2-loaded platelets were challenged with 0.06 or 0.2 IU ml^{-1} thrombin and the fluorescent signals recorded. Maximal concentrations of cytosolic free calcium reached upon activation were calculated from these signals and are indicated at the end of each tracing (expressed in nM). The values measured in resting platelets ranged between 50 and 60 nM. These tracings were obtained in one single experiment representative of three. Platelets were incubated for 5 min at 37 °C with aspirin and BN 52021 (0.1 mM both) or their solvent before additon of thrombin. These data were obtained with the collaboration of Dr M.S. Selak (Temple University)

REFERENCES

Benveniste, J., and Vargaftig, B.B. (1983). 'An ether lipid with biological activities: platelet-activating factor (PAF-acether)'. In H.K. Mangold and F. Paltauf (eds.) *Ether Lipids: Biochemical Aspects* Academic Press, New York, pp. 355–376.

Bourgain, R.H., Maes, L., Braquet, P., Andries, R., Touqui,L., and Braquet, M. (1985).'The effect of 1-O-alkyl-2-acetyl-*sn*-glycero-3-phosphocholine (PAF-acether) on the arterial wall', *Prostaglandins*, **30**, 185–197.

Chignard, M., Coeffier, E., and Benveniste, J. (1986). 'Role of PAF-acether and related ether-lipid metabolism in platelets'. In J. Westwick, M.F. Schully, D.E. McIntyre and V.V. Kakkav (eds.) *Advances in Medicine and Biology. Mechanisms of Stimulus Response Coupling in Platelets*, Plenum Press, New York, (in press).

Chignard, M., Le Couedic, J.P., Tence, M., Vargaftig, B.B., and Benveniste, J. (1979). 'The role of platelet-activating factor in platelet aggregation', *Nature*, **179**, 799–800.

Chignard, M., Le Couedic, J.P., Vargaftig, B.B., and Benveniste, J. (1980). 'Platelet-activating factor (PAF-acether) secretion from platelets: effect of aggregating agents', *Brit. J. Hematol.*, **46**, 455–464.

Grynkiewicz, G., Poenie, M., and Tsien, R.Y. (1985). 'A new generation of Ca^{2+} indicators with greatly improved fluorescent properties', *J. Biol. Chem.*, **260**, 3440–3450.

Lalau-Keraly, C., Delautier, D., Delabassee, D., Chignard, M., and Benveniste, J. (1984). 'Inhibition by ticlopidine of PAF-acether-induced *in vitro* aggregation of rabbit and human platelets', *Thromb. Res.*, **34**, 463–471.

Nunez, D., Chignard, M., Korth, R., Le Couedic, J.P., Norel, X., Spinnewyn, B., Braquet, P., and Benveniste, J. (1986). 'Specific inhibition of PAF-acether-induced platelet activation by BN 52021 and comparison with the PAF-acether inhibitors kadsurenone and CV 3988', *Eur. J. Pharmacol.*, **123**, 197–205.

Pinckard, R.N., McManus, L., Halonen, M., and Hanahan, D.J. (1981). 'Acetyl glyceryl ether phosphorylcholine: platelet-activating factor', *Int. Archs Allergy appl. Immun.*, **66**, 127–136.

Roubin, R., Tence, M., Mencia-Huerta, J.M., Arnoux, B., Ninio, E., and Benveniste, J. (1983). 'A chemically defined monokine: macrophage-derived platelet-activating factor (PAF-acether)', In E. Pick (ed.) *Lymphokines*, Academic Press, New York, pp. 249–276.

Selak, M.S., and Smith, J.B. (1986). 'Antagonism of platelet-activating factor-induced calcium mobilisation in platelets and neutrophils', (submitted).

Shen, T.Y., Hwang, S.B., Chang, N.M., Doebber, T.W., Lam, M.H.T., Wu, M.S., Xui Wang, Gui Quin Han, and Run Zhi, L.I. (1985). 'Characterization of a platelet-activating factor receptor antagonist isolated from haifenteng (Piper futokadsura). 'Specific inhibition of *in vitro* and *in vivo* platelet-activating factor-induced effects', *Proc. Natl. Acad. Sci. USA*, **82**, 672–676.

Terashita, Z.I., Tsushima, S., Yoshioka, Y., Nomura, H., Inada, Y., and Nishikawa, K. (1983). 'CV 3988, a specific antagonist of platelet-activating factor (PAF)', *Life Sci.*, **32**, 1975-1982.

Tsien, R.Y., Rink, T.J., and Poenie, M. (1985). 'Measurement of cytosolic free Ca^{2+} in individual small cells using fluorescence microscopy with dual excitation wavelengths', *Cell Calcium*, **6**, 145–157.

Vargaftig, B.B., Chignard, M., Benveniste, J., Lefort, J., and Wal, F. (1981). 'Background and present status of research on platelet-activating factor (PAF-acether)', *Ann. N.Y. Acad. Sci.*, **370**, 119–137.

Vargaftig, B.B., Chignard, M., Le Couedic, J.P., and Benveniste, J. (1980). 'One, two, three or more pathways for platelet aggregation', *Acta Med. Scand. (supplement)*, **642**, 23–29.

Pathophysiology of
Platelet Activating Factor

25

Acute Lung Injury Induced by Intravascular Platelet Activating Factor

Linda M. McManus

INTRODUCTION

The lung is a particularly sensitive target organ for the development of acute allergic and inflammatory tissue injury. Diverse etiologic agents can induce acute and/or chronic host−defense responses in the lung and activate protective inflammatory mediators and inflammatory cells. However, excessive activation or alterations of the homeostatic regulation of these inflammatory responses may result in severe tissue injury and organ dysfunction.

Unequivocal evidence for the role of any one cell or mediator in effecting acute pulmonary tissue injury is, at present, circumstantial. Indeed, it is likely that a complex series of interrelated events with interacting cells and mediator systems are involved in the pathogenesis of most pulmonary inflammatory reactions and tissue injury. Operationally, it has been difficult to elucidate the mechanism(s) by which a given inflammatory cell or mediator participates in these reactions. Nevertheless, intense research efforts to probe such interactions should provide an in-depth understanding of the molecular mechanisms by which inflammatory mediators and cells act to modulate acute and chronic lung injury. This information will undoubtedly clarify the pathogenesis and point to potential treatment of human pulmonary disorders.

In view of the above, platelet activating factor or PAF, as a relatively new and potent mediator of inflammatory reactions, also has been implicated in events associated with acute pulmonary injury and will be the focus of the following discussion.

HISTORICAL

Structural characterization of PAF as an unusual family of closely-related phospholipids (Demopoulos *et al.*, 1979; Pinckard *et al.*, 1984; Weintraub *et al.*, 1985) permitted rapid advancement of our understanding of its potent biological activities associated with allergy and inflammation. Prior to its structural identification, however, several studies had suggested that PAF was involved in systemic IgE-mediated, acute allergic reactions. First, PAF was characterized as a mediator released by antigen-stimulated, IgE-sensitized leukocytes and was detected in a bioassay based upon platelet stimulation (Henson 1970, 1976, 1977; Benveniste *et al.*, 1972). Second, intravenous antigen administration into rabbits sensitized to produce specific antibodies of only the IgE class of immunoglobulin initiated acute, but reversible, cardiovascular, pulmonary and intravascular alterations, including thrombocytopenia (Halonen and Pinckard, 1975; Halonen *et al.*, 1976). This platelet alteration occurred after intravascular platelet aggregates were sequestered in the pulmonary microvasculature (Pinckard *et al.*, 1977); additionally, after their return to the circulation, these platelets were unresponsive to further *in vitro* PAF stimulation (Henson and Pinckard, 1977). Using this same experimental animal model, PAF was isolated directly from the peripheral blood following antigen challenge (Pinckard *et al.*, 1979); further, concomitant *in vivo* platelet activation was indicated by the intravascular accumulation of platelet factor 4 (PF4) (McManus *et al.*, 1979). These observations suggested that the PAF produced following antigen challenge may have been responsible for platelet stimulation and possibly other systemic anaphylactic sequellae of this acute allergic reaction.

The above evidence for the participation of PAF in systemic IgE-mediated events was indirect, i.e. cause and effect could not be documented. However, once the chemical structure of PAF was known, this problem operationally was more approachable. Thus, the intravenous administration of PAF into normal rabbits was evaluated (Halonen *et al.*, 1980; McManus *et al.*, 1980). Direct comparisons between the effects observed following PAF infusion and those which followed antigen challenge indicated that identical intravascular, circulatory and respiratory alterations developed. Taken altogether, these results provided strong evidence that PAF was a central mediator of acute allergic reactions in rabbits. Because of both the severe hemodynamic and mechanical pulmonary alterations associated with systemic allergic reactions, more recent efforts have focused upon assessment of its role as a mediator of acute lung tissue injury.

CURRENT PERSPECTIVES

The effects of a single intravenous infusion of purified PAF (1-*O*-hexadecyl-2-acetyl-*sn*-glycero-3-phosphocholine) have now been extensively studied. As a result, the kinetics of the acute alterations associated with a 15 s bolus infusion of PAF in the rabbit have been established. Within $30-60$ s following PAF infusion, dynamic lung compliance decreases and total pulmonary resistance increases (Halonen *et al.*, 1980; Lefer *et al.*, 1984). Concomitantly, profound increased right ventricular pressure and systemic hypotension develop (Halonen *et al.*, 1980; Lefer *et al.*, 1984). During this same period ($30-120$ s), thrombocytopenia, basopenia and neutropenia occur in concert with the intravascular accumulation of PF4 and thromboxane B_2

(TxB$_2$) (McManus *et al.*, 1980, 1983; Camussi *et al.*, 1983). These severe physiological alterations are reversible with most parameters at normal levels within 60 min. Many of these effects of PAF infusion also have been observed in experimental animal models other than the rabbit including the rat, mouse, guinea pig, dog, pig and baboon (Vargaftig *et al.*, 1980; Demopoulos *et al.*, 1981; Page *et al.*, 1982; Lanara *et al.*, 1982; Bessin *et al.*, 1983; Feuerstein *et al.*, 1984; Doebber *et al.*, 1984; Kenzora *et al.*, 1984; Darius *et al.*, 1986).

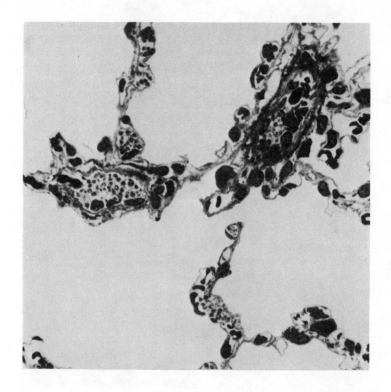

Figure 1. AGEPC-induced intravascular pulmonary platelet and neutrophil aggregation and arteriolar constriction in the rabbit. Thirty seconds following an intravenous bolus of AGEPC (0.5 μg kg^{-1}), the lungs were inflated with fixative *in situ* prior to routine processing for light and electron microscopic examination. Extensive platelet aggregates are present in the pulmonary microvasculature. Toluidine blue ($\times$ 670)

The acute thrombocytopenia induced by PAF infusion likely developed largely as a consequence of intravascular platelet aggregation, i.e. peripheral blood smears obtained within 30 s following PAF infusion frequently contained large platelet aggregates. These aggregates were then trapped within the lung microvasculature as elucidated by light and electron microscopy (Figures 1 and 2; Lewis *et al.*, 1983;

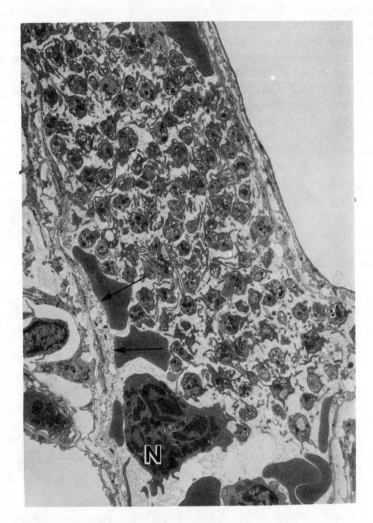

Figure 2.   Ultrastructural appearance of the pulmonary microvasculature 30 seconds after AGEPC infusion in the rabbit. All platelets have developed features associated with activation (shape change, granule centralization, pseudopodia formation, or aggregation). A neutrophil (N) also has pseudopodia. Note the swollen endothelial cell (arrows) (× 3,520)

Lellouch-Tubiana *et al.*, 1985; McManus and Pinckard, 1985). Chromium-labeled platelet studies have confirmed this preferential organ sequestration and documented that the platelets in the circulation at 60 min following PAF infusion were the same platelets which were sequestered in the pulmonary vasculature at 30 s (McManus *et al.*, 1980); interestingly, the platelet release reaction, as estimated by the significant increase in intravascular PF4 levels, occurred within seconds after the platelets were lodged in the pulmonary microvasculature. Not surprisingly, the intravascular eleva-tions in plasma TxB_2 levels also occurred simultaneously (McManus *et al.*, 1983; Lefer *et al.*, 1984). Although the origin of thromboxane remains to be established, *in vitro* studies have documented that PAF stimulates rabbit platelets to produce this arachidonic acid metabolite (McManus *et al.*, 1983), and, therefore, suggests the possible platelet derivation of this other potent lipid inflammatory mediator.

In keeping with the above, the secondary effects of platelet-derived mediators in promoting PAF-induced physiologic alterations have been suggested inasmuch as platelet depletion eliminated the pulmonary mechanical changes (decreased dynamic compliance and increased total pulmonary resistance) following PAF infusion (Halonen *et al.*, 1981). Additional support for this hypothesis was provided in studies which demonstrated that inhibition of platelet activation by the administration of prostacyclin (PGI_2) also abrogated PAF-induced lung mechanical changes (Halonen *et al.*, 1985). Since anti-histamine treatment also inhibited these lung mechanical alterations following PAF infusion, a role for platelet-derived histamine was sugges-ted (Vargaftig *et al.*, 1982; Halonen *et al.*, 1985). Of interest, the circulatory altera-tions and apnea which follow PAF infusion were not affected by these interventions (Halonen *et al.*, 1981, 1985). Thus, the combined results of the above studies indicate that PAF-mediated pulmonary alterations have a primary (hemodynamic) and plate-let-dependent (lung mechanical) component in the rabbit. Of note, these observations should not be generalized for other animals including humans since species differen-ces in platelet responsiveness to PAF stimulation are well-documented (McManus *et al.*, 1981; Cargill *et al.*, 1983; Hadvary and Baumgartner, 1983). Similarly, since platelet histamine content is diverse between species, this difference also could alter or change the character of the acute physiologic pulmonary responses to PAF.

Acute neutropenia induced by PAF infusion also was a prominent feature and likely was a result of sequestration of these cells in the pulmonary microvasculature (Fig-ures 1 and 2; Camussi *et al.*, 1983; Lewis *et al.*, 1983; Lellouch-Tubiana *et al.*, 1985; McManus and Pinckard, 1985). A reversible event, precise quantitation of this appa-rent preferential organ distribution of neutrophils after PAF administration remains to be conclusively established. Moreover, PAF-induced alterations in lung function in neutropenic animals must be evaluated. Intravascular neutrophil activation after PAF infusion also remains to be assessed. Although increased plasma levels of lysosomal hydrolases have been observed in rats following PAF infusion, the neutrophil did not appear to be the source of these enzymes since comparable amounts of lysosomal hydrolases were detected in neutropenic animals (Doebber *et al.*, 1984). The sequen-tial effects of intravascular neutrophil activation could be considerable since the neutrophils are sequestered in close proximity to the underlying pulmonary vascular endothelium. Direct stimulation of intravascular neutrophils by PAF is suggested by *in vitro* studies which have demonstrated that PAF is chemotactic for isolated human neutrophils and stimulates them to aggregate, to generate both highly reactive oxy-gen-derived free radicals and arachidonate metabolites (leukotrienes), and to release a variety of lysosomal enzymes (cf., O'Flaherty 1982). Such secondary, intravascular mediators released from PAF-activated neutrophils *in vivo* could have profound deleterious effects on the vascular endothelium and underlying structures. Indeed, focal pulmonary vascular endothelial cell alterations are observed following PAF infusion (Figure 2).

Acute pulmonary vascular alterations resulting from intravascular PAF are considerable. PAF-induced right ventricular hypertension is associated with prominent microscopic pulmonary artery vasoconstriction (McManus and Pinckard, 1985; Lellouch-Tubiana *et al.*, 1985). Whether or not this response is due to direct or secondary effects of PAF on the pulmonary vasculature remains to be established although it appears to be unaffected by chlorpheniramine but inhibited by diethylcarbamazine (Kenzora *et al.*, 1984; Halonen *et al.*, 1985). Although PAF has been shown to increase vascular permeability when injected into the skin (Humphrey *et al.*, 1982; Bjork and Smedegard, 1983; Archer *et al.*, 1984), similar effects of PAF on the pulmonary vasculature have been more difficult to document and some controversy exists (Worthen *et al.*, 1983; Heffner *et al.*, 1983; Hamasaka *et al.*, 1984). Explanations for the discrepancies in this area deserve further attention inasmuch as the development of pulmonary edema likely plays an important role in the development of lung diseases of diverse etiologies.

The acute pulmonary pathophysiologic effects of PAF infusion have now been rigorously evaluated in a variety of animal models as summarized above. However, little attention has been focused upon delayed pulmonary alterations since most measured parameters were returned to normal within 60 min. An exception of note, however, was the identification of focal, periarterial hemorrhage which occurred within 60 min following PAF infusion in the rabbit (McManus and Pinckard, 1985). In more recent investigations, the later consequences of PAF infusion have been assessed since resolution of the periarterial hemorrhage would be expected to have an additional inflammatory component (L.M. McManus, unpublished observations). These preliminary studies unexpectedly have demonstrated the accumulation of eosinophils in and around pulmonary arteries. A subendothelial distribution of eosinophils was observed within 6 h after PAF infusion (Figure 3). Subsequently, eosinophils also were prevalent within the vascular media and adventitia by 24 h (Figure 4). Maximum eosinophil deposition occurred within 24–48 h and declined thereafter. In all cases, periarterial eosinophil accumulation was focal, i.e. not all vascular intima, media, or adventitia of similarly-sized arteries were similarly involved. This pattern seemed to reflect the equally focal distribution of periarterial hemorrhage observed at 60 min following PAF infusion (McManus and Pinckard, 1985). Although the precise mediator mechanism which promotes this pulmonary eosinophil accumulation remains to be established, these initial exciting observations indicate that additional studies must be performed to further characterize these events and to assess the consequences of this late-phase inflammatory reaction upon pulmonary function. Because of the biological potential of the eosinophil and the implication of this cell in human pulmonary diseases of allergic origin, additional studies are clearly required.

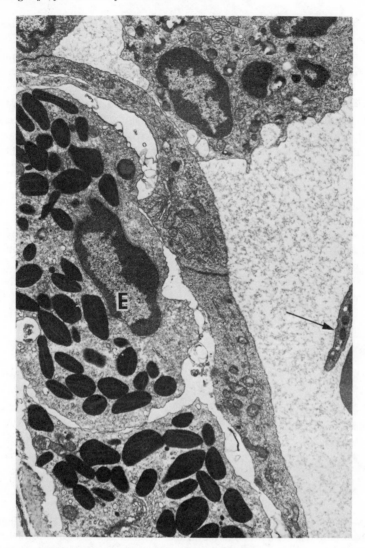

Figure 3.   Ultrastructural detail of AGEPC-induced pulmonary arterial eosinophil infiltrate in the rabbit. Six hours after intravenous AGEPC infusion (0.5 μg kg^{-1}), eosinophils (E) are present beneath the vascular endothelium. Another leukocyte is present on the luminal surface of the endothelium and a discoid platelet is nearby (arrow) ($\times$ 9,360)

FUTURE DIRECTIONS

As outlined above, a spectrum of effects are now known to follow the intravascular infusion of PAF. The pulmonary alterations induced by this potent lipid mediator are diverse but potentially of importance as they may occur in pulmonary disease. Thus, additional efforts to dissect the role of PAF in promoting acute lung injury are required. For instance, while intravascular PAF induces acute alterations, intratracheal PAF also initiates pathophysiologic events (Patterson and Harris, 1983; Denjean *et al.*, 1983). The precise mechanisms by which any of these alterations develop must be elucidated if interventions are planned. In this regard, these studies must include assessment of species variation as well as dose, route and PAF carrier effects. Certainly, an acute bolus of PAF would be expected to have a different effect in comparison to a slower, chronic infusion of PAF whether it be instilled into the airways or infused into the vasculature.

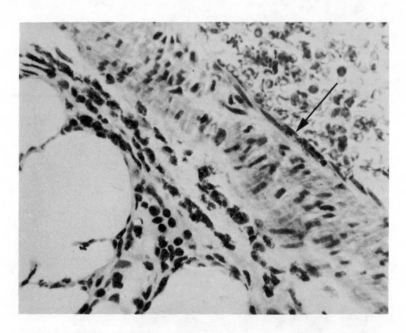

Figure 4. Light microscopic appearance of pulmonary eosinophil accumulation 24 h post-AGEPC infusion in the rabbit. Eosinophils are focally distributed beneath the vascular endothelium (arrow) and in the adjacent adventitia (× 580)

In addition to the above, studies to characterize the primary vs. secondary effects of PAF are necessary, i.e. does PAF directly promote pulmonary alterations, or does it merely initiate the generation of other biologically potent mediators which then act to cause the observed pathophysiology? Indeed, multimediator synergism may actually result in enhanced biological efficacy and may be an important mechanistic aspect of both host defense and undesired tissue injury. Because of the spectrum of secondary mediators which can be derived from activated, intravascular inflammatory cells, such primary, PAF-initiated events must be established in order to plan interventions for treatment of human disease. Similarly, the contributory roles of the various inflammatory cells including the platelet, neutrophil, eosinophil and vascular endothelial cell also must be characterized in PAF-promoted reactions.

Finally, the definition of possible sources of PAF which may target the lungs (or other organs for that matter) must be defined. For instance, during systemic IgE-mediated reactions, the lungs appear to be selectively targeted. If IgE-sensitized cells such as the circulating basophil are the primary source of PAF during this reaction, therefore, why does the lung receive the main impact of this allergic response? Does the lung serve as a first-pass target? Are PAF receptors predominantly located in the pulmonary microvasculature? Do other cells, e.g. the vascular endothelium, produce PAF during this reaction? In addition to consideration of allergic reactions, the sources of PAF during other inflammatory events also should be considered. In this regard, recent studies indicating that PAF is present in dog lung surfactant (this volume) and accumulates in bronchial alveolar lavage fluid following hypoxia (Prevost *et al.*, 1983) suggest that this mediator also is formed as a result of non-immunologic stimuli. This is particularly critical in view of the observations that alveolar macrophages produce PAF and these cells would be expected to be an important front-line host defense component.

In summary, in view of the potent biological activities of PAF, its role in the initiation of acute and possibly chronic tissue injury is suggested and definitive experiments to assess this possibility are mandated. The considerations listed above are only but a few which will be required to understand the role of PAF in promoting acute lung injury. These efforts, along with the development of specific antagonists of PAF, likely will yield therapeutic interventions designed to prevent and treat PAF-mediated pulmonary reactions as they occur in man.

ACKNOWLEDGMENTS

The author acknowledges the typing of this manuscript by Adelaida Garcia. Supported in part by USPHS Grants HL 28724 and HL 22555.

REFERENCES

Archer, C.B., Frohlich, W., Page, C.P., Paul, W., Morley, J., and MacDonald, D. M. (1984). 'Synergistic interaction between prostaglandins and PAF-acether in experimental animals and man', *Prostaglandins*, **27**, 495–501.

Benveniste, J., Henson, P.M., and Cochrane, C.G. (1972) 'Leukocyte-dependent histamine release from rabbit platelets. 'The role of IgE, basophils, and a platelet activating factor', *J. Exp. Med.*, **136**, 1356–1377

Bessin, P., Bonnet, J., Apffel, D., Soulard, C., Desgroux, L., Pelas, I., and Benveniste, J. (1983). 'Acute circulatory collapse caused by platelet-activating factor (PAF-acether) in dogs', *Eur. J. Pharmacol.*, **86**, 403–413.

Bjork, J., and Smedegard, G. (1983). 'Acute microvascular effects of PAF-acether, as studied by intravital microscopy', *Eur. J. Pharmacol.*, **96**, 87–94.

Camussi, G., Tetta, C., and Bussolino, F. (1983). 'Inhibitory effect of prostacyclin (PGI$_2$) on neutropenia induced by intravenous injection of platelet-activating factor (PAF) in the rabbit', *Prostaglandins*, **25**, 343–351.

Cargill, D.I., Cohen, D.S., Van Valen, R.G., Klimek, J. J., and Levin, R.P. (1983). 'Aggregation, release and desensitization induced in platelets from five species by platelet activating factor (PAF)', *Thrombos. Haemostas.*, **49**, 204–207

Darius, H., Lefer, D.J., Smith, J.B., and Lefer, A.M. (1986). 'Role of platelet-activating factor-acether in mediating guinea pig anaphylaxis', *Science*, **232**, 58–60.

Demopoulos, C.A., Pinckard, R.N., and Hanahan, D.J. (1979). 'Platelet-activating factor. Evidence for 1-0-alkyl-2-acetyl-*sn*-glyceryl-3-phosphorylcholine as the active component (A new class of lipid chemical mediators)', *J. Biol. Chem.*, **254**, 9355–9358.

Demopoulos, C.A., Tsabikakis, G.E., and Kapoulas, V.M. (1981). 'Intravascular pathobiology of acetyl glyceryl ether phosphorylcholine (AGEPC), a synthetic platelet-activating factor (PAF). I. Intravenous infusion in guinea pigs', *Immunol. Letters*, **3**, 133–135.

Denjean, A., Arnoux, B., Masse, R. Lockhart, A., and Benveniste, J. (1983). 'Acute effects of intratracheal administration of platelet-activating factor in baboons', *J. Appl. Physiol.*, **55**, 799-884.

Doebber, T.W., Wu, M.S., and Shen, T.Y. (1984). 'Platelet activating factor intravenous infusion in rats stimulates vascular lysosomal hydrolase secretion independent of blood neutrophils', *Biochem. Biophys. Res. Comm.*, **125**, 980–987.

Feuerstein, G., Boyd, L.M., Ezra, D., and Goldstein, R.E. (1984). 'Effect of platelet-activating factor on coronary circulation of the domestic pig', *Am. J. Physiol.*, **246**, H466–H471.

Hadvary, P., and Baumgartner, H.R. (1983). 'Activation of human and rabbit blood platelets by synthetic structural analogs of platelet activating factor', *Thrombos. Res.*, **30**, 143–156.

Halonen, M., and Pinckard, R.N. (1975). 'Intravascular effects of IgE antibody upon basophils, neutrophils, platelets and blood coagulation in the rabbit', *J. Immunol.*, **115**, 519–524.

Halonen, M., Fisher, H.K., Blair, C., Butler, C., and Pinckard, R.N. (1976). 'IgE-induced respiratory and circulatory changes during systemic anaphylaxis in the rabbit', *Amer. Rev. Resp. Dis.*, **114**, 961–969.

Halonen, M., Palmer, J.D., Lohman, I.C., McManus, L.M., and Pinckard, R.N. (1980). 'Respiratory and circulatory alterations induced by acetyl glyceryl ether phosphorylcholine (AGEPC), a mediator of IgE anaphylaxis in the rabbit', *Amer. Rev. Resp. Dis.*, **122**, 915–924.

Halonen, M., Palmer, J.D., Lohman, C., McManus, L.M., and Pinckard, R.N. (1981). 'Differential effects of platelet depletion on the cardiovascular and pulmonary alterations of IgE anaphylaxis and AGEPC infusion in the rabbit', *Amer. Rev. Resp. Dis.*, **124**, 416–421.

Halonen, M., Lohman, I.C., Dunn, A.M., McManus, L.M., and Palmer, J.D. (1985). 'Participation of platelets in the physiologic alterations of the AGEPC response and of IgE anaphylaxis in the rabbit. Effects of PGI$_2$ inhibition of platelet function', *Am. Rev. Resp. Dis.*, **131**, 11–17.

Hamasaka, Y., Mojarad, M., Saga, T., Tai, H., and Said, S.I. (1984). 'Platelet-activating factor raises airway and vascular pressures and induces edema in lungs perfused with platelet-free solution', *Am. Rev. Respir. Dis.*, **129**, 742–746.

Heffner, J.E., Shoemaker, S.A., Canham, E.M., Patel, M., McMurtry, I.F., Morris, H.G., and Repine, J.E. (1983). 'Acetyl glyceryl ether phosphorylcholine stimulated human platelets cause pulmonary hypertension and edema in isolated rabbit lungs. Role of thromboxane A$_2$', *J. Clin. Invest.*, **71**, 351–357.

Henson, P.M. (1970). 'Release of vasoactive amines from rabbit platelets induced by sensitized mononuclear leukocytes and antigen', *J. Exp. Med.*, **131**, 287–306.

Henson, P.M. (1976). 'Activation and desensitization of platelets by platelet-activating factor (PAF) derived from IgE-sensitized basophils, I. Characteristics of the secretory response', *J. Exp. Med.*, **143**, 937–951.

Henson, P.M. (1977). 'Activation of rabbit platelets by platelet-activating factor derived from IgE-sensitized basophils. Characteristics of the aggregation and its dissociation from secretion'. *J. Clin. Invest.*, **60**, 481–490.

Henson, P.M., and Pinckard, R.N. (1977). 'Basophil derived platelet activating factor (PAF) as an *in vivo* mediator of acute allergic reactions. Demonstration of specific desensitization of platelets to PAF during IgE-induced anaphylaxis in the rabbit'. *J. Immunol.*, **119**, 2179–2184.

Humphrey, D.M., McManus, L.M., Satouchi, K., Hanahan, D.J., and Pinckard, R.N. (1982). 'Vasoactive properties of acetyl glyceryl ether phosphorylcholine (AGEPC) and AGEPC analogues', *Lab. Invest.*, **46**, 422–427.

Kenzora, J.L., Perez, J.E., Bergmann, S.R., and Lange, L.G. (1984). 'Effects of acetyl glyceryl ether of phosphorylcholine (platelet-activating factor) on ventricular preload, afterload, and contractility in dogs', *J. Clin. Invest.*, **74**, 1193–1203.

Lanara, E., Vakirtzi-Lemonias, C., Kritikou, L., and Demopoulos, C.A. (1982). 'Response of mice and mouse platelets to acetyl glyceryl ether phosphorylcholine', *Biochem. Biophys. Res. Comm.*, **109**, 1148–1156.

Lefer, A.M., Muller, H.F., and Smith, J.B. (1984). 'Pathophysiological mechanisms of sudden death induced by platelet activating factor', *Br. J. Pharmacol.*, **83**, 125–130.

Lellouch-Tubiana, A., Lefort, J., Pirotzky, E., Vargaftig, B.B., and Pfister, A. (1985). 'Ultrastructural evidence for extravascular platelet recruitment in the lung upon intravenous injection of platelet-activating factor (PAF-acether) in guinea-pigs', *Br. J. Exp. Path.*, **66**, 345–355.

Lewis, J.C., O'Flaherty, J. T., McCall, C.E., Wykle, R.L., and Bond, M.G. (1983). 'Platelet-activating factor effects on pulmonary ultrastructure in rabbits', *Exp. Mole. Pathol.*, **38**, 100–108.

McManus, L.M., and Pinckard, R.N. (1985). 'Kinetics of acetyl glyceryl ether phosphorylcholine (AGEPC)-induced acute lung injury in the rabbit,' *Amer. J. Pathol.*, **121**, 55–68.

McManus, L.M., Fitzpatrick, F.A., Hanahan, D.J., and Pinckard, R.N., (1983). 'Thromboxane B$_2$ release following acetyl glyceryl ether phosphorylcholine (AGEPC) infusion in the rabbit', *Immunopharm.*, **5**, 197–207.

McManus, L.M., Hanahan, D.J., and Pinckard, R.N. (1981). 'Human platelet stimulation by acetyl glyceryl ether phosphorylcholine (AGEPC)', *J. Clin. Invest.*, **67**, 903–906.

McManus, L.M., Hanahan, D.M., Demopoulos, C.A., and Pinckard, R.N. (1980). 'Pathobiology of the intravenous infusion of acetyl glyceryl ether phosphorylcholine (AGEPC), a synthetic platelet-activating factor (PAF), in the rabbit', *J. Immunol.*, **124**, 2919-2924.

McManus, L.M., Morley, C.A., Levine, S.P., and Pinckard, R.N. (1979). 'Platelet-activating factor (PAF) induced release of platelet factor 4 (PF4) *in vitro* and during IgE anaphylaxis in the rabbit', *J. Immunol.*, **123**, 2835–2841.

O'Flaherty, J.T. (1982). 'Biology of disease. Lipid mediators of inflammation and allergy', *Lab. Invest.*, **47**, 314–329.

Page, C.P., Paul, W., and Morley, J. (1982). 'An *in vivo* model for studying platelet aggregation and disaggregation', *Thrombos. Haemostas.*, **47**, 210–213.

Patterson, R., and Harris, K.E. (1983). 'The activity of aerosolized and intracutaneous synthetic platelet activating factor (AGEPC) in rhesus monkeys with IgE-mediated airway responses and normal monkeys', *J. Lab. Clin. Med.*, **102**, 933–938.

Pinckard, R.N., Jackson, E.M., Hoppens, C., Weintraub, S.T., Ludwig, J.C., McManus, L.M., and Mott, G.E. (1984). 'Molecular heterogeneity of platelet-activating factor produced by stimulated human polymorphonuclear leukocytes', *Biochem. Biophys. Res. Comm.*, **122**, 325–332.

244New Horizons in Platelet Activating Factor Research

Pinckard, R.N., Farr, R.S., and Hanahan, D.J. (1979). 'Physicochemical and functional identity of platelet-activating factor (PAF) released in vivo during IgE anaphylaxis with PAF released in vitro from IgE sensitized basophils', J. Immunol., 123, 1847–1857.
Pinckard, R.N., Halonen, M., Palmer, J.D., Butler, C., Shaw, J.O., and Henson, P.M. (1977). 'Intravascular aggregation and pulmonary sequestration of platelets during IgE-induced systemic anaphylaxis in the rabbit. Abrogation of lethal anaphylactic shock by platelet depletion', J. Immunol., 119, 2185–2193.
Prevost, M.C., Cariven, C., Simon, M.F., Chap, H., and Douste-Blazy, L. (1983). 'Platelet-activating factor (PAF-acether) is released into rat pulmonary alveolar fluid as a consequence of hypoxia', Biochem. Biophys. Res. Comm., 119, 58–63.
Vargaftig, B.B., Lefort, J., Chignard, M., and Benveniste, J. (1980). 'Platelet-activating factor induces a platelet-dependent bronchoconstriction unrelated to the formation of prostaglandin derivatives', Eur. J. Pharmacol., 65, 185–192.
Vargaftig, B.B., Lefort, J., Wal, F., Chignard, M., and Medeiros, M.C. (1982). 'Non-steroidal anti-inflammatory drugs if combined with anti-histamine and antiserotonin agents interfere with the bronchial and platelet effects of 'platelet-activating factor' (PAF-acether)', Eur. J. Pharmacol., 82, 121–130.
Weintraub, S.T., Ludwig, J.C., Mott, G.E., McManus, L.M., Lear,. C., and Pinckard, R.N. (1985). 'Fast atom bombardment-mass spectrometric identification of molecular species of platelet-activating factor produced by stimulated human polymorphonuclear leukocytes', Biochem. Biophys. Res. Comm., 129, 868–876.
Worthen, G.S., Goins, A.J., Mitchel, B.C., Larsen, G.L., Reeves, J.R., and Henson, P.M. (1983). 'Platelet-activating factor causes neutrophil accumulation and edema in rabbit lungs'. Chest., 83, 13S–15S.

New Horizons in Platelet Activating Factor Research
Edited by C. M. Winslow and M. L. Lee
© 1987 John Wiley & Sons Ltd.

26

The Role of Platelet Activating Factor of Endothelial Origin in the Pathophysiology of the Inflammatory Reaction

G. Camussi, F. Bussolino, C. Tetta and P.R. Caldwell

INTRODUCTION

Platelet activating factor (PAF) may be regarded as an acute phase reactant in the inflammatory response. It causes aggregation of platelets (Benveniste *et al.*, 1972) and neutrophils (Camussi *et al.*, 1980, 1981; O'Flaherty *et al.*, 1981; Shaw *et al.*, 1981) and release of mediators, vasoconstriction and vasodilation (Pinckard *et al.*, 1980; Humphrey *et al.*, 1982) through a direct action on vascular smooth muscle cells (Findley *et al.*, 1981; Stimler *et al.*, 1981), enhanced vascular permeability (Humphrey *et al.*, 1982, 1984) with extravasation of plasma proteins (McManus *et al.*, 1981; Sanchez Crespo *et al.*, 1982) and edema formation, and it induces chemotaxis and granule secretion by neutrophils (O'Flaherty *et al.*, 1981; Shaw *et al.*, 1981) and monocytes (Yasaka *et al.*, 1982). Recent evidence shows that the endothelium is involved in the inflammatory response through several mechanisms. Endothelial cells metabolize vasoactive substances such as bradykinin, angiotensin, histamine and serotonin and release prostacyclin and other arachadonic acid metabolites. In addition, the endothelium binds chemotactic peptides such as C5a and has receptors for C3b, Fc and procoagulant peptides. We have found that endothelium may also release PAF both *in vivo* and *in vitro* (Camussi *et al.*, 1983a,b). Studies on endothelial cells in culture have also shown that PAF production maybe triggered by a variety of stimuli (Cammusi *et al.*, 1983a; Prescott *et al.*, 1984; McIntyre *et al.*, 1985). This report presents additional features of PAF release by endothelium and its relation to the inflammatory response.

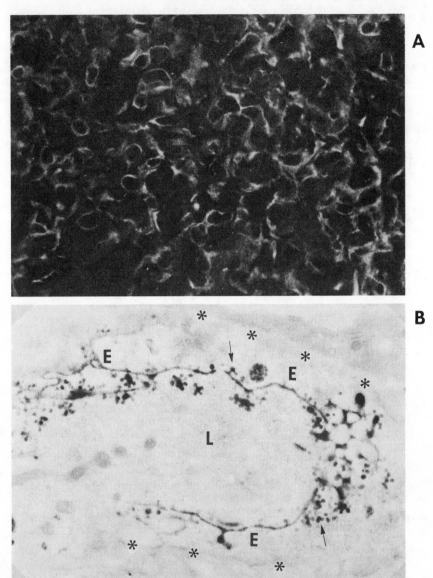

Figure 1.   A.   Immunofluorescence micrograph showing *in vitro* binding of Gt anti-Rb ACE antibodies to the alveolar capillary walls of a normal rabbit. The staining pattern resulting from the binding of the antibody to the surface of pulmonary endothelial cells is linear (× 390).
B.   Immunoelectron micrograph of lung in a rabbit injected with peroxidase-labeled Gt anti-Rb ACE antibodies as described by Barba *et al.* (1983). The reaction product is irregularly distributed along the surface of alveolar capillary endothelium (E), in endothelial caveolae (arrows), and in cytoplasmic vacuoles. (L) Lumen of the alveolar capillary. Asterisks: alveolar basement membrane (× 6,500)

Release of PAF in antibody mediated endothelial injury in two animal models

Goat antibodies to rabbit pulmonary angiotensin converting enzyme (Gt anti-Rb ACE) bind to the surface of the pulmonary endothelium and in the caveolae (Barba *et al.*, 1983; Caldwell *et al.*, 1981; Ryan *et al.*, 1976) (Figures 1A and B). The interaction *in vivo* results in aggregation of the membrane immune complexes (Figure 2A) and fixation of C3 with swelling and detachment of endothelial cells and massive accumulation of platelets and neutrophils (PMN) and deposition of fibrin in the pulmonary capillaries leading to fatal pulmonary edema (Figures 2B, 3A and B). PAF release occurs within 5 min after the intravenous administration of Gt anti-Rb ACE antibodies which initiates these events (Camussi *et al.*, 1983b). Depletion of PMN by nitrogen mustard pretreatment reduces but does not abolish PAF release, an observation consistent with PAF production by antibody stimulated pulmonary endothelium (Camussi *et al.*, 1983b).

Reduction of the dosage of Gt-anti Rb ACE antibodies permitted the study of survivors receiving several intravenous injections of antibodies and in these animals a loss of ACE from the pulmonary endothelium was documented over a period of four days by immunocytochemistry and tissue ACE activity assay (Barba *et al.*, 1983). This was presumed to result from shedding of the immune complex, an example of antigenic modulation. Over the period of four days, the PAF release decreased to become undetectable on the fourth day. Animals made tolerant to Gt IgG survived three additional weeks of injections of Gt anti-Rb ACE IgG. By way of contrast, when monovalent Gt anti-Rb ACE Fab were administered in the same protocol, there was no aggregation of endothelial membrane ACE, no deposition of C3, and no shedding of immune complexes. Yet, PAF release developed after a delay on the fourth day. Concomitantly the animals became dyspneic and died. Histologic examination revealed platelet aggregates in the pulmonary capillaries, an influx of neutrophils and numerous eosinophils with swelling of the endothelium. PAF release in this Fab model may be mainly from inflammatory cells, although a contribution by injured endothelium is not excluded (work in progress).

Transplantation of a renal allograft into a rabbit presensitized with rabbit skin allografts resulted in immediate binding of antibodies and complement to glomerular and peritubular capillary endothelium. PAF could be assayed within 5 min in the venous effluent. This was followed by an influx of platelets and subsequently PMN (Ito *et al.*, 1984) (Figure 4). The observed binding of platelet derived cationic proteins to glomerular anionic sites indicates an intravascular release of mediators from platelets. Thus PAF release occurs early in both models of divalent antibody mediated endothelial injury and may play a role in the development of inflammatory response.

PAF production by endothelial cells *in vitro*

The results of studies performed *in vitro* using cultured human endothelial cells have confirmed the ability of endothelium to produce PAF (Camussi *et al.*, 1983a; Prescott

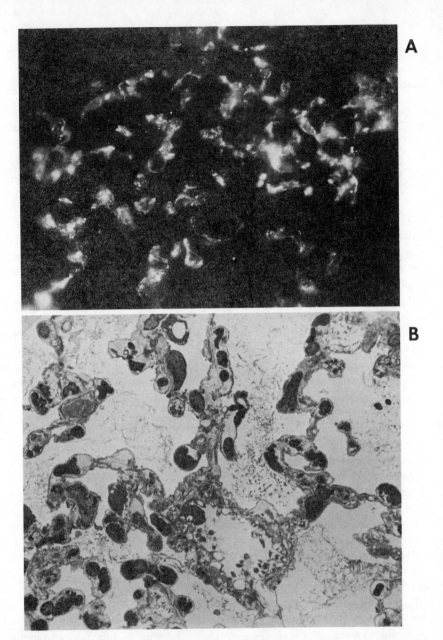

Figure 2. A. Immunofluorescence micrograph showing a granular distribution of Gt IgG along alveolar capillary walls after intravenous injection of Gt anti-Rb ACE antibodies. The redistribution of ACE immunocomplexes (analogous to patching) at the surface of the alveolar endothelial cells occurs within 5 min after the intravenous administration of the antibodies. Concomitantly PAF is released in the circulation ($\times$ 390)

B. Light micrograph of the lung in a rabbit injected with Gt anti-Rb ACE antibodies. Swelling, vacuolization and detachment of endothelial cells, intravascular accumulation of PMN and platelets and edema of alveolar septa are observed. The alveolar accumulation of proteinaceous material and fibrin is consistent with a condition of pulmonary edema ($\times$ 520)

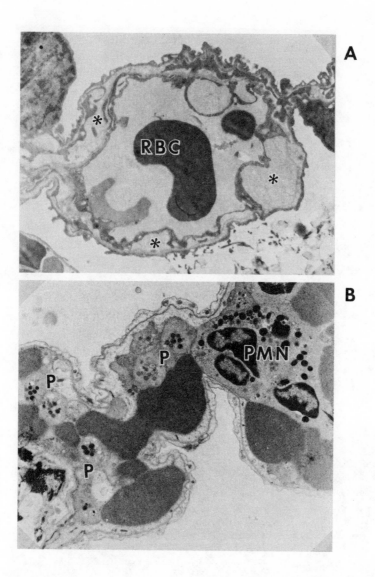

Figure 3. A. Electron micrograph of the lung of a rabbit injected with Gt anti-ACE antibodies. Swelling and detachment of the endothelium from the alveolar basement membrane with formation of endothelial blebs (asterisks) are seen. RBC: red blood cells (× 6,500)
B. Electron micrograph of the lung of a rabbit injected with Gt anti-ACE antibodies. Accumulation of platelets (P) and PMN in the lumens of alveolar capillaries (× 3,900)

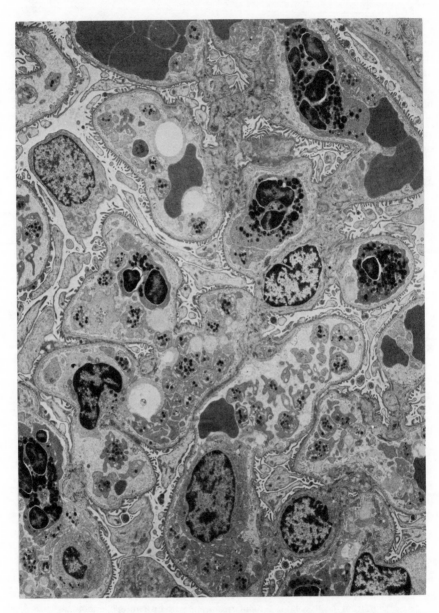

Figure 4.   Electron micrograph of a part of a glomerulus in a rabbit renal allograft undergoing hyperacute rejection; 60 min after revascularization platelets and PMN obliterate the glomerular capillaries. Intravascular PAF release is detectable within 10 min after revascularization and throughout most of the 60 min of observation (× 420)

et al., 1984). Several stimuli were found to be able to induce PAF production by endothelium. The results obtained with different stimuli vary with respect to the amount of PAF that remains associated with cells or is released into the supernatant. Thrombin as well as histamine and bradykinin have been shown to induce production of PAF, which remains mainly cell-associated without significant release into the supernatant (Prescott *et al.*, 1983; McIntyre *et al.*, 1985). However, if thrombin was added repeatedly in order to exhaust the ability of the endothelial cells to produce prostacyclin (PGI_2) or if the cells were preincubated with indomethacin which prevents the synthesis PGI_2, the release of PAF was detectable in the supernatant (Camussi *et al.*, 1983a). Other stimuli such as calcium ionophore, A23187, angiotensin II, vasopressin, and antibodies reacting with antigens expressed on the surface of endothelial cells induced not only PAF production but also release of PAF into the supernatant (Camussi *et al.*, 1983a). In spite of the difference between the amount of PAF in the supernatant of stimulated cultured endothelial cells detected by us (Camussi *et al.*, 1983a) and by McIntyre *et al.*, (1985) (a difference mainly due to the use by the latter investigators of gelatin-coated tissue culture dishes as gelatin binds PAF), at the same time it is evident that a certain amount of PAF remains associated with endothelial cells. This observation is consistent with the existence of a putative receptor for PAF on these cells or with an intracellular role of this mediator. The prolonged association of PAF with endothelium may mediate the direct interaction of these cells with platelets and inflammatory cells such as PMN and monocytes and may be a factor in rendering the vascular surface thrombogenic. In addition, these data suggest that nonimmunological stimuli generated during the inflammatory reactions contribute to the release of PAF *in vivo*.

Effects of platelet activating factor on endothelial cells in culture

PAF produces a concentration and temperature dependent increase in calcium uptake by endothelial cells in culture, accompanied by a rise in membrane associated calcium (Bussolino *et al.*, 1985). This effect was blunted by pre-exposure of the cells to PAF, consistent with deactivation by occupation of a putative PAF receptor. PAF also stimulates calcium efflux from calcium preloaded endothelial cells (Bussolino *et al.*, 1985). Thus, these effects of PAF on calcium homeostasis may provide a mechanism for influencing the calcium dependent functions of the endothelial cell cytoskeleton. Support for this hypothesis comes from the observation that after incubation with 1–100 nM PAF endothelial cells tend to round up and separate. There is disorganization of microfilaments of actin and myosin with altered distribution of these elements (work in progress). All these alterations are consistent with a contraction of endothelial cells induced by PAF.

New Horizons in Platelet Activating Factor Research

CONCLUSIONS

PAF appears to be an acute phase reactant in immunologic endothelial injury. *In vitro* it has been shown that, after appropriate stimulation, PAF is synthesized by and released from endothelium. PAF, in turn, may interfere with the cytoskeletal function of endothelium through its effects on calcium homeostasis. These observations warrant further study of the role of PAF in the inflammatory response.

ACKNOWLEDGMENTS

We are grateful to Mr Jerry Verdi for photographical assistance and to Ms Veronica Sanfilippo for typing the manuscript.

This work was supported by grant AMAI36807 of the National Institute of Arthritis, Diabetes and Digestive and Kidney Diseases, National Institute of Health, Bethesda, Maryland.

REFERENCES

Barba, L.M., Caldwell, P.R.B., Downie, G.H., Camussi, G., Brentjens, J.R., and Andres, G. (1983). 'Lung injury mediated by antibodies to endothelium. I. In the rabbit a repeated interaction of heterologous anti-angiotensin converting enzyme antibodies with alveolar endothelium results in resistance to immune injury through antigenic modulation', *J. Exp. Med.*, **158**, 2141–2158.

Benveniste, J., Henson, P.M., and Cochrane, C.G. (1972). 'Leukocyte-dependent histamine release from rabbit platelets. The role of IgE, basophils and a platelet-activating factor', *J. Exp. Med.* **136**, 1356–1377.

Bussolino, F., Aglietta M., Sanavio, F., Stacchini, A., Lauri, D., and Camussi, G. (1985). 'Alkyl-ether phosphoglycerides influence calcium fluxes into human endothelial cells', *J. Immunol.*, **135**, 2748–2753.

Caldwell, P.R.B., Wigger, J.H., Fernandez, L.T., D'Alisa, R.M., Tse-Eug, D., Butler, V.P., and Gigli, I. (1981). 'Lung injury induced by antibody fragments to angiotensin converting enzyme', *Am. J. Pathol.*, **105**, 54–64.

Camussi, G., Bussolino, F., Tetta, C., Brusca, R., and Ragni, R. (1980). 'The binding of platelet-activating factor (PAF) to polymorphonuclear neutrophils (PMN) as a trigger of immune-induced PMN aggregation', *Pan. Med.*, **22**, 1–5.

Camussi, G., Tetta, C., Bussolino, F., Caligaris-Cappio, F., Masera, C., and Segoloni, G. (1981). 'Mediators of immune complex induced aggregation of polymorphonuclear neutrophils. II. Platelet-activating factor as the effector substance of immune-induced aggregation', *Int. Arch. Allergy Appl. Immunol.*, **64**, 25–41.

Camussi, G., Aglietta, M., Malavasi, F., Tetta, C., Piacibello, W., Sanavio, F., and Bussolino, F. (1983a). 'The release of platelet-activating factor from human endothelial cells in culture', *J. Immunol.*, **131**, 2397–2403.

Camussi, G., Pawlowski, I., Bussolino, F., Caldwell, P., Brentjens, J., and Andres, G. (1983b). 'Release of platelet-activating factor in rabbits with antibody mediated injury of the lung. The role of polymorphonuclear neutrophils and pulmonary endothelial cells', *J. Immunol.*, **131**, 1802–1806.

Findley, S.R., Lichtenstein, L.M., Hanahan, D.J., and Pinckard, R.N. (1981). 'The contraction of guinea pig ileal smooth muscle by acetyl glyceryl ether phosphorylcholine", *Amer. J. Physiol.*, **241**, C, 130−133.

Humphrey, D.M., McManus, L., Satouchi, K., Hanahan, D.J., and Pinckard, R.N. (1982). 'Vasoactive properties of acetyl glyceryl ether phosphorylcholine and analogs', *Lab. Invest.*, **46**, 422−427.

Humphrey, D.M., McManus L., Hanahan,D.J., and Pinckard, R.N. (1984). 'Morphologic basis of increased vascular permeability induced by acetyl glyceryl ether phosphorylcholine', *Lab. Invest.*, **50**, 16−25.

Ito, S., Camussi, G., Tetta, C., Milgrom, F., and Andres, G. (1984). 'Hyperacute renal allograft rejection in the rabbit. The role of platelet-activating factor and of cationic proteins derived from polymorphonuclear leukocytes and from platelets', *Lab Invest.*, **51**, 148−161.

McIntyre, T.M., Zimmerman, G.A., Satoh, K., and Prescott, S.M. (1985). 'Cultured endothelial cells synthesize both platelet-activating factor and prostacyclin in response to histamine, bradykinin, and adenosine triphosphate', *J. Clin. Invest.*, **76**, 271−278.

McManus, L.M., Pinckard, R.N., Fitzpatrick, F.A., O'Rourke, R.A., Drawford, M.H., and Hanahan, D.J. (1981). Acetyl glyceryl ether phosphorylcholine. Intravascular alterations following intravenous infusion into the baboon', *Lab. Invest.*, **45**, 303−307.

O'Flaherty, J.R., Wykle, R.L., Miller, C.H., Lewis, J.C., Waite, M., Bass, D.A., McCall, C.E., and Dechatelet, L.R. (1981). '1-0-alkyl-2-acetyl-*sn*-glyceryl-3-phosphorylcholine: A novel class of neutrophil stimulants', *Am. J. Pathol.*, **103**, 70.

Pinckard, R.N., Kniker, W.T., Lee, L., Hanahan, D.J., and McManus, L.M. (1980). 'Vasoactive effect of 1-0-alkyl-2-acetyl-*sn*-glyceryl-3-phosphorylcholine (AGEPC) in human skin (abstract)', *J. Allergy Clin. Immunol.*, **65**, 196.

Prescott, S.M., Zimmerman, G.A., McIntyre, T.M. (1984). 'Human endothelial cells in culture produce platelet-activating factor (1-alkyl-2-acetyl-*sn*-glyceryl-3-phosphocholine) when stimulated with thrombin', *Proc. Natl. Acad. Sci. USA.*, **81**, 3534−3538.

Ryan, V.S., Ryan, J.W., Whitaker, C., Chiu, A. (1976). 'Localization of angiotensin converting enzyme (Kinase II). II. Immunocytochemistry and immunofluorescence', *Tissue & Cell.*, **8**, 125−135.

Sanchez Crespo, M., Alonso, F., Inarrea, P., Alvarez, V., and Egido, J. (1982). 'Vascular actions of synthetic PAF-acether (a synthetic platelet-activating factor) in the rat: evidence for a platelet independent mechanism', *Immunopharmacology.*, **4**, 173−185.

Shaw, J.O., Pinckard, R.N., Ferrigni, K.S., McManus, L., and Hanahan, D.J. (1981). 'Activation of human neutrophils with 1-0-hexadecyl octadecyl-2-acetyl-*sn*-glyceryl-3-phosphorylcholine (platelet activating factor)', *J. Immunol.*, **127**, 1250−1255.

Stimler, N.P., Bloor, C.M., Hugli, T.E., Wykle, R.L., McCall, C.E., and O'Flaherty, J.R. (1981). 'Anaphylactic actions of platelet activating factor', *Am. J. Pathol.*, **105**, 64−69.

Yasaka, T., Boxer, L.A., and Baehner, R.L. (1982). 'Monocytes aggregation and superoxide anion release in response to formylmethionyl-leucylphenylalanine (FMLP) and platelet activating factor (PAF)', *J. Immunol.*, **128**, 1939−1944.

New Horizons in Platelet Activating Factor Research
Edited by C. M. Winslow and M. L. Lee
© 1987 John Wiley & Sons Ltd.

27

Platelet Activating Factor: Effects on Human and Guinea Pig Heart Preparations

Roberto Levi, T.Y. Shen, Sam J. Yee, Donna A. Robertson,
Arturo Genovese, O. Wayne Isom and Karl H. Krieger

The remarkable cardiac depressant effects of platelet-activating factor (PAF) were first reported by Halonen and associates (1980). Upon intravenous infusion of the semisynthetic PAF, acetyl glyceryl ether phosphorylcholine (AGEPC) (Demopoulos *et al.*, 1979) in the rabbit, they noted increase in right ventricular pressure and systemic hypotension. These changes appeared both qualitatively and quantitatively indistinguishable from those which characterize IgE anaphylaxis in the rabbit. We soon discovered (Burke *et al.*, 1982a) that AGEPC depresses left ventricular contractility and coronary flow in the isolated guinea pig heart, and is equipotent with leukotriene (LT) D_4 (Burke *et al.*, 1981). PAF-induced negative inotropism and decreased coronary flow were also described by Benveniste *et al.*, (1983) in the guinea pig and by Bessin *et al.*, (1983) in the dog. Confirmation of the potent cardiac depressant effects of PAF was later obtained in the rabbit (Kenzora *et al.*, 1984) and in the dog (Kenzora *et al.*, 1984; Vemulapalli *et al.*, 1984; Sybertz *et al.*, 1985).

In humans, a dramatic fall in cardiac index, probably reflecting the negative inotropic effect of PAF, has been reported by Gateau and colleagues (1984). That PAF has direct potent negative inotropic effects on the human heart has been demonstrated in our laboratory using surgical specimens of right atrium (Robertson *et al.*, 1986). As shown in Figure 1, the human right atrial pectinate muscle preparation is highly sensitive to PAF: the threshold concentration for the negative inotropic effect of AGEPC is approximately 10 pM, the maximum effect (i.e. a 45 percent decrease in contractility) occurs at 30 nM, and the approximate ED_{50} is 0.5 nM. The de-acetylated derivative lyso-GEPC is ineffective, indicating that the 2-acetyl moiety is necessary for the effects of AGEPC on the human heart. Alloatti *et al.*, (1986) have made similar observations in surgical specimens of human papillary muscle excised from the left ventricle. Further data from our laboratory (Robertson *et al.*, 1986) indicate that the potent negative inotropic effect of PAF in the human atrial myocardium does not involve cholinergic mechanisms, is not mediated by 5-lipoxygenase metabolites, but is antagonized by drugs known to block the platelet effects of PAF such as compound CV-3988 (Terashita *et al.*, 1983, 1985) and triazolobenzodiazepines (Kornecki *et al.*, 1984).

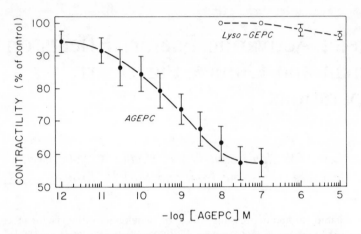

Figure 1. Effects of AGEPC and lyso-GEPC on spontaneously beating human right atrial pectinate muscles. Pectinate muscles were isolated as previously described (Guo *et al.*, 1983). Horizontal scale: concentration of AGEPC or lyso-GEPC. AGEPC and lyso-GEPC were synthesized and purified by Pinckard and associates, as previously described (Demopoulos *et al.*, 1979). Points represent maximum changes in contractility from control before AGEPC or lyso-GEPC (means ± S.E.M., $n = 5-6$)

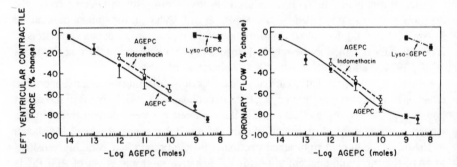

Figure 2. Effects of AGEPC and lyso-GEPC on isolated guinea-pig hearts perfused at constant pressure. AGEPC or lyso-GEPC was injected intra-aortically. AGEPC was administered in the absence or presence of indomethacin (1 μg ml^{-1}). Horizontal scale: dose of AGEPC or lyso-GEPC. Left panel: maximum percent change in left ventricular contractile force from control period before AGEPC. Right panel: maximum percent change in coronary flow. Points represent means (± S.E.M., $n = 4-5$ hearts). Reproduced from Levi *et al.*, 1984, by permission of the American Heart Association Inc.

Given the prominent cardiac effects of PAF (Burke *et al.*, 1981; Benveniste *et al.*, 1983; Bessin *et al.*, 1983) and its major role in immediate hypersensitivity (Pinckard *et al.*, 1982), we questioned whether PAF may be a mediator of cardiac anaphylaxis. Accordingly we:

1. Quantified the effects of PAF in the isolated heart from non-sensitized guinea pigs.
2. Ascertained its release during anaphylaxis.
3. Assessed whether cardiac PAF is released in functionally relevant quantities (Levi *et al.*, 1984).

As shown in Figure 2, in the isolated guinea pig heart perfused at constant pressure, a bolus intracoronary injection of 100 fmole AGEPC caused an approximate 20 percent decrease in left ventricular contractile force and an approximate 30 percent decrease in coronary flow rate. The dose-dependent decrease in contractility and flow reached a maximum of about 85 percent with 3 nmole AGEPC. The approximate ED_{50} was 3 pmole. AGEPC also caused conduction arrhythmias, ranging from second degree atrioventricular conduction block at the low doses, to complete atrioventricular dissociation at the high ones. The larger the dose of AGEPC, the longer the duration of the arrhythmia (Figure 3). On the contrary, the de-acetylated derivative of AGEPC, lyso-GEPC, which is devoid of any other known biological activity (Pinckard *et al.*, 1982), had negligible effects on flow and contractility and caused no arrhythmias (see Figures 2 and 3).

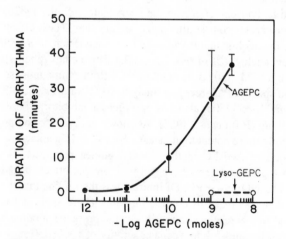

Figure 3. Arrhythmogenic effects of AGEPC on isolated guinea-pig hearts perfused at constant pressure. Arrhythmias include second-degree atrioventricular block and/or complete dissociation. Same experiments as in Figure 2.

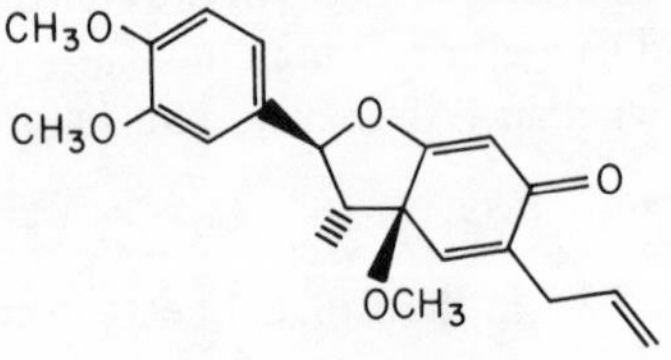

KADSURENONE

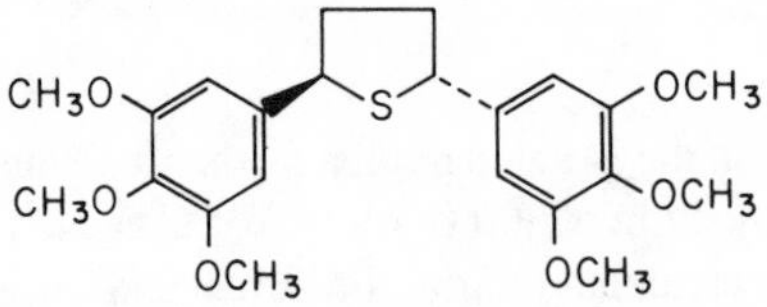

COMPOUND L-653,150

Figure 4. Structures of kadsurenone and
compound L-653,150

   The PAF-induced decrease in myocardial contractility and coronary flow in the
guinea pig heart is most probably a primary phenomenon, i.e. not mediated by arachidonate metabolites with negative inotropic and coronary vasoconstricting effects.
Indeed, neither indomethacin (see Figure 2), nor compound FPL 55712 (Levi *et al.*,
1984), at concentrations which effectively block prostaglandin synthesis (Allan and
Levi, 1981) and leukotriene effects in the heart (Burke *et al.*, 1982b), modified the
effects of PAF on cardiac contractility and coronary flow. These effects were however
antagonized by the neolignan derivative kadsurenone (Shen *et al.*, 1985) and by the
synthetic lignan analog (DL)-*trans*-2,5-bis(3,4,5-trimethoxyphenyl)tetrahydrothio-
phene, compound L-653,150 (Biftu *et al.*, 1986). Both compounds (see Figure 4) are
competitive and specific PAF-receptor antagonists (Hwang *et al.*, 1985; Biftu *et al.*,
1986). Compound L-653,150 is also a 5-lipoxygenase inhibitor, whereas kadsurenone
has no such activity (Biftu *et al.*, 1986). As shown in Figure 5, compound L-653,150
(1 μM) was slightly more potent than kadsurenone (1 μM) in antagonizing the cardiac
depressant effects of AGEPC in the isolated guinea pig heart. Both compounds
antagonized to a greater extent the negative inotropic effect than the decrease in
coronary flow caused by AGEPC. Of interest was the finding that the 20 ng dose of
AGEPC caused no decrease in contractility in the presence of kadsurenone, but
actually induced an increase in contractility in the presence of compound L-653,150.
It is unlikely that the anti-5-lipoxygenase activity of L-653,150 may account for its
greater antagonism of PAF's cardiac effects as compared with kadsurenone. Indeed,
as already mentioned, leukotrienes do not mediate the cardiac effects of PAF, since
PAF's effects on the guinea pig heart are not affected by compound FPL 55712 (Levi
et al., 1984).

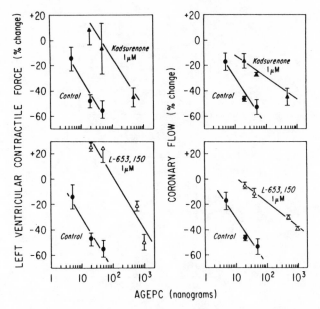

Figure 5. Dose–response relationships for the effects of AGEPC on left ventricular contractile force and coronary flow rate in isolated guinea-pig hearts perfused at constant pressure in the absence or presence of kadsurenone (1 μM) or compound L-653,150 (1 μM). Each point (mean ± S.E.M., n = 3–4 hearts)

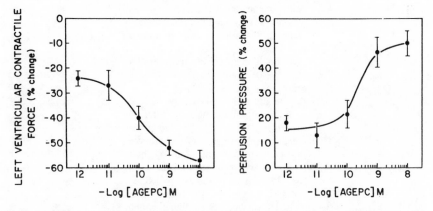

Figure 6. Effects of AGEPC on isolated guinea pig hearts perfused at constant flow. The flow rate was adjusted to yield the same perfusion pressure as in Figure 2. The indicated concentration of AGEPC was perfused through the heart for 10 min, followed in turn by the next higher concentration. Left panel: left ventricular contractile force during AGEPC perfusion, maximum percent change from control. Right panel: coronary perfusion pressure during AGEPC perfusion, maximum percent change from control. Points represent means (± S.E.M., n = 6 hearts). Reproduced from Levi *et al.*, 1984, with permission of the American Heart Association Inc.

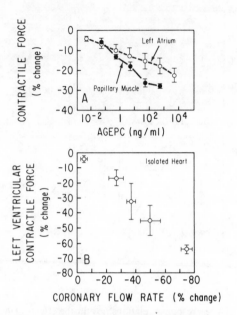

Figure 7.   A.   Concentration−respon-
se curves for the negative inotropic
effect of AGEPC on the electrically
paced left atrium and right ventricular
papillary muscle of the guinea-pig. Each
point (mean ± S.E.M., n = 3−6)
represents the maximum decrease in
contractility at each concentration of
AGEPC (data from Levi *et al.*, 1984).
Please note that AGEPC concentrations
of $10^{-2}-10^4$ ng ml^{-1} correspond to concentrations of 20 pM 20 μM^{-1}.
B.   Relationship between the decrease
in left ventricular contractile force and
in coronary flow rate in isolated guinea-
pig hearts perfused at constant pressure.
AGEPC was administered by bolus
intracoronary injections of 5 pg−1.5 μg
(i.e. $10^{-14}-3\times10^{-9}$ moles). Maximum
decreases in contractility (ordinate) are
plotted against corresponding maximum
decreases in coronary flow (abscissa).
Same experiments as in Figure 2.

Because the administration of AGEPC into the Langendorff heart perfused at constant pressure caused a decrease in both contractility and coronary flow, we evaluated
the possiblity that the decrease in contractility might be secondary to the decrease in

coronary flow. For this, we studied the effects of AGEPC in the isolated guinea pig heart perfused at constant flow. As shown in Figure 6, AGEPC caused a decrease in left ventricular contractile force and an increase in perfusion pressure as a function of its concentration. Thus, it is clear that AGEPC decreased contractility independently of coronary flow changes, since the flow was maintained constant. On the other hand, the increase in perfusion pressure observed in hearts perfused at constant flow, suggested that AGEPC increased coronary vascular resistance. Because this could have produced regional shunting and ischemia, which may have contributed to arrhythmias and negative inotropism, we assessed the effects of AGEPC in the electrically paced, isolated left atrium and right ventricular papillary muscle of the guinea pig (Levi *et al.*, 1984). In these preparations, changes in contractility are totally independent of changes in sinus rate and coronary flow. As a function of its concentration, AGEPC caused a negative inotropic effect in the left atrium and the right papillary muscle (Figure 7A). Again, lyso-GEPC had negligible effects (Levi *et al.*, 1984). As shown in Figure 7B, a linear correlation exists between the decrease in left ventricular contractile force and the decrease in coronary flow caused by AGEPC in isolated guinea pig hearts perfused at constant pressure. Further, it is apparent that the decrease in contractility in the left atrium and papillary muscle reaches a maximum of 20–30 percent, as compared with an approximate 65 percent decrease in the whole heart. Thus, it is probable that in the whole heart, as well as *in vivo*, the direct negative inotropic effect of PAF is amplified by local ischemia possibly resulting from the increase in coronary vascular resistance. This reasoning probably applies also to LTC_4, and in part to PGD_2, other mediators of immediate hypersensitivity (Anhut *et al.*, 1978; Levi *et al.*, 1985; Hattori and Levi, 1986). However, although the cardiac effects of PAF resemble those of sulfidopeptide leukotrienes and vasoconstricting prostaglandins, and although PAF is known to induce the release of thromboxane (Tx) A_2 and leukotrienes in other organs (McManus *et al.*, 1980, 1983; Voelkel *et al.*, 1982), our evidence suggests that the effects of PAF on the heart are not mediated by arachidonate metabolites.

Because PAF had potent primary cardiac depressant effects, closely resembling the contractile failure and decreased coronary flow which characterize cardiac anaphylaxis, the question arose whether PAF is produced during cardiac anaphylaxis, and—if so—in amounts sufficient to account for the observed contractile failure, reduction in coronary flow and arrhythmias. We found that during anaphylaxis in the isolated guinea pig heart, a PAF is released into the coronary effluent which has physicochemical and functional properties identical to AGEPC (Levi *et al.*, 1984). As shown in Figure 8, both histamine and PAF were released into the coronary effluent during the anaphylactic crisis. Whereas histamine release reached a maximum within 2 min after antigen and declined rapidly, PAF release was maximal between 4 and 6 min after antigen and declined slowly thereafter. Changes in functional parameters following antigen included (Figure 8): tachycardia, arrhythmias, a prolonged decrease in left ventricular contractile force and coronary flow. Histamine, a potent positive chronotropic and arrhythmogenic agent, is most probably responsible for the tachycardia and arrhythmias (Wolff and Levi, 1986). It is likely that sufficient PAF is released during cardiac anaphylaxis to account for the observed contractile failure and reduction in coronary flow. Indeed, given the coronary flow rates during anaphylaxis, the concentration of PAF in the cardiac effluent approximated 14–20 pM (Levi *et al.*, 1984). This concentration of AGEPC administered continuously at constant flow induced significant reduction in left ventricular contractility and increase in perfusion pressure (See Figure 6). Thus, it appears that the quantity of PAF released from the heart during anaphylaxis is sufficient to cause cardiac dysfunction, although it may not be sufficient to account entirely for the decrease in contractility and coronary flow. Moreover, we probably underestimated the total amount of PAF synthesized at the sites of action within the myocardium, since significant amounts of this phospholipid may have become tightly bound and retained within the myocardium.

As already mentioned, several other mediators with effects similar to PAF are released during cardiac anaphylaxis and each and all contribute to the derangement in cardiac function (Figure 9) (Levi *et al.*, 1982, 1984, 1985; Wolff and Levi, 1986). Following an antigen–antibody reaction, histamine is promptly released, and tachycardia and arrhythmias ensue (see Figures 8 and 9). After a short delay, PAF, leukotrienes and prostaglandins are generated, causing a marked decrease in coronary flow and a protracted negative inotropic effect. TxA_2 is another major contributor to anaphylactic coronary vasoconstriction (Allan and Levi, 1981). The metabolites of arachidonic acid interact with histamine by modulating its release and its effects (Levi *et al.*, 1982). Leukotrienes potentiate and prolong the tachyarrhythmic effects of histamine (Levi *et al.*, 1980; Burke *et al.*, 1982b), whereas PGE_2 attenuates these effects. In addition, PGE_2 could increase, and PGD_2 decrease, the quantity of histamine released from the anaphylactic heart (Allan and Levi, 1980). Thus an intricate interrelationship exists between the various mediators of immediate hypersensitivity. In all likelihood, PAF is a major participant in this interplay of mediators, and either modulates or is modulated by the other autacoids. Indeed, LTD_4 and PAF have been shown to potentiate each other's effects on the primate lung (Patterson *et al.*, 1984), whereas PGD_2 has been reported to inhibit PAF-induced human platelet activation (Bushfield *et al.*, 1985).

Further, it is important to appreciate that during the course of systemic anaphylactic reactions, the heart becomes the target of mediators released intracardially (Capurro and Levi, 1975), as well as of mediators reaching the left side of the heart from the lung (Zavecz and Levi, 1977). Thus, anaphylactic cardiac dysfunction results from a double immunological insult, both cardiac and pulmonary. Future research will eventually determine the extent of the contributory role of PAF to cardiac anaphylaxis and will define the nature of its interactions with the other mediators.

In conclusion, PAF is one of the most potent negative inotropic agents in animals and humans. The cardiac effects of PAF are primary and direct. Indeed, in the guinea pig as well as in the human heart, PAF effects do not require the presence of platelets and are not secondary to the concomitant decrease in coronary flow. Furthermore, although the cardiac effects of PAF resemble those of leukotrienes and certain

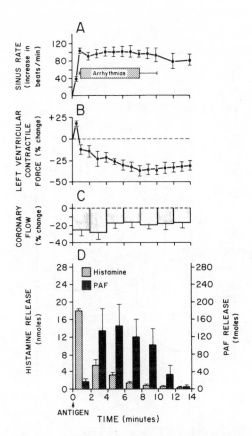

Figure 8. Changes in cardiac function and release of two mediators (histamine and PAF) during cardiac anaphylaxis. All values represent means (± S.E.M.) from seven hearts passively sensitized *in vivo* with guinea-pig anti-DNP-BGG and challenged *in vitro* with DNP-BSA (antigen) at time = 0.

A and B. Change in rate (A) and ventricular contractility (B) at the time indicated, compared with the control period preceding antigenic challenge. Inset in A. Ends of shaded bar indicate time of onset and termination of arrhythmias (second and third-degree A-V block and idioventricular rhythms). C. Changes in average coronary flow rate during 2-minute intervals compared with control period. D. Release of histamine and PAF into the coronary effluent during 2 min intervals following challenge. Reproduced from Levi *et al.*, 1984, by permission of the American Heart Association Inc.

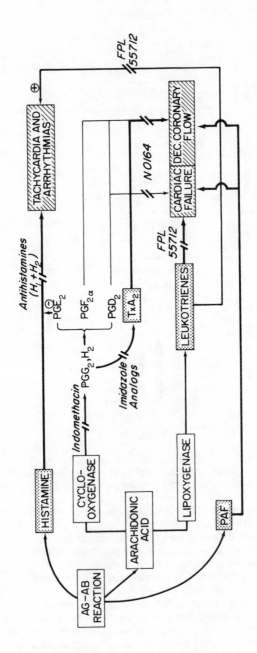

Figure 9. Proposed scheme for the actions and interactions among various mediators of cardiac anaphylaxis

prostaglandins, PAF's effects do not depend on the release of these mediators, and are specifically antagonized by drugs known to block the platelet effects of PAF. The availability of molecules which specifically antagonize the effects of PAF will certainly allow a better understanding of the actions of this potent autacoid and perhaps facilitate the uncovering of new pathophysiological implications.

ACKNOWLEDGMENTS

We wish to thank Dr R. Neal Pinckard for the gift of AGEPC and Drs S.-B. Hwang and T.W. Doebber for helpful suggestions. Ms I.L. Stellaccio provided excellent secretarial assistance.

Supported by NIH Grants HL 34215 and 18828; by a PMAF predoctoral fellowship; by a NATO-CNR Fellowship and by E.N. Dana-Charitable Trust.

REFERENCES

Allan, G., and Levi, R. (1980). 'Pharmacological studies on the role of prostaglandins in cardiac hypersensitivity reactions'. In A. Scriabine, A.M. Lefer and F.A. Kuehl, Jr., (eds.) *Prostaglandins and Renal Function*, Spectrum Publications, Inc., New York, pp. 223–237.

Allan, G., and Levi, R. (1981). 'Thromboxane and prostacyclin release during cardiac immediate hypersensitivity reactions *in vitro*', *J. Pharmacol. Exp. Ther.*, **217**, 157–161.

Alloatti,G., Montrucchio,G., Mariano,F., Tetta, C., De Paulis, R., Morea, M., Emanuelli, G., and Camussi, G. (1986). 'Effect of platelet-activating factor (PAF) on human cardiac muscle', *Int. Archs. Allergy Appl. Immunol.*, **79**, 108–112.

Anhut, H., Bernauer, W., and Peskar, B.A. (1978). 'Pharmacological modification of thromboxane and prostaglandin release in cardiac anaphylaxis', *Prostaglandins*, **15**, 889–900.

Benveniste, J., Boullet, C., Brink, C., and Labat, C. (1983). 'The actions of PAF-acether (platelet-activating factor) on guinea-pig isolated heart preparations', *Br. J. Pharmacol.*, **80**, 81–83.

Bessin, P., Bonnet, J., Apffel, D., Soulard, C., Desgroux, L., Pelas, I., and Benveniste, J. (1983). 'Acute circulatory collapse caused by platelet-activating factor (PAF-acether) in dogs', *Eur. J. Pharmacol.*, **86**, 403–413.

Biftu, T., Gamble, N.F., Hwang, S.-B., Chabala, J.C., Doebber, T. W., Dougherty, H.W., and Shen, T.Y. (1986). 'L-653,150 a dual inhibitor of 5-lipoxygenase and platelet-activating factor', *Adv. Prostaglandins, Thromboxane and Leukotriene Res.*, (in press).

Burke, J.A., Levi, R., and Corey, E. (1981). 'Cardiovascular effects of pure synthetic leukotrienes C and D', *Fed. Proc.*, **40**, 1015.

Burke, J.A., Levi, R., Hanahan, D.J., and Pinckard, R.N. (1982a). 'Cardiac effects of acetyl glyceryl ether phosphorylcholine', *Fed. Proc.*, **41**, 823.

Burke, J.A., Levi, R., Guo, Z.-G., and Corey, E. (1982b). 'Leukotrienes C_4, D_4 and E_4: Effects on human and guinea-pig cardiac preparations *in vitro*', *J. Pharmacol. Exp. Ther.*, **221**, 235–241.

Bushfield, M., McNichol, A., and MacIntyre, D. E. (1985). 'Inhibition of platelet-activating-factor-induced human platelet activation by prostaglandin D_2 *Biochem. J.*, **232**, , 267–271.

Capurro, N., and Levi, R. (1975). 'The heart as a target organ in systemic allergic reactions', *Circulation Res.*, **36**, 520–528.

Demopoulos, C.A., Pinckard, R.N., and Hanahan, D.J. (1979). 'Platelet-activating factor, evidence for 1-0-alkyl-2-acetyl-*sn*-glyceryl-3-phosphorylcholine as the active component (a new class of lipid chemical mediators)', *J. Biol. Chem.*, **254**, 9355−9358.

Gateau, O., Arnoux, B., Deriaz, H., Viars, P., and Benveniste, J. (1984). 'Acute effects of intratracheal administration of PAF-acether (Platelet-activating factor) in humans', *Amer. Rev. Respir. Dis.*, **129**, A3.

Guo, Z.-G., Levi, R., Aaronson, L.M., and Gay, W.A. (1983). 'The isolated human pectinate muscle: a reliable preparation of human cardiac tissue', *J. Pharmacol. Meth.*, **9**, 127−135.

Halonen, M., Palmer, J.D., Lohman, I.C., McManus, L.M., and Pinckard, R.N. (1980). 'Respiratory and circulatory alterations induced by acetyl glyceryl ether phosphorylcholine, a mediator of IgE anaphylaxis in the rabbit', *Amer. Rev. Resp. Dis.*, **122**, 915−924.

Hattori, Y., and Levi, R. (1986). 'Effect of PGD_2 on cardiac contractility: a negative inotropism secondary to coronary vasoconstriction conceals a primary positive inotropic action', *J. Pharmacol. Exper. Ther.*, **237**, 719−724.

Hwang, S.-B., Li, C.-L., Lam, M.-H., and Shen, T.Y. (1985). 'Characterization of cutaneous vascular permeability induced by platelet-activating factor in guinea pigs and rats and its inhibition by a platelet-activating factor receptor antagonist', *Laboratory Investign.*, **52**, 617−630

Kenzora, J.L., Perez, J.E., Bergmann, S.R., and Lange, L.G. (1984). 'Effects of acetyl glyceryl ether of phosphorylcholine (platelet-activating factor) on ventricular preload, afterload, and contractility in dogs', *J. Clin. Investign.*, **74**, 1193−1203.

Kornecki, E., Ehrlick, Y.H., and Lenox, R.H. (1984). 'Platelet-activating factor-induced aggregation of human platelets specifically inhibited by triazolobenzodiazepines', *Science.*, **226**, 1454−1456.

Levi, R., Burke, J.A., Holland, B.A., and Green, F. J. (1980). 'Immediate hypersensitivity reactions of the heart: reduction of tachycardia and arrhythmias by the SRS-A antagonist FPL 55712', *Immunopharmacol.*, **2**, 173−176.

Levi, R., Burke, J.A., and Corey, E. (1982). 'SRS-A, leukotrienes, and immediate hypersensitivity reactions of the heart'. In B. Samuelsson and R. Paoletti, (eds.) *Leukotrienes and Other Lipoxygenase Products*, Raven Press, New York, pp. 215−222.

Levi, R., Burke, J.A., Guo, Z.-G., Hattori, Y., Hoppens, C.M., McManus, L.M., Hanahan, D.J., and Pinckard, R.N. (1984). 'Acetyl glyceryl ether phosphorylcholine (AGEPC): A putative mediator of cardiac anaphylaxis in the guinea pig', *Circulation Res.*, **54**, 117−124.

Levi, R., Hattori, Y., Burke, J.A., Guo, Z.-G., Hachfeld del Basso, U., Scott, W. A., and Rouzer, C.A. (1985). 'Leukotriene C_4 is released from the anaphylactic heart: a case for its direct negative inotropic effect'. In J.M. Bailey (ed.) *Prostaglandins, leukotrienes, and lipoxins: Biochemistry, Mechanisms of Action and Clinical Applications*, Plenum Press, New York, pp.275−288.

McManus, L.M., Hanahan, D.J., Demopoulos, C.A., and Pinckard, R.N. (1980). 'Pathobiology of the intravenous infusion of acetyl glyceryl ether phosphorylcholine (AGEPC), a synthetic platelet-activating factor (PAF), in the rabbit', *J. Immunol.*, **124**, 2919−2924.

McManus, L.M., Fitzpatrick, F.A., Hanahan, D.J., and Pinckard, R.N. (1983). 'Thromboxane $B_2(TxB_2)$ release following acetyl glyceryl ether phosphorylcholine (AGEPC) infusion in the rabbit', *Immunopharmacol.*, **5**, 197−207.

Patterson, R., Bernstein, P.R., Harris, K.E., and Krell, R.D. (1984). 'Airway responses to sequential challenges with platelet-activating factor and leukotriene D_4 in Rhesus monkeys', *J. Lab. Clin. Med.*, **104**, 340−345.

Pinckard, R.N., McManus, L.M., and Hanahan, D.J. (1982). 'Chemistry and biology of acetyl glyceryl ether phosphorylcholine (platelet-activating factor)'. In G. Weissmann (ed.) *Adv. Inflammation Res.*, Raven Press, New York, Vol.4, pp. 147−180.

Robertson, D.A., Levi, R., Genovese, A., Krieger, K.H., and Isom, O.W. (1986). 'Negative inotropic effects of platelet-activating factor in human myocardium: a pharmacological study', *Fed. Proc.*, **45**, 685.

Shen, T.Y., Hwang, S.-B., Chang, M.N., Doebber, T.W., Lam, M.-H. T., Wu, M.S., Wang, X., Han, G.Q., and Li, R.Z. (1985). 'Characterization of a platelet-activating factor receptor antagonist isolated from haifenteng (*Piper Futokadsura*): Specific inhibition of *in vitro* and *in vivo* platelet-activating factor-induced effects', *Proc. Natl. Acad. Sci. (USA)*, **82**, 672–676.

Sybertz, E.J., Watkins, R.W., Baum,T., Pula, K., and Rivelli, M. (1985). 'Cardiac, coronary and peripheral vascular effects of acetyl glyceryl ether phosphorylcholine in the anesthetized dog', *J. Pharmacol. Exp. Ther.*, **232**, 156–162.

Terashita, Z.-I., Tsushima, S., Yoshioka, Y., Nomura, H., Inada, Y. and Nishikawa, K. (1983). 'CV-3988 — A specific antagonist of platelet activating factor (PAF)', *Life Sciences*, **32**, 1975–1982.

Terashita, Z.-I., Imura, Y., and Nishikawa, K. (1985). 'Inhibition by CV-3988 of the binding of ^{3}H-platelet-activating factor (PAF) to the platelet', *Biochem. Pharmacol.*, **34**, 1491–1495.

Vemulapalli, S., Chiu, P.J.S., and Barnett, A. (1984). 'Cardiovascular and renal action of platelet-activating factor in anesthetized dogs', *Hypertension*, **6**, 489–493.

Voelkel, N.F., Worthen, S., Reeves, J.T., Henson, P.M., and Murphy, R.C. (1982). 'Nonimmunological production of leukotrienes induced by platelet-activating factor', *Science*, **218**, 286–288.

Wolff, A.A., and Levi, R. (1986). 'Histamine and cardiac arrhythmias', *Circulation Res.*, **58**, 1–16.

Zavecz, J.H., and Levi, R. (1977). 'Separation of primary and secondary cardiovascular events in systemic anaphylaxis', *Circulation Res.*, **40**, 15–19.

New Horizons in Platelet Activating Factor Research
Edited by C. M. Winslow and M. L. Lee
© 1987 John Wiley & Sons Ltd.

28

Parasympathetic Action of Platelet Activating Factor in Lung

Norma P. Stimler-Gerard

INTRODUCTION

The ether phospholipid derivative, PAF (1-0-alkyl-2-0-acetyl-*sn*-glycero-3-phosphoryl-choline) is a novel and potent anaphylactoid mediator (Henson, 1969, 1970; Siraganian and Osler, 1971; Benveniste *et al.*, 1972). In addition to its actions on circulatory cells (reviewed in O'Flaherty and Wykle, 1983) and its ability to enhance vascular permeability in human and guinea-pig skin (Pinckard *et al.*, 1980; Stimler *et al.*, 1981), PAF contracts isolated preparations of smooth muscle-containing tissues, including the guinea-pig ileum, parenchymal tissues from guinea-pig, rat, rabbit and human lung (Stimler *et al.*, 1981; Findlay *et al.*, 1981; Stimler and O'Flaherty, 1983; Camussi *et al.*, 1983; Stimler *et al.*, 1983) and canine trachea in situ (Leff *et al.*, 1986).

In the guinea-pig, contractile responses of isolated lung parenchymal tissues induced by PAF are independent of platelets and neutrophils (Stimler and O'Flaherty, 1983; Lefort *et al.*, 1984). PAF releases significant quantities of thromboxane A_2 but no detectable histamine or leukotrienes from guinea-pig lung tissues (Stimler and O'Flaherty, 1983). However, since pretreatment with indomethacin inhibits only the rate of contraction and has no effect on the magnitude of the response, it appears that thromboxane release plays a role only in the early phase of the contraction. These findings led us to consider a number of other potential mechanisms by which PAF might stimulate contractions of isolated guinea-pig lung tissues. The current report describes studies using inhibitors of parasympathetic responses. Both atropine and the neurotoxin, tetrodotoxin, are shown to block a component of PAF-induced contractions, and the data demonstrate parasympathetic as well as potentially direct mechanisms for PAF-induced contractile responses in the lung.

METHODS

Reagents and buffers

Acetylcholine chloride, atropine sulfate, hexamethonium bromide, histamine phosphate, indomethacin, physostigmine, and tetrodotoxin were obtained from Sigma Chemical Co., St Louis, MO. Synthetic PAF (1-0-hexadecyl-2-0-acetyl-rac-3-phosphocholine) was a generous gift of Dr Robert L. Wykle, Department of Biochemistry, Bowman Gray School of Medicine, Winston-Salem, NC. Leukotrienes C_4 and D_4 were obtained from Dr J. Rokach, Merck Frosst, Canada, Inc., Dorval, Quebec. PGF_{2a} was obtained from Upjohn, Kalamazoo, MI, and the thromboxane A_2 analog, U-46619 was obtained from Cayman Chemical Co., Ann Arbor, MI. The buffer used throughout the experiments was a modified Tyrode's solution, pH 7.4 (Brocklehurst, 1978). PAF was stored in methanol at -20 °C under nitrogen. Before use it was dried under nitrogen and redissolved in Tyrode's buffer containing 0.25 percent BSA at concentrations such that addition of 10 μl to the organ bath (2 ml) resulted in the desired PAF concentration and a fixed amount of BSA (1.25 μg ml^{-1}). Control experiments using BSA alone showed that it did not produce any of the responses observed. All other agonists were similarly diluted into the tissue bathing fluid from concentrated stock solutions. Studies of the effects of antagonists on subsequent responses to PAF or other agonists were performed by diluting the antagonist into the tissue bathing fluid 10 min prior to addition of agonist. Concentrated solutions of indomethacin in DMSO were prepared daily and diluted into the tissue bathing fluid so that the DMSO concentration did not exceed 0.1 percent. This quantity of DMSO had no effect on the tissue responses studied.

Tissue preparations

Guinea pig lung parenchymal strips were prepared from lungs perfused with Tyrode's buffer as previously described (Stimler et al., 1981). Tissues were mounted in organ baths filled with Tyrode's buffer at 37 °C, aerated with 95 percent O_2, 5 percent CO_2, and were attached to force displacement transducers (FT03C; Grass Instrument Co., Quincy, MA) under a resting tension of 300 mg. Tissues were equilibrated for 20–60 min at this tension, and contractile responses stimulated by addition of agonists to the bathing fluid were recorded for at least 10 min (Grass Model 7 polygraph, Quincy, MA). Responses were recorded in a non-cumulative manner, and because PAF is highly tachyphylactic for these tissues (Stimler et al., 1981) a fresh lung strip was used for each measurement. At least 20 parenchymal strips were prepared from each animal and used in two groups of ten on a single day. Tissues were first challenged with ACh (2 μg ml^{-1}). Antagonist was then added to the bathing fluid of six of the ten tissues and incubated for 10 min. All tissues were then challenged with PAF or another agonist to determine the effect of the drug on the elicited tissue response. Results are reported as the increase in tension induced by a particular agonist relative to the contraction caused by 11 μM ACh. The rate of contraction was determined from the increase in tension per minute relative to ACh (i.e. percentage of ACh min^{-1}. The mean $\pm$ S.E. of at least four individual responses was determined for each data point and the significance of the findings was determined using a two-sample Student's t-test at each PAF concentration.

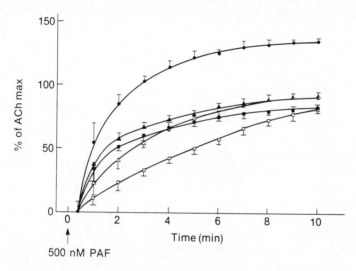

Figure 1. Contractile response of guinea-pig lung parenchymal tissues to 500 nM PAF in Tyrode's buffer alone ($\bullet$), in Tyrode's buffer with 10 nM tetrodotoxin ($\blacksquare$), 1μM atropine ($\blacktriangle$), with 10 μM indomethacin and 10 nM tetrodotoxin ($\square$), and with 10 μM indomethacin and 1 μM atropine ($\triangle$). Responses are expressed as the percentage of the response to 11 μM ACh (mean $\pm$ S.E.M., $n = 10$ for each curve)

RESULTS AND DISCUSSION

The contractile response of isolated guinea-pig lung strips to 500 nM PAF is shown in Figure 1. When tetrodotoxin at 10 nM was added to the tissue bathing fluid 10 min prior to addition of PAF, the magnitude of this contraction was inhibited by 40 percent (significant at $p < 0.005$). Atropine, at 1μM, inhibited the PAF response by 33 percent (significant at $p < 0.005$). The rate of contraction was not effected by either drug. Previous studies of the mechanism of action of PAF in contracting guinea-pig lung parenchymal tissues showed that the phospholipid is a potent stimulus for the release of spasmogenic cyclooxygenase metabolites of arachidonic acid, particularly thromboxane A$_2$. However, in the presence of indomethacin at a concentration which completely blocks PAF-induced thromboxane release, the magnitude of the contractile responses elicited by PAF are not inhibited (Stimler and O'Flaherty, 1983). When PAF responses were studied in the presence of combinations of indomethacin and tetrodotoxin the result was an attenuation of the rate of contraction, with no further inhibition in the magnitude of the response over that observed with tetrodotoxin alone (Figure 1). Increasing the concentration of tetrodotoxin to 50 nM did not further inhibit PAF-induced responses in these tissues. Similarly, the combination of atropine with indomethacin had no more effect than either drug alone, and increasing the atropine concentration to 10 μM did not further inhibit the magnitude of the contractions.

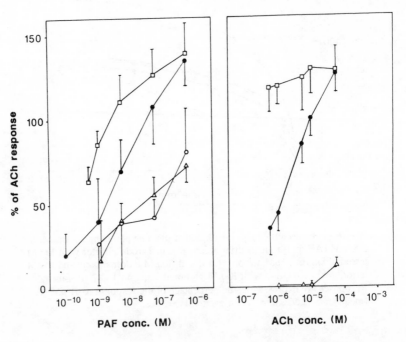

Figure 2.   (Left) Dose−response curves for PAF-induced contraction of guinea-pig lung parenchymal strips in Tyrode's buffer alone (●), in Tyrode's buffer containing 10 nM tetrodotoxin (○), 1 μM atropine (△), or 20 μM physostigmine (□).
(Right) Dose−response curves for ACh in Tyrode's buffer alone (●), in the presence of 1 μM atropine (△) or 20 μM physostigmine (□). The magnitude of each response is expressed as the percentage of the response to 11 μM ACh (mean ± S.E.M. for at least four responses at each concentration)

The effect of parasympathetic inhibition on the dose−response curve for PAF-induced contraction of guinea-pig lung parenchymal strips is shown in Figure 2. The data indicate non-competitive inhibition since regression analysis indicates a non-parallel shift of the dose−response curve in the presence of these drugs, possibly indicating an additional mechanism of action on the tissue.

Table 1. Specificity of Parasympathetic Inhibitors on Guinea-Pig Lung Parenchymal Strips

Agonist (M)		Inhibitor	
		Tetrodotoxin (10 nM)	Atropine (1 μM)
PAF	(5×10^{-7})	60 ± 18	67 ± 14
ACh	(1.1×10^{-5})	98 ± 19	0 ± 0
Hist	(1.8×10^{-6})	105 ± 32	96 ± 13
LTC$_4$	(5×10^{-9})	92 ± 10	87 ± 6
LTD$_4$	(5×10^{-9})	109 ± 18	93 ± 18
PGF$_{2a}$	(1×10^{-5})	97 ± 16	122 ± 22
U 46619	(1×10^{-8})	107 ± 21	106 ± 18

Agonists were added to the tissue bathing fluid from concentrated aqueous stock solutions 10 min before addition of the agonist. Responses are reported as a percentage of the control response in the absence of the drug and are the mean $\pm$ S.E.M. of eight to ten responses.

Specificity studies of both tetrodotoxin and atropine were carried out using a number of additional agonists known to be involved in hypersensitivity reactions (Table 1). Tetrodotoxin at 10 nM significantly inhibited contractile responses induced by PAF but did not effect responses to leukotrienes C$_4$ and D$_4$, PGF$_{2a}$, the stable thromboxane A$_2$ analog, U-46619, histamine or acetylcholine. Atropine at 1 μM effectively blocked responses to exogenous ACh (Figure 2, Table 1) and significantly inhibited the contractions induced by PAF, but like tetrodotoxin, atropine had no significant effect on responses to the other agonists tested.

To further support the evidence that PAF induces release of endogenous ACh from lung tissues, the effect of the cholinesterase inhibitor, physostigmine, was assessed (Figure 2). This inhibitor significantly potentiates tissue responses to ACh at suboptimal concentrations by inhibiting degradation of the agonist. Physostigmine has a similar effect on contractile responses to PAF at concentrations between 10^{-9} and 5×10^{-8}M (Figure 2). The preganglionic blocker, hexamethonium, at 3 mM, had no effect on PAF-induced contractions of the tissue (not shown).

These data clearly demonstrate an action of PAF on parasympathetic neurons in lung parenchymal tissues to stimulate the release of endogenous neurotransmitter substances. The difference in the degree of inhibition caused by tetrodotoxin compared to atropine (Figure 1), although not statistically significant, may reflect the release of substance P, since this peptide is now believed to contribute to parasympathetic responses in the lung as well (Lundberg and Saria, 1982). Lack of inhibition by hexamethonium limits the action of the phospholipid to a ganglionic or post-ganglionic site. In addition, the incomplete blockade of PAF-induced contractions in these tissues, even in the presence of elevated concentrations of the parasympathetic inhibitors, suggest that additional, perhaps direct actions of PAF may be in effect. A schematic model for the mechanisms of action of PAF in lung is depicted in Figure 3.

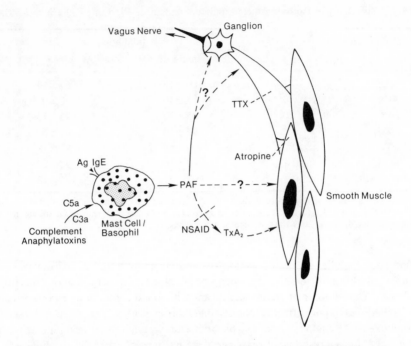

Figure 3. Schematic representation of the mechanisms of action of PAF for contracting guinea-pig lung parenchymal tissues. PAF is released from inflammatory cells upon immunologic or other stimulation. Released PAF stimulates neurotransmitter release from parasympathetic neurons, responses which are blocked pre-synaptically by tetrodotoxin or post-synaptically by atropine. PAF also stimulates release of cyclooxygenase metabolites (TxA_2) which can be blocked by indomethacin or other NSAIDs. There may additionally be a direct effect of PAF on smooth muscle. (Stimler-Gerard, 1986)

To our knowledge the data presented here provide the first evidence that PAF stimulates neuronal tissues, and this result may have important ramifications in studies on the mechanism of smooth muscle contraction associated with allergic bronchospasms. At present, evidence for activation of both humoral and autonomic pathways in these responses is available, however, the interrelationship of the two systems is poorly reconciled (Nadel, 1980). Based upon the results presented here, we hypothesize that PAF constitutes a link between immunologically stimulated humoral and autonomic pathways in the lung.

ACKNOWLEDGMENTS

Supported in part by NIH Grant HL 36162.

Dr Stimler-Gerard is the recipient of National Heart Lung and Blood Institute Research Career Development Award HL 01777.

REFERENCES

Benveniste, J., Henson, P.M., and Cochrane, C.G. (1972). 'Leukocyte-dependent histamine release from rabbit platelets. The role of IgE basophils and a platelet-activating factor', *J. Exp. Med.*, **136**, 1356–1377.

Brocklehurst, W.E. (1978). 'The handling and assay of mediators in hypersensitivity reactions', *Handbook of Experimental Immunology.*, Blackwell, Oxford, pp.46.1–46.20.

Camussi, G., Montruccio, G., Antro, C., Bussolino, F., Tetta, C., and Emanuelli, G. (1983). 'Platelet-activating factor-mediated contraction of rabbit lung strips: pharmacologic modulation', *Immunopharmacol.*, **6**, 87–96.

Findlay, S.R., Lichtenstein, L.M., Hanahan, D.J., and Pinckard, R.N. (1981). 'Contraction of guinea pig ileal smooth muscle by acetyl glyceryl ether phosphorylcholine', *Am. J. Physiol.*, **241**, C130–C133.

Henson, P.M. (1969). 'Role of complement and leukocytes in immunologic release of vaso-active amines from platelets', *Fed. Proc.*, **28**, 1721–1728.

Henson, P.M. (1970). 'Release of vasoactive amines from rabbit platelets induced by sensitized mononuclear leukocytes and antigen', *J. Exp. Med.*, **131**, 287–306.

Leff, A.R., White, S.R., Munoz, N., Popovich, K.J., Shioya, T., and Stimler-Gerard, N.P. (1986). 'Parasympathetic mediation of PAF-induced contraction in canine trachealis *in vivo.*, *J. Appl. Physiol.*, (submitted).

Lefort, J., Rotilio, D., and Vargaftig, B.B. (1984). 'The platelet-independent release of thromb-oxane A_2 by PAF-acether from guinea pig lungs involves mechanisms distinct from those for leukotriene', *Br. J. Pharmac.*, **82**, 565–575.

Lundberg, J.M. and Saria, A. (1982). 'Bronchial smooth muscle contraction induced by stimulation of capsaicin-sensitive sensory neurons', *Acta. Physuiol. Scand.*, **116**, 473–476.

Nadel, J.A. (1980). 'Autonomic regulation of airway smooth muscle'. In J.A. Nadel (ed.) *Physiology and Pharmacology of the Airways*, Marcel Dekker, New York, pp.217–257.

O'Flaherty, J.T., and Wykle, R.L. (1983). 'Mediators of anaphylaxis', *Clinics in Lab. Med.*, **3**, 619–643.

Pinckard, R.N., Knicker, W.T., Lee, L., Hanahan, D.J., and McManus, L.M. (1980). 'Vaso-active effects of 1-0-alkyl-2-acetyl-*sn*-glyceryl-3-phosphocholine (AcGEPC) in human skin', *J. Allergy Clin. Immunol.*, **65**, 196.

Siraganian, R.P., and Osler, A.G. (1971). 'Destruction of rabbit platelets in the allergic response of sensitized leukocytes. II Evidence for basophil involvement', *J. Immunol.*, **106**, 1252–1259.

Stimler, N.P., Bloor, C.M., Hugli, T.E., Wykle, R. L., McCall, C.E., and O'Flaherty, J.T. (1981). 'Anaphylactic actions of platelet-activating factor', *Am. J. Pathol.*, **105**, 64–69.

Stimler, N.P., Gerard, C., and O'Flaherty, J.T. (1983). 'Contraction of human lung tissues by platelet-activating factor (AAGPC)'. In J. Benveniste and B. Arnoux (eds.) *Platelet-Activating Factor, INSERM Symp. No. 23*, Elsevier, Amsterdam, pp.195–204.

Stimler, N.P., and O'Flaherty, J.T. (1983). 'Spasmogenic properties of platelet-activating factor: Evidence for a direct mechanism in the contractile response of pulmonary tissues', *Am. J. Pathol.*, **113**, 75–84.

Stimler-Gerard, N.P. (1986). 'Parasympathetic stimulation as a mechanism for PAF-induced contractile responses in lung', *J. Pharm. Exp. Therap.*, **237**, 209–213.

New Horizons in Platelet Activating Factor Research
Edited by C. M. Winslow and M. L. Lee
© 1987 John Wiley & Sons Ltd.

29

The Inhibitory Activity of Brotizolam and Related Compounds on Platelet Activating Factor Induced Effects *In Vitro* and *In Vivo*

J. Casals-Stenzel

INTRODUCTION

In the attempts to find a structure with PAF antagonistic activity, brotizolam, a thieno-triazolodiazepine (Figure 1) attracted attention. This drug has been described as an agent with hypnogenic, anxiolytic, anticonvulsant and muscle relaxant properties (Kuhn *et al.*, 1983) and is used as a hypnotic.

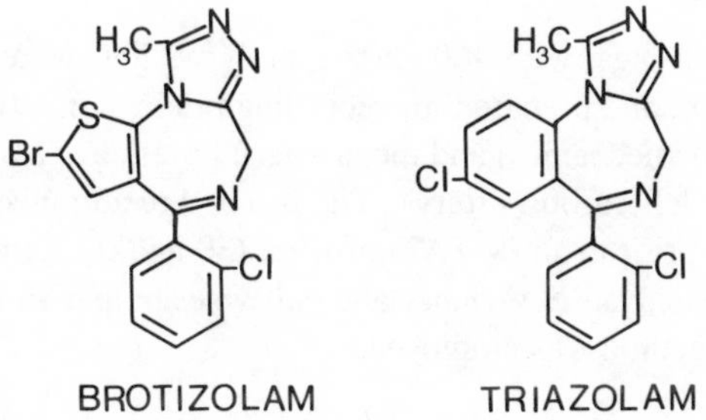

Figure 1. Structure of the triazolodiazepines

A recent study has shown that other triazolodiazepines like triazolam (Pakes *et al.*, 1981) and alprazolam (Dawson *et al.*, 1984) inhibit specifically the PAF-induced aggregation of human platelets (Kornecki *et al.*, 1984).

In the present study, the inhibitory property of brotizolam on PAF-induced effects *in vitro* and *in vivo* has been evaluated in comparison to related compounds.

MATERIALS AND METHODS

In vitro platelet aggregation

Platelets were prepared from human venous blood. Platelet aggregation was determined according to the method of Born and Cross (1963). Aggregation was induced by PAF, ADP, adrenaline, serotonin (5-HT), arachidonic acid (AA) or collagen in final concentrations of 0.05, 1, 10, 500 μM, and 0.1 μg ml^{-1}, respectively. IC_{50} values were calculated by linear regression analysis of log concentration versus percent inhibition.

In vivo platelet aggregation

Circulating platelets labeled with ^{111}Indium were continuously monitored in guinea-pigs using the method of Page *et al.*, (1982). The experiments were performed with Pirbright white guinea-pigs, 400−500 g body weight anesthetized with urethan (1.6 g kg^{-1} i.p.). Accumulation or aggregation of platelets was indicated by an increase of the γ-count rate in the thoracic region. 10−15 min after the i.v. injection of labeled platelets, aggregation was induced by an i.v. infusion of PAF (30 ng (kg min)$^{-1}$). The animals were treated with the test compounds either orally 1 h or intravenously 10 min before PAF infusion.

Respiratory function and arterial pressure

Pirbright white guinea-pigs, with 400−500 g body weight, were anesthetized with urethan (1.6 g kg^{-1} i.p.) and prepared for recording tidal volume (intratracheal cannula, Buxco pulmonary mechanics) and mean arterial pressure (MAP measured continuously through the left carotid artery). The drugs wre administered orally 1 h or intravenously 10 min prior to an i.v. PAF infusion (30 ng (kg $\times$ min)$^{-1}$). For statistical analysis, one way analysis of variance and pairwise comparison of mean values by the Newman-Keuls method was employed.

RESULTS AND DISCUSSION

Effects on human platelet aggregation *in vitro*

Brotizolam and triazolam inhibited concentration dependently the PAF induced platelet aggregation (Figure 2). Brotizolam was fourteen times as potent as triazolam.

Both compounds showed no or only a weak effect on the aggregation induced by ADP, adrenaline (Adr), serotonin (5-HT), collagen (Coll) and arachidonic acid (AA), a fact which implies a specific action of these drugs against PAF. These *in vitro* findings are in close accord, however, with the results published by Kornecki *et al.*, 1984. They found that the triazolobenzodiazepines alprazolam and triazolam were potent inhibitors of PAF induced platelet aggregation and shape change.

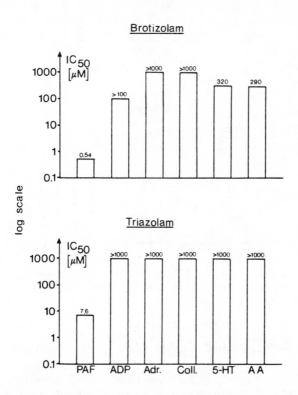

Figure 2. Inhibition of human platelet aggregation by brotizolam and triazolam *in vitro*; IC_{50}-values (μM) on top of the columns

In contrast, flunitrazepam and diazepam, two benzodiazepines lacking of the triazole ring, were considerably less effective in inhibiting the PAF induced platelet aggregation (Figure 3). They inhibited also the aggregation induced by the other aggregating agents, i.e. they did not show any specificity in their antiaggregatory effect. This difference between benzodiazepines with and without triazole ring was also pointed out in the work of Kornecki *et al.*, 1984. The inhibitory activity of benzodiazepines like flurazepam and diazepam on ADP, adrenaline and arachidonic acid induced platelet aggregation has also recently been described (Romstedt *et al.*, 1985).

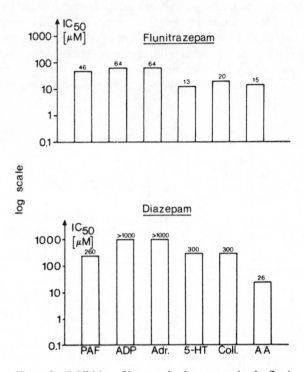

Figure 3.   Inhibition of human platelet aggregation by flunitrazepam and diazepam *in vitro*; IC_{50}-values (μM) on top of
the columns

Effects on platelet aggregation in guinea-pigs

To show that these *in vitro* results are transferable to *in vivo* conditions, the activity
of brotizolam and triazolam on PAF-induced platelet aggregation was also studied in
anesthetized guinea-pigs. Figure 4 shows typical time-responses to PAF alone and to
PAF after oral pretreatment with brotizolam or triazolam.

The γ-radiation recorded from the thoracic region increased rapidly 1–2 min after
the beginning of the PAF-infusion, reaching a maximum which was maintained up to
the end of the experiment (death of the animal at 15 min). This effect reflects a retention (accumulation and aggregation) of labeled platelets in the pulmonary capillary
system.

Brotizolam or triazolam inhibited dose-dependently the proaggregatory action of
PAF. Doses of 5 mg kg^{-1} p.o. of brotizolam and 50 mg kg^{-1} p.o. of triazolam gave
approximately half-maximal responses. Therefore, brotizolam showed its protective
effect against PAF in doses ten to fifteen times as low as triazolam.

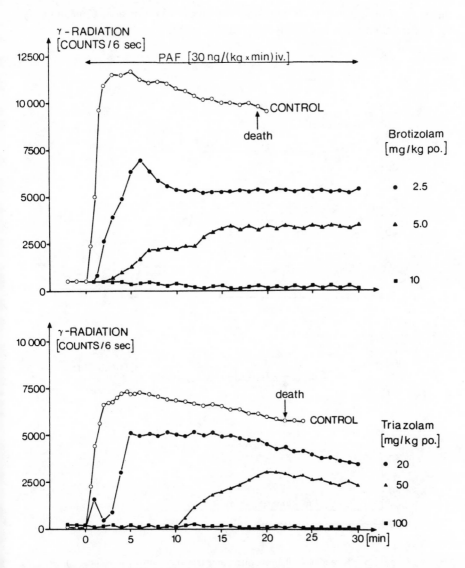

Figure 4.   Inhibition of PAF-induced accumulation of ¹¹¹In-labeled platelets in the lung of anesthetized guinea-pigs by oral brotizolam and triazolam given 1 h prior to PAF infusion. Each curve represents a typical time−response of one animal

Effects on respiratory function and mean arterial pressure in guinea pigs

The continuous i.v. infusion of PAF provoked also within 1.5 min a lung reaction characterized by a continuous decrease in tidal volume (Figure 5) which ended with the death of the animal 15–20 min after start of the PAF infusion. Concomitantly, mean arterial pressure was deeply lowered (Figure 6).

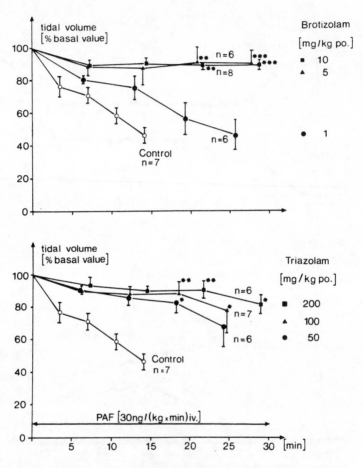

Figure 5.   Effect of oral brotizolam and triazolam on tidal volume in guinea pigs receiving an i.v. infusion of PAF. The drugs were administered 1 h prior to PAF. Points and vertical bars represent the mean ± S.E.M.; significant difference from control: ***$p < 0.001$, **$p < 0.01$, *$p < 0.05$

Under these conditions, pretreatment with brotizolam and triazolam 1 h prior to PAF protected the animals from death and inhibited dose-dependently the PAF-induced decrease in tidal volume (Figure 5) and mean blood pressure (Figure 6).

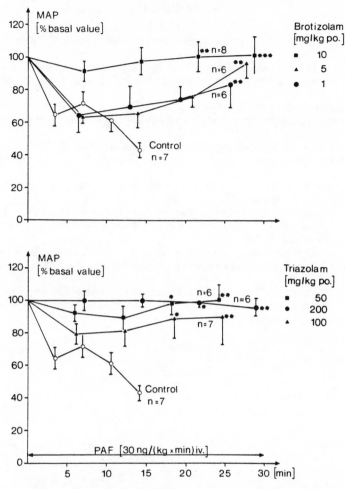

Figure 6. Effect of oral brotizolam and triazolam on mean arterial pressure (MAP) in guinea pigs receiving an i.v. infusion of PAF. The drugs were administered 1 h prior PAF. Points and vertical bars represent the mean ± S.E.M.; significant difference from control, $***p < 0.001$, $**p < 0.01$, $*p < 0.05$

The doses needed for the complete inhibition of the hypotensive effect were higher than those required for the total blocking of the PAF induced bronchoconstriction. This difference can be explained by the fact that the PAF induced lung reaction is mainly mediated by platelets while the hypotension is not platelet dependent (Vargaftig *et al.*, 1980).

In conclusion, brotizolam and triazolam, both triazolodiazepines, are potent and specific antagonists to PAF *in vitro* and *in vivo* models.

REFERENCES

Born, G.V.R., and Cross, M.J. (1963). 'The aggregation of blood platelets', *J. Physiol. (Lond).*, **168**, 178–179.

Dawson, G.W., Jue, S.G., and Brogden, R.N. (1984). 'Alprazolam, a review of its pharmacodynamic properties and efficacy in the treatment of anxiety and depression', *Drugs.*, **27**, 132–147.

Kornecki, E., Ehrlich, Y.H., and Lenox, R.H. (1984). 'Platelet-activating factor-induced aggregation of human platelets specifically inhibited by triazolobenzodiazepines', *Science.*, **226**, 1454–1456.

Kuhn, F.J., Böke-Kuhn, K., Danneberg, P., Lehr, E., and Stockhaus, K. (1983). 'Pharmacology and hypnogenic properties of brotizolam in animals', *Br. J. Clin. Pharmac.*, **16**, 253S–260S.

Page, C.P., Paul, W., and Morley, J. (1982). 'An *in vivo* model for studying platelet aggregation and disaggregation', *Thromb. Haemostas.*, **47**, 210–213.

Pakes, G.E., Brodgen, R.N., Heel, R.C., Speight, T.M., and Avery, G.S. (1981). 'Triazolam: A Review of its Pharmacological Properties and Therapeutic Efficacy in Patients with Insomnia', *Drugs*, **22**, 81–110.

Romstedt, K., and Huzoor-Akbar (1985). 'Benzodiazepines inhibit human platelet activation: comparison of the mechanism of antiplatelet actions of flurazepam and diazepam', *Thrombosis Res.*, **38**, 361–374.

Vargaftig, B.B., Lefort, J., Chignard, M., and Benveniste, J. (1980). 'Platelet-activating factor induces a platelet-dependent bronchoconstriction unrelated to the formation of prostaglandin derivatives', *Eur. J. Pharmacol.*, **65** 185–192.

New Horizons in Platelet Activating Factor Research
Edited by C. M. Winslow and M. L. Lee
© 1987 John Wiley & Sons Ltd.

30

A Role for Platelet Activating Factor in Neuronal Function: Specific Inhibition of Platelet Activation by Triazolobenzodiazepines and Interactions of PAF with Cultured Neural Cells

E. Kornecki, R.H. Lenox, D.H. Hardwick and Y.H. Ehrlich

Platelet activating factor (PAF) is a naturally occurring ether-phospholipid (1-0-alkyl-2-acetyl-*sn*-glyceryl-3-phosphoryl choline), which acts as an inter-cellular messenger in the communication of a variety of cells (for review see Chapter 1). We have reported previously (Kornecki *et al.*, 1984) that a class of neuroactive drugs, the triazolobenzodiazepines, act as potent and specific antagonists of PAF-induced platelet responses. The present report summarizes these studies and present recent results from our laboratory indicating a role for PAF in regulating the function of cells in the nervous system.

TRIAZOLOBENZODIAZEPINES ARE SPECIFIC ANTAGONISTS OF PLATELET ACTIVATING FACTOR

It is known that clacium-dependent protein phosphorylation activity plays a key role in agonist-induced cellular-responses (for review, see Ehrlich, 1984). DeLorenzo *et al.*, (1981) reported that calcium-dependent protein phosphorylation activity in neuronal membranes can be inhibited by benzodiazepines. Since platelets possess benzodiazepine receptors (Wang *et al.*, 1980), and platelet activation by agonists involves calcium-dependent protein phosphorylation systems (Hathaway and Adelstein, 1979; Nishizuka, 1984), we tested whether platelet activation by various agonists could be inhibited by benzodiazepines.

Table 1.   IC$_{50}$ Values of Drugs Tested for Inhibition of PAF-Induced Aggregation of Human Platelets

Drugs Tested	IC$_{50}$ Values (μM)
Triazolam	0.3
Alprazolam	0.5
Ro 5-4864	45.0
Chlordiazepoxide	67.0
Diazepam	130.0
Adinazolam	500.0

Gel-filtered platelets (2×10^8 ml^{-1}) were prepared and assayed as described by Kornecki *et al.*, (1984). The final concentration of PAF used was 51 nM.

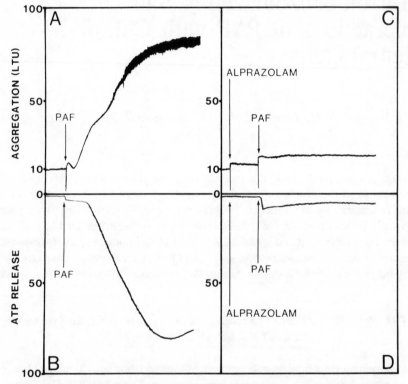

Figure 1.   Inhibition of PAF-induced platelet shape change, aggregation and granular secretion by alprazolam. Gel-filtered human platelets were used in these experiments as detailed in the legend to Table 1. The concentration of alprazolam shown here was 10 μM

The benzodiazepines most commonly prescribed, diazepam and chlordiazepoxide, were tested at a concentration range of 0.1-40 μM and had no detectable effects on either the initial velocity nor on the extent of aggregation of human platelets stimulated by ADP, thrombin, epinephrine, the calcium ionophore A23187, collagen or arachidonate. A separate subclass of these drugs are the triazolobenzodiazepines, including alprazolam and triazolam. The primary clinical use of alprazolam is in the treatment of panic disorder with or without agoraphobia, and triazolam is used as a short acting sleep medication. Neither alprazolam nor triazolam had significant effects on platelet aggregation activated by any of the agonists mentioned above. In contrast, the triazolabenzodiazepines alprazolam and triazolam potently blocked platelet aggregation induced by PAF (see Table 1). We have also found that not only the aggregation, but also platelet shape change as well as PAF-induced granular secretion from human platelets (monitored by measuring ATP release) were inhibited by both alprazolam and triazolam (see Figure 1). Similar results were obtained with rabbit platelets (see Figure 2). The mechanism of action of these drugs in inhibiting PAF-mediated platelet activation was indicated by the finding that increasing concentrations of PAF competitively reversed this inhibition (Kornecki *et al.*, 1984). We have concluded from these studies that the triazolobenzodiazepines triazolam and alprazolam are specific and competitive antagonists of PAF action.

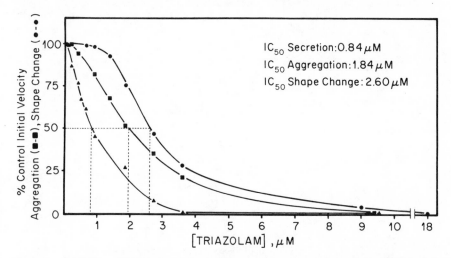

Figure 2. Inhibition of PAF-induced shape change, aggregation and secretion of rabbit platelets by triazolam. In these experiments we used gel-filtered platelets obtained from rabbits, and the PAF concentration used was 0.47 nM

Table 1 shows that a selective ligand of the peripheral benzodiazepine receptor, Ro5-4864, was about 100-times less potent than triazolam or alprazolam in inhibiting PAF action. In addition, Ro5-4864 did not block the inhibitory effect of alprazolam or triazolam on PAF-induced platelet function. Therefore, binding to the platelet benzodiazepine receptor does not appear to be involved in the inhibition of PAF-induced platelet activation by triazolobenzodiazepines, and it is more likely that direct interaction of these drugs with PAF-receptor(s) is the underlying mechanism. Studies of structure–function relationships also began to shed light on the structural requirements necessary for inhibiting the action of PAF by triazolobenzodiazepines. As shown in Figure 3 and Table 1, the presence of a triazole ring in the structure is needed for potent inhibition of PAF action. On the other hand, substitutions at the C-1 position of the triazole ring of alprazolam, as is the case in the drug called adinazolam, result in complete loss of activity of this drug as a PAF antagonist. It appears that triazolobenzodiazepines with appropriate substitutions could serve as potent antagonists of PAF-induced cellular responses. Such drugs may prove to be useful in the treatment of various clinical disorders resulting from pathophysiological activity of PAF.

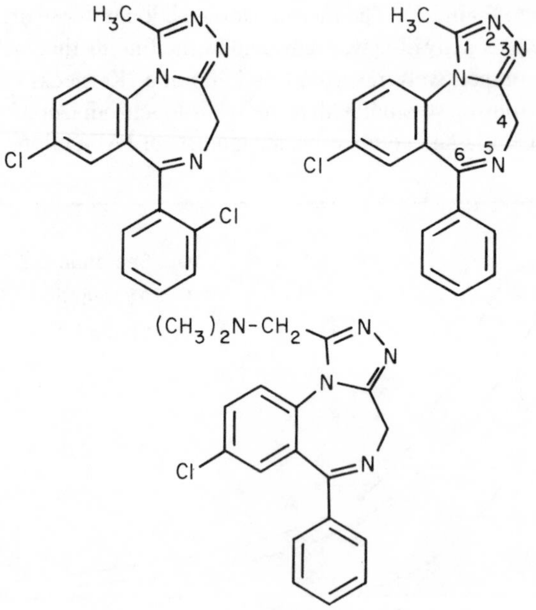

Figure 3.   Comparison of the structures of alprazolam, triazolam and adinazolam

INTERACTIONS OF PAF WITH NEURAL CELLS

Since the psychotropic drugs triazolam and alprazolam were found to be potent and specific inhibitors of PAF-mediated cellular responses, we have suggested that the mechanism of action of these drugs may involve interactions with processes mediated by PAF or PAF-like ether-phospholipids in the central nervous system. This possibility is supported by reports (Blank *et al.*, 1981; Chapter 2) that the brain contains relatively high levels of enzymes for the biosynthesis and degradation of ether-phospholipids. However, effects of PAF on the function of neuronal cells have never been reported. We have initiated this line of investigation by examining the interactions of PAF with a homogenous population of a cloned neuronal cell line.

Cloned cells of the line designated NG108-15 have been extensively investigated in recent years as a model system in studies of various neuronal functions (Nirenberg *et al.*, 1983; Hamprecht *et al.*, 1985). Under standard growth conditions NG108-15 cells divide rapidly and exhibit an exponential growth curve. However, when these cells are exposed in culture to agents which induce neuronal differentiation, their growth is arrested, and they develop a multitude of morphological, physiological and biochemical properties characteristic of mature neurons (Nirenberg *et al.*, 1983; Ehrlich *et al.*, 1986). One of the main morphological mainfestations of this differentiation is the extension of long processes called neurites. Differentiation of NG108-15 cells in culture can be quantitated by determining the percentage of cells that, under the influence of a differentiating agent, cease multiplying and extend neurites. Using this criterion, our initial studies have determined that PAF can induce neuronal differentiation.

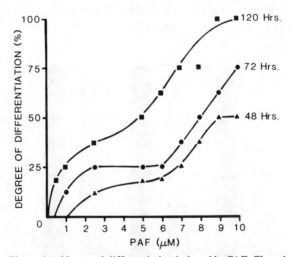

Figure 4.   Neuronal differentiation induced by PAF. Cloned cells of the neural line NG108-15 were grown in a DMEM medium containing 1 percent fetal calf serum, supplemented with the PAF concentrations indicated in the figure. Morphological differentiation was quantitated by determining the percentage of cells in the dish bearing neurites

NG108-15 cells are grown in our laboratory in a DMEM medium supplemented with fetal calf serum as described by Nirenberg *et al.*, (1983) or in a chemically defined, serum-free medium (Ehrlich *et al.*, 1986). We have observed that addition of PAF to the growth medium of cultured NG108-15 cells induced growth arrest and morphological differentiation. The differentiating effect of PAF on neuronal cells was found to be both concentration- and time-dependent. In serum containing medium, maximal differentiation required treatment of the cells with 10 μM PAF for a period of four to five days (see Figure 4). With lower concentrations of PAF, the rate of differentiation was slower. In experiments to be reported in detail elsewhere, we have found that in serum-free medium PAF was about ten-times more potent in inducing differentiation of NG108-15 cells than in serum- containing media. Under these conditions, as little as 50 nM PAF induced measurable neuronal differentiation.

Increasing the dose of PAF beyond the levels which induce maximal differentiation revealed that, at relatively high concentrations, PAF is cytotoxic to NG108-15 cells. The cytotoxic effects of PAF were dose and time-dependent. As seen in Figure 5, a differentiating concentration of PAF (10 μM) had no cytotoxic effect on NG108-15 cells grown in a serum-containing medium. A slightly higher level, 12.5 μM PAF, caused growth arrest and differentiation within the first 24 h of treatment, but no cell death. After 48 h exposure of the cells to 12.5 μM PAF, however, cytotoxicity was in evidence and cell death rapidly progressed over time. Figure 5 also demonstrates that at higher PAF concentrations, this process was accelerated. As might be expected, with cells grown in a chemically defined serum-free medium the neurotoxic doses of PAF showed a shift to the left as compared to the results depicted in Figure 5.

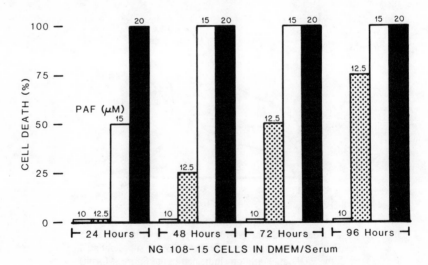

Figure 5.   Neurotoxicity of PAF, NG108-15 cells were grown in the presence of varying concentrations of PAF as described in the legend to Figure 4. Cell death was quantitated by determining the decrease in number of viable cells

The biochemical mechanisms underlying the neurotropic effects of PAF reported above are currently under investigation. In initial studies we have loaded NG108-15 cells with the calcium probe aequorin, and were able to measure a significant PAF-induced rise in free intracellular Ca^{2+}-ions concentrations in these neural cells (Kornecki and Ehrlich, 1986). Previous studies of non-neural cells have shown that increased levels of intracellular ionized calcium is an early event in processes leading to either cell differentiation or programmed cell-death, depending on the magnitude of the initial rise (Leonard and Salpeter, 1979). Our findings suggest that such series of events may be induced by PAF in neuronal cells.

In summary, we have demonstrated that neurotropic drugs are potent and specific antagonists of PAF-induced platelet responses, and that PAF itself can exert specific effects on the function of neural cells. In the mature brain, PAF or PAF-like phospholipids may be involved in cell—cell communications. Antagonism of this process by triazolam or alprazolam could play a role in mechanisms underlying the therapeutic effects of these drugs. In the developing nervous system, low levels of PAF produced by neuronal and/or glial cells may play a role in cell differentiation (see Figure 4). Indeed, neuronal dysfunction has been found in individuals with Zellweger Syndrome, a genetic disorder in which there is lack of enzymes needed for the synthesis of ether-phospholipids (Datta *et al.*, 1984). Our finding that, at higher levels, PAF is cytotoxic to neural cells (see Figure 5), also suggests the possibility that PAF may be one of the circulation factors responsible for the irreversible neuronal degeneration associated with spinal cord injury, trauma and stroke. Further studies of the interaction of PAF with the function of neuronal cells could provide new insights into the role of ether-phospholipids in the regulation of neurophysiological events and the treatment of pathological states in the nervous system.

REFERENCES

Blank, M.L., Lee, T., Fitzgerald, V., and Snyder, F. (1981). 'A specific acetylhydrolase for 1-alkyl-2-acetyl-1-*sn*-glycero-3-phosphocholine (a hypotensive and platelet-activating lipid)', *J. Biol. Chem.*, **256**, 175–178.

Datta, N.S., Wilson, G.N., and Hajra, A.K. (1984). 'Deficiency of enzymes catalyzing the biosynthesis of glycerol-ether lipids in Zellweger syndrome', *N. Eng. J. Med.*, **311**, 1080–1083.

DeLorenzo, R.J., Burdette, S., and Holderness, J. (1981). 'Benzodiazepine inhibition of the calcium-calmodulin protein kinase system in brain membrane', *Science.*, **213**, 546–549.

Ehrlich, Y.H. (1984). 'Protein phosphorylation: Role in the regulation and adaptation of neuronal receptors.' In A. Lajtha, (ed.) *Handbook of Neurochemistry*, 2nd edn, Plenum Press, New York, pp. 541–574.

Ehrlich, Y.H., Garfield, M.G., Davis, T.B., Kornecki, E., Chaffee, J.E., and Lenox, R.H. (1986). 'Extracellular protein phosphorylation systems in the regulation of neuronal function.' In W. Gispen and A. Routtenberg, (eds.) *Progress in Brain Research*. Elsevier, Amsterdam, (in press).

Hamprecht, B., Glaser, T., Reiser, G., Bayer, E., and Propst, F. (1985). 'Culture and characteristics of hormone-responsive neuroblastoma X glioma cells', *Mehods in Enzymology.*, **109**, 316–341.

Hathaway, D.R., and Adelstein, R.S. (1979). 'Human platelet myosin light chain kinase requires the calcium binding protein calmodulin for activity', *Proc. Natl. Acad. Sci., U.S.A.*, **76**, 1653–1657.

Kornecki, E., and Ehrlich, Y.H. (1986). 'Platelet activating factor (PAF) stimulates calcium uptake in intact neural cells', *Transactions of Am. Soc. Neurochemistry.*, **17**, (abstract).

Kornecki, E., Ehrlich, Y.H., and Lenox, R.H. (1984). 'Platelet-activating factor-induced aggregation of human platelets specifically inhibited by triazolobenzodiazepines', *Science.*, **226**, 1454–1456.

Leonard, J.P., and Salpeter, M.M. (1979). 'Agonist-induced myopathy at the neuromuscular junction is mediated by calcium', *J. Cell Biol.*, **82**, 811–819.

Nirenberg, M., Wilson, S., Higashida, H., Rotter, A., Krueger, K., Busis, N., Ray, R., Kenimer, J.G., and Adler, M. (1983). 'Modulation of synapse formation by cyclic adenosine monophosphate', *Science.*, **222**, 793–799.

Nishizuka, Y. (1984). 'Turnover of inositol phospholipids and signal transduction', *Science.*, **225**, 1365–1370.

Wang, J.K.T., Taniguchi, T., and Spector, S. (1980) 'Properties of [³H] diazepam binding sites on rat blood platelets. *Life Sci.*, **27**, 1881–1888

New Horizons in Platelet Activating Factor Research
Edited by C. M. Winslow and M. L. Lee
© 1987 John Wiley & Sons Ltd.

31

CV 3988, a Platelet Activating Factor Antagonist and Ethanol Protect Against Endotoxin-Induced Hemodynamic Alterations in Rats

Shih-Wen Chang, Christian O. Feddersen, Peter M. Henson and Norbert F. Voelkel

INTRODUCTION

The adult respiratory distress syndrome (ARDS) is a common clinical disorder characterized by pulmonary hypertension, increased pulmonary vascular permeability and decreased lung compliance. Since gram-negative sepsis is a common antecedent to ARDS, and since injection of bacterial endotoxin reproduces many of the hemodynamic and pulmonary vascular changes of sepsis, endotoxin administration has been studied as an animal model of ARDS (Newman, 1985). Despite many studies, the pathogenesis of both human ARDS and endotoxemia in animals are still unclear, and the mortality of human ARDS remained close to 60 percent (Fowler *et al.*, 1985).

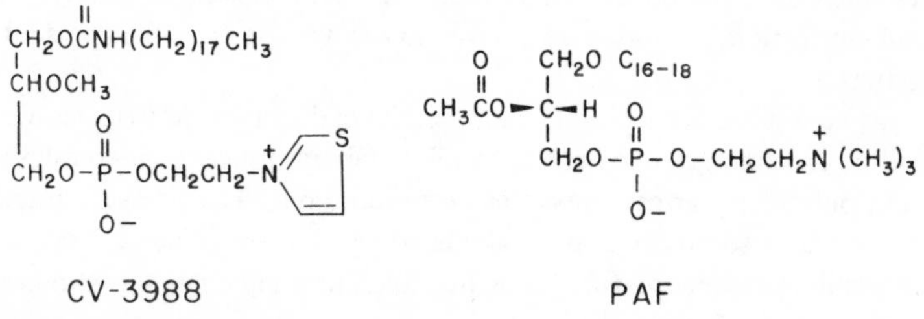

Figure 1.   Structure of CV 3988 and PAF

293

Platelet activating factor (PAF), 1-O-alkyl-2-acetyl-sn-glycero-3-phosphocholine (Figure 1), is a potent ether lipid produced by inflammatory cells. *In vitro*, PAF causes platelet aggregation and serotonin release, neutrophil activation, smooth muscle contraction and endothelium-dependent vascular relaxation (Pinckard *et al.*, 1983; Kasuya *et al.*, 1984). *In vivo*, injection of PAF causes systemic hypotension with cardiac depression (Bessin *et al.*, 1983). Previous investigations have documented the release of PAF in anaphylactic shock (Henson, 1970), after infusion of immune aggregates (Inarrea *et al.*, 1983) and in association with antibody-mediated lung injury (Camussi *et al.*, 1983).

Recently, PAF has been suggested as an important mediator in endotoxic shock. PAF is released from splenic and peritoneal macrophages after experimental gram-negative sepsis (Inarrea *et al.*, 1985) and is found in high concentrations in rat blood after intravenous injection of endotoxin (Doebber *et al.*, 1985). In addition, three structurally different PAF receptor antagonists, CV 3988, kadsurenone and BN 52021, prevented and reversed experimental endotoxic shock (Terashita *et al.*, 1985; Doebber *et al.*, 1985; Adnot *et al.*, 1985).

Since endotoxemia causes major alterations of pulmonary hemodynamics including pulmonary hypertension and loss of hypoxic pulmonary vasoconstriction (Newman, 1985), we wondered whether PAF, in addition to mediating the systemic hemodynamic effects, also influenced pulmonary hemodynamics. To answer this question we studied the effect of a specific PAF receptor antagonist, CV 3988, on the systemic and pulmonary hemodynamic changes after intraperitoneal injection of bacterial endotoxin in awake, catheterized rats.

METHODS

Male Sprague−Dawley rats (290−350 g) were purchased from a commercial vendor (Sasco, Omaha, NE) and allowed free access to food and water. After anesthesia with ketamine (50−100 mg kg^{-1}) and xylazine(5 mg kg^{-1}) i.m., catheters were placed in the carotid artery, jugular veins and pulmonary artery as described previously (Stanbrook *et al.*, 1984). The location of the pulmonary artery catheter was verified by the characteristic pulmonary artery pressure tracing displayed on an oscilloscope. After catheterization, the rats were allowed to recover for 24−48 h and studied without anesthesia.

The rats were placed in a plastic chamber, the catheters were irrigated with heparinized saline and connected to two Statham P23 Db transducers. Heart rates and mean aortic and pulmonary artery pressures wre monitored. The pressure tracings were displayed on an oscilloscope and calculated by a Data-General Nova computer. Hypoxic challenges were performed by flushing the study chamber with gas containing 8 percent O_2 for 5 min. The hypoxic pressor response was calculated as the difference between the maximal mean pulmonary artery pressure during hypoxia and the mean pulmonary artery pressure immediately preceding hypoxia. Cardiac output was measured using the dye-dilution method (Coleman, 1974; Huber *et al.*, 1976). Systemic vascular resistance and total pulmonary resistance were obtained by dividing mean aortic and pulmonary artery pressures by the cardiac output.

Since CV 3988, RS-2-methoxy-3-(octadecylcarbamoyloxy) propyl-2-(3-thiazolio) ethyl phosphate (Figure 1), is a specific antagonist of PAF at the receptor sites of platelets, and since rat platelets lack PAF receptors (Terashita *et al.*, 1985b), we wondered whether CV 3988 would inhibit the vascular effects of PAF in rats. CV 3988 was a kind gift of Dr Walter Pickett (Lederle Laboratory, American Cyanamid Co., NJ). In four catheterized rats, PAF (10 ng 0.1 ml^{-1} saline with 0.25 percent bovine serum albumin, Sigma) was injected intravenously during an ongoing hypoxic pulmonary vasoconstriction. Following the administration of CV 3988 (10mg kg^{-1} i.v.), the PAF injection was repeated during the subsequent hypoxic challenges. The effect of PAF on mean aortic and pulmonary artery pressures before and after CV 3988 were compared. In three additional rats that did not receive CV 3988, PAF was injected during five successive hypoxic challenges to demonstrate that tachyphylaxis to PAF did not occur.

Twenty-four catheterized rats were divided into four experimental groups: control ($n = 5$), endotoxin ($n = 7$), endotoxin plus CV 3988 ($n = 6$) and endotoxin plus ethanol ($n = 6$). Endotoxin (*S. enteritidis* lipopolysaccharide B, Difco Laboratories, Detroit, MI) 20 mg kg^{-1} was given i.p. at time zero. CV 3988 (dissolved in 30 percent ethanol) was given i.v. 10 mg kg^{-1} 10 min before endotoxin and 5 mg kg^{-1} 1 h later. Equal volumes of 30 percent ethanol were given to the fourth group of rats which served as the vehicle control. Heart rates, mean aortic and pulmonary artery pressures, cardiac outputs and hypoxic pressor responses were monitored for 90 min before and 120 min after endotoxin. Arterial blood gas and blood counts were obtained before and 70 min after endotoxin.

The means of the four groups were compared by a one-way analysis of variance using the method of Scheffe for multiple comparison (Steel and Torrie, 1960). For each group, values before and after endotoxin were compared using a paired t-test. To compare the blood pressure changes over time in the four groups of rats, we used a non-parametric test described by Zerbe (1979) for comparing time–response curves. Differences were considered significant when $p < 0.05$.

RESULTS

Injection of 10 ng PAF caused transient decreases in mean aortic and pulmonary artery pressures. The maximal decrease was observed 1 min after PAF injection and averaged 23 ± 2 percent of the baseline aortic pressure and 35 ± 5 percent of the hypoxic pressor response (mean ± S.E.M., $n = 7$). CV3988 blocked the hypotensive effect of PAF in both the systemic and pulmonary circulation (maximal decrease after CV 3988 were 7 ± 3 percent of the aortic pressure and 3 ± 1 percent of the hypoxic pressor response).

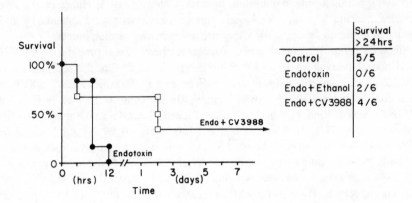

Figure 2.   Effect of CV 3988 and ethanol on endotoxin induced hypotension. Shown are means (and S.E.M. bars) of blood pressure (B.P.) changes as percent change from pre-endotoxin baseline

Treatment with CV 3988 or ethanol resulted in mean plasma ethanol levels of 62 ± 7 mg dl^{-1} 80 min after endotoxin ($n = 4$). Figure 2 shows the effect of CV 3988 and ethanol on the blood pressure changes after endotoxin. Endotoxin caused a significant decrease in mean aortic pressure 30 and 60 min after injection. The PAF receptor antagonist, CV 3988, but not the vehicle control, ethanol, attenauted the endotoxin-induced hypotension.

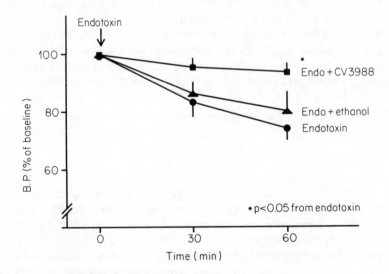

Figure 3.   Cardiac output (C.O.) 30 min after endotoxin. Endo=endotoxin

On the other hand, the cardiac depression 30 min after endotoxin was significantly improved by pretreatment with either ethanol dissolved CV 3988 or ethanol alone (Figure 3). This suggested that the protection of the cardiac output was attributable to ethanol.

Pulmonary artery pressure decreased after endotoxin, although total pulmonary resistance rose (data not shown). Both CV 3988 and ethanol attenuated these changes in pulmonary hemodynamics, but the protection was not statistically significant due to the large scatter in the data.

Figure 4 shows the hypoxic pressor response (HPR) as a percent of the pre-endotoxin baseline for the four groups of animals 30 min after endotoxin. Endotoxin caused a marked depression of the hypoxic pressor response which was significantly attenuated by CV 3988 but not by ethanol. The hypoxic pressor responses at 60 min after endotoxin showed a similar pattern of changes in these four groups (data not shown).

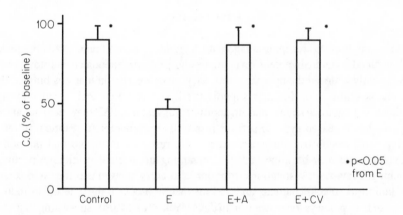

Figure 4.   Hypoxic pressor response (HPR) 30 min after endotoxin.
E = endotoxin, E + A = endotoxin/ethanol, E + CV = endotoxin/CV 3988

Figure 5 shows the survival data for the four groups of animals. In contrast to the endotoxin group in which all rats died within the first 24 h, four of the endotoxin plus CV 3988 rats were alive at the end of 24 h and two of them survived to seven days after endotoxin. Thus, CV 3988 appeared to prolong the survival of endotoxin-treated rats. CV 3988 was ineffective against the endotoxin-induced leukopenia, hypocapnia or metabolic acidosis.

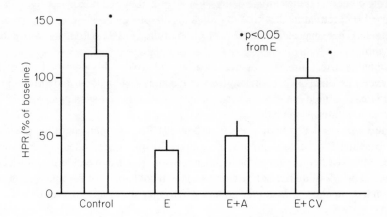

Figure 5.   Effect of CV 3988 on survival of endotoxin-treated rats.
E = endotoxin, E + A = endotoxin/ethanol, E + CV = endotoxin/CV 3988

DISCUSSION

In this study the PAF receptor antagonist CV 3988, at a dose that effectively blocked PAF induced systemic hypotension in unanesthetized rats, attenuated endotoxic shock and partially restored the hypoxic pulmonary vasoconstriction that was blunted during endotoxemia. Our findings support the hypothesis that PAF is an important mediator in endotoxic shock, and, in addition, suggest that PAF may mediate, at least in part, the decreased hypoxic pressor response after endotoxin treatment in rats.

Hypoxic vasoconstriction is a characteristic response in the normal pulmonary circulation and may be important in maintaining the normal ventilation-perfusion matching. Previous investigations from our laboratory showed that the cyclooxygenase inhibitors meclofenamate and indomethacin blocked the endotoxin-induced decrease in hypoxic vasoconstriction in dogs (Weir *et al.*, 1976), suggesting that vasodilator prostaglandins may be responsible. However, in a recent study in unanesthetized sheep, the decreased hypoxic pressor response following endotoxemia was not affected by meclofenamate (Hutchison *et al.*, 1985). Therefore, the decreased pulmonary vascular reactivity in this setting cannot be attributed entirely to vasodilator prostaglandins. Since endotoxin causes an elevation of blood PAF levels (Doebber *et al.*, 1985) and since exogenous PAF in our study inhibits hypoxic pulmonary vasoconstriction, PAF may be an important contributor to the decreased vascular reactivity after endotoxin. Moreover, since PAF stimulates the release of prostaglandins in some species (Bessin *et al.*,1983), the action of PAF may be related in part to that of vasodilator prostaglandins. An unexpected finding of this study was the protective effect of ethanol against endotoxin-induced cardiac depression. As an effective hydroxyl radical scavenger (Feierman *et al.*, 1985), ethanol may have beneficial effects during endotoxemia by reducing oxidant damage from stimulated granulocytes (Bernard *et al.*, 1984). In addition, ethanol may modulate the biosynthesis of arachidonic acid metabolites (Wescott and Murphy, 1985) and may impair the migration of polymorphonuclear leukocytes (Astry *et al.*, 1983). Both of these effects potentially may attenuate the toxic response to endotoxin. However, since the mechanism of myocardial dysfunction in endotoxin shock is still unclear (Parker and Adams, 1985), the explanation for the observed ethanol effect must remain speculative.

The possibility that the beneficial effect of CV 3988 observed in this study was due to actions other than PAF receptor blockade cannot be completely excluded. However, previous studies suggested that CV 3988 is a specific antagonist of PAF receptor both *in vitro* and *in vivo* (Terashita *et al.*, 1983). In addition, other structurally different PAF receptor blockers also blocked endotoxin-induced hypotension (Doebber *et al.*, 1985; Adnot *et al.*, 1985). Taken together, these studies suggest an important role for PAF in endotoxic shock.

To the extent that CV 3988 did not completely prevent the hypotensive effect of endotoxin and was ineffective against the endotoxin-induced leukopenia, hypocapnia and metabolic acidosis, one needs to postulate either an excessive level of PAF (thus overcoming the blocking effect of CV 3988) or the presence of other inflammatory mediators. Indeed increased levels of histamine, kinins, prostaglandins and leukotrienes have all been reported during and following endotoxemia (Brigham *et al.*, 1983; Hagmann *et al.*, 1985). It is likely that these, and perhaps other as yet undescribed inflammatory mediators interact to provide the hemodynamic and metabolic changes of endotoxemia.

REFERENCES

Adnot, S., Lefort, J., Lagente, V., Braquet, P., and Vargaftig, B.B. (1985). 'Interference of BN 52021, a PAF-acether antagonist, with endotoxin-induced hypotension in the guinea pig', *Lancet.*, (in press).

Astry, C.L., Warr, G.A., and Jakab, G.J. (1983). 'Impairment of polymorphonuclear leukocyte immigration as a mechanism of alcohol-induced suppression of pulmonary antibacterial defenses',*Am. Rev. Resp. Dis.*, **128**, 113–117.

Bernard, G.R., Lucht, W.D., Niedermeyer, M.E., Snapper, J.R., Ogletree, M.L., and Brigham, K.L. (1984). 'Effect of N-acetyl-cysteine on the pulmonary response to endotoxin in the awake sheep and upon *in vitro* granulocyte function', *J. Clin. Invest.*, **73**, 1772–1784.

Bessin, P., Bonnet, J., Apffel, D., Soulard, C., Desgroux, I., Pelas, I., and Benveniste, J. (1983). 'Acute circulatory collapse caused by platelet-activating factor in dogs' *Eur. J. Pharm.*, **86**, 403–413.

Brigham, K.L., Begley, C.J., Bernard, G.R., Hutchison, A.A., Loyd, J.E., Lucht, W.D., Meyrick, B., Newman, J.H., Niedermeyer, M.E., Ogletree, M.L., Sheller, J.R., and Snapper, J.R. (1983). 'Septicemia and lung injury', *Clin. Lab. Med.*, **3**, 719–744.

Camussi, G., Pawlowski, I., Bussolino, F., Caldwell, P.R.B., Brentjens, J., and Andres, G. (1983). 'Release of platelet activating factor in rabbits with antibody-mediated injury of the lung: the role of leukocytes and of pulmonary endothelial cells', *J. Immunol.*, **131**, 1802–1807.

Coleman, T.G. (1974). 'Cardiac output by dye dilution in the conscious rat', *J. Appl. Physiol.*, **37**, 452–455.

Doebber, T.W., Wu, M.S., Robbins, J.C., Choy, B.M., Chang, M.N., and Shen, T.Y. (1985). 'Platelet activating factor involvement in endotoxin-induced hypotension in rats. Studies with PAF-receptor antagonist kadsurenone', *Biochem. Biophys. Res. Comm.*, **127**, 799–808.

Feierman, D.E., Winston, G.W., and Cederbaum, A.I. (1985). 'Ethanol oxidation by hydroxyl radicals: role of iron chelates, superoxide and hydrogen peroxide', *Alcoholism: Clin. Exp. Res.*, **9**, 95–102.

Fowler, A.A., Hamman, R.F., Zerbe, G.O., Benson, K.N., and Hyers, T.M. (1985). 'Adult respiratory distress syndrome: prognosis after onset', *Am. Rev Respir. Dis.*, **132**, 472–478.

Hagmann, W., Denzlinger, C., and Keppler, D. (1985). 'Production of peptide leukotrienes in endotoxin shock', *FEBS.*, **180**, 309–313.

Henson, P.M. (1970). 'Release of vasoactive amines from rabbit platelets induced by antiplatelet antibody in the presence and absence of complement' *J. Immunol.*, **104**, 924–934.

Huber, F., Sodal, I.E. and Weil, J.V. (1976). 'On-line cardiac output by digital computer', *J. Appl. Physiol.*, **40**, 266–268.

Hutchison, A.A., Ogletree, M.L., Snapper, J.R., and Brigham K.L. (1985). 'Effect of endotoxemia on hypoxic pulmonary vasoconstriction in unanesthetized sheep', *J. Appl. Physiol.*, **58**, 1463–1468

Inarrea, P., Alonso, F., and Sanchez Crespo, M. (1983). 'Platelet activating factor: an effector substance of the vasopermeability changes induced by the infusion of immune aggregates in the mouse', *Immunopharm.*, **6**, 7–14.

Inarrea, P., Gomez-Cambronero, J., Pascual, J., del Carmen Ponte, M., Hernando, L., and Sanchez Crespo, M. (1985). 'Synthesis of PAF-acether and blood volume changes in gram-negative sepsis', *Immunopharm.*, **9**, 45–52.

Kasuya, Y., Masuda, Y., and Shigenobu, K. (1984). 'Possible role of endothelium in the vasodilator response of rat thoracic aorta to platelet activating factor', *J. Pharmacobiodyn.*, **7**, 138–142.

Newman, J.H. (1985). 'Sepsis and pulmonary edema', *Clin. Chest Dis.*, **6**, 371–391.

Parker, J.L., and Adams, H.R. (1985). 'Development of myocardial dysfunction in endotoxin shock' *Am. J. Physiol.*, **248**, H818–H826.

Pinckard, R.N., McManus, L.M., Halonen, M., Humphrey, D.M., and Hanahan, D.J. (1983). 'Acetyl glyceryl phosphorylcholine: a model anaphylactomimetic mediator', J.T. August (ed.) *Biological Response Mediators and Modulators*, Academic Press, New York, pp. 67–82.

Stanbrook, H.S., Morris, K.G., and McMurtry, I.F. (1984). 'Prevention and reversal of hypoxic pulmonary hypertension by calcium antagonists', *Am. Rev. Respir. Dis.*, **130**, 81–85.

Steel, R.G.D., and Torrie, J.H.(1960). *Principles and Procedures of Statistics*, McGraw-Hill, New York.

Terashita, Z-I., Tsushima, S., Yoshioka, T., Nomura, B., Inada, Y., and Nishikawa, K. (1983). 'CV-3988, a specific antagonist of platelet activating factor', *Life Sci.*, **32**, 1975–1982.

Terashita, Z-I., Imura, Y., Nishikawa, K., and Sumida, S. (1985a). 'Is platelet activating factor a mediator of endotoxin shock?' *Eur. J. Pharm.*, **109**, 257-261.

Terashita, Z-I., Imura, Y., and Nishikawa, K. (1985b). 'Inhibition by CV 3988 of the binding of H³-platelet activating factor to the platelet', *Biochem. Pharm.*, **34**, 1491–1495.

Weir, E.K., Mlczoch, J., Reeves, J.T., and Grover, R.F. (1976). 'Endotoxin and prevention of hypoxic pulmonary vasoconstriction', *J. Lab. Clin. Med.*, **88**, 975–983.

Wescott, J.Y., and Murphy R.C. (1985). 'Effect of alcohols on arachidonic acid metabolism in murine mastocytoma cells and human polymorphonuclear leukocytes', *Biochim. Biophys. Acta.*, **833**, 262–271.

Zerbe, G.O. (1979). 'Randomization analysis of growth and dose response curves', *J. Am. Stat. Assoc.*, **74**, 215–221.

New Horizons in Platelet Activating Factor Research
Edited by C. M. Winslow and M. L. Lee
© 1987 John Wiley & Sons Ltd.

32

Role of Perfusion Medium in the Effects of Platelet Activating Factor-Acether on Isolated Rabbit Lung *In Situ*

B. Arnoux and C.N. Gillis

Benveniste *et al.*, (1972) described the release of platelet-activating factor (PAF) from antigen-stimulated rabbit basophils. This factor, identified as 1-0-alkyl-2-acetyl-*sn*-glycerophosphocholine was named PAF-acether or AGEPC (Benveniste *et al.*, 1979; Demopoulos *et al.*, 1979) and was synthetized in 1980 (Godfroid *et al.*, 1980). Release of this phospholipid from other cells including phagocytic cells and platelets of rabbits, rats, guinea-pigs and humans has also been described (Roubin *et al.*, 1983). PAF-acether not only aggregates platelets, but also affects several other tissues and organs (Benveniste *et al.*, 1983). Thus, PAF-acether, after intravenous (i.v.) or intratracheal administration, increases vascular and bronchial smooth muscle tone in guinea-pig, rabbit, baboon and man (Vargaftig *et al.*, 1980; McManus *et al.*, 1980; Denjean *et al.*, 1983; Gateau *et al.*, 1983). The latter reports indicated that PAF-acether-induced bronchoconstriction required platelets but was independent of arachidonic acid metabolites. Using more sensitive techniques, Page *et al.*, (1984) reported a temporal dissociation between bronchoconstriction and platelet lung accumulation after PAF-acether challenge in guinea-pigs. The dissociation between PAF-acether effects on smooth muscle and blood cells was confirmed by studies on guinea-pig isolated lung perfused with blood cells-free medium (Hamasaki *et al.*, 1984). In this model, vascular and airway responses were observed after i.v. administration of PAF-acether and there was no clear relationship to the cyclooxygenase pathway of arachidonate metabolism.

The aim of the present study was two-fold: first to confirm, in another species, namely the rabbit, the effect of PAF-acether on pulmonary vascular smooth muscle in the absence of blood cells, and second, to study the relationship between the chemical composition of the perfusion medium and the involvement of arachidonic metabolism in the PAF-acether response.

MATERIALS AND METHODS

Animal preparation

Twenty-eight New Zealand male rabbits weighing 2.5 ± 0.2 kg were anesthetized with a mixture of allobarbital (50 mg ml^{-1}), and urethane (200 mg ml^{-1}) administrated into the marginal ear vein. Animals received heparin (500 IU, i.v.) immediately before the surgical procedure, and were sacrificed by an overdose of anesthetic. The trachea was intubated after which the chest was opened and the main pulmonary artery and the left atrium were canulated. Lungs were perfused via the pulmonary artery, at a flow rate of 20 ml min^{-1} with Krebs–Henseleit medium (see below). To remove blood cells from the pulmonary vascular space, the lung preparation was perfused for 10 min before challenge with PAF-acether. Lungs were ventilated with room air at constant pressure and frequency by means of a respirator (Harvard Apparatus, tidal volume 10 ml kg^{-1}, rate 35 min^{-1}). PAF-acether (a gift of Prof. J.J. Godfroid, Université Paris VII, France) at a dose of 1 μg per kg of body weight, was injected directly as a bolus (1–3 μl of stock PAF-acether solution in 200 μl of perfusion medium) into the pulmonary artery. Perfusion pressure, i.e., the pressure in the pulmonary artery as well as left atrial and airway pressures were measured 10 min before and 20 min after PAF-acether challenge, by mean of pressure transducers and a Grass polygraph recorder.

In order to assess the possible role of the cyclooxygenase pathway in PAF-acether-induced effects, some animals were pretreated with indomethacin (10 mg kg^{-1}) 30 min before their sacrifice.

Perfusion medium

Krebs-Henseleit media was prepared freshly for each experiment and had the following composition: NaCl, 6.9 g l^{-1}; KCl, 0.35 g l^{-1}; CaCl$_2$ 2H$_2$0, 0.37 g l^{-1}; KH$_2$PO$_4$, 0.16 g l^{-1}; MgSO$_4$ 7H$_2$0, 0.29 g l^{-1}; NaHCO$_3$, 2.2 g l^{-1} and D-glucose 2 g l^{-1}. The pH was adjusted to 7.4 and the medium was aerated with O$_2$ and CO$_2$ (95 percent and 5 percent respectively) at 37 °C. For some experiments, dextran, 3 percent (M.W. 60–80000, United States Biochemical Corporation), or albumin fraction V, 3 percent, (Sigma) was added to the perfusion medium. When animals were pretreated with indomethacin, this compound was also added in the perfusion medium (5 μg ml^{-1}).

Analysis of arachidonic acid metabolites

5ml samples of the lung effluent were collected 60 s before and 15, 30, 45, 60, 90, 180, and 600 s after PAF-acether challenge. Arachidonic acid metabolites were extracted from the perfusion medium according to classical methods (Mencia-Huerta *et al.*, 1983; Peter *et al.*, 1984). Extracts were stored at -20 °C under nitrogen until analyzed by high performance liquid chromatography (Rainin) with a C-18 reverse phase column (250 × 4.6 mm; 5 μm, Rainin). Lipoxygenase metabolites were analysed with a mobile phase: methanol: water (34:66 percent) at 254 nm and the cyclooxygenase products with acetonitrile: water (33:67 percent, pH 7.4) at 194 nm.

RESULTS

Injection of a PAF-acether bolus immediately increased perfusion pressure, which reached its maximum 90 s later. Pressure was constant for 30 s and returned to the control value within 15−20 min. A similar increase in perfusion pressure was noted with each perfusion medium used (Table 1). Treatment with indomethacin did not alter the constrictor action of PAF-acether on vascular smooth muscle when Krebs-albumin medium was used. However, this effect of PAF-acether was not seen when Krebs−dextran medium was used to perfuse lung from indomethacin-pretreated animals (Table 1).

Table 1.   Effect of PAF-Acether (i.v. 1 μg kg^{-1}) on perfusion pressure in isolated rabbit lung perfused *in situ*

Perfusion medium	n	Perfusion Pressure (cm H_2O)[1]	
		Control	+ 90 s
Krebs	3	11.33 ± 0.88	25.00 ± 3.06[3]
Krebs−Dextran	4	12.00 ± 1.58	26.75 ± 5.34[3]
Krebs−Albumin	4	8.00 ± 1.08	16.13 ± 2.40[2]
Krebs−Dextran−Indo	4	11.67 ± 0.88	12.33 ± 0.33[4]
Krebs−Albumin−Indo	4	9.13 ± 1.42	17.00 ± 2.04[3]

[1]   mean ± S.E.M., Paired *t*-Test
[2] $p<0.01$
[3] $p<0.05$
[4]   not significant

Peak inspiratory pressure was increased only when PAF-acether was administered in the presence of Krebs −albumin medium (Table 2). Pretreatment with indomethacin decreased the effect of PAF-acether but the response was still significantly greater than when the other perfusion media were used (Table 2). The maximum increase occurred 80−90 s after the i.v. injection of PAF-acether. Although airway pressure gradually decreased, even 20 min later it had still not completely returned to baseline values.

Table 2. Effect of PAF-Acether (i.v. 1 μg kg^{-1}) on peak inspiratory pressure in isolated rabbit lung perfused *in situ*

| Perfusion medium | n | Peak Inspiratory Pressure (cm H$_2$O)[1] | |
		Control	+ 90 s
Krebs	3	14.00 ± 0.58	14.00 ± 0.58[3]
Krebs–Dextran	4	14.33 ± 0.33	14.33 ± 0.33[3]
Krebs–Albumin	4	15.33 ± 0.33	20.00 ± 2.89[2]
Krebs–Dextran–Indo	4	14.00 ± 1.73	14.00 ± 1.73[3]
Krebs–Albumin–Indo	4	15.75 ± 0.48	17.88 ± 0.52[2]

[1] mean ± S.E.M., Paired *t*-Test
[2] $p < 0.01$
[3] not significant

Arachidonic acid metabolites

We could not detect either cyclooxygenase and lipoxygenase products of arachidonic acid metabolism in the perfusion medium after PAF-acether challenge. There were no compounds which co-chromatographed with PGE$_2$, PGD$_2$, PGF$_{2a}$, 6-keto PGF$_{1a}$, thromboxane B$_2$, leukotrienes C$_4$, D$_4$, or B$_4$, each of which were used as reference compounds.

DISCUSSION

Our results show that PAF-acether causes vasoconstriction and increases the peak inspiratory pressure of isolated rabbit lung *in situ* and that these effects are seen in the absence of platelets and/or polymorphonuclear leukocytes. These data therefore confirm the observation of Hamasaki *et al.*, (1984) obtained with guinea-pig lungs. The PAF-acether-vascular effect was always present, regardless of the perfusion medium used. Pretreatment with indomethacin does not change the vascular PAF-acether response when Krebs-albumin medium was used, but abolished the latter when Krebs – dextran medium perfused the lung. Two of the media used contained albumin or dextran and thus had increased oncotic pressure. However, the Krebs – albumin medium also had lipids present, since the latter are normal contaminants of albumin fraction V. It was only when Krebs-albumin was used that we noted the airway response and indomethacin did not inhibit the bronchial muscle action of PAF-acether. Thus, as previously described the PAF-acether action in the rabbit lung seems also to depend on the presence of contaminating lipids. Furthermore, the absence of cyclooxygenase products, (in the presence of indomethacin) did not alter the airway action of PAF-acether, confirming observations with other experimental species (Vargaftig *et al.*, 1982; Denjean *et al.*, 1983).

In conclusion, the PAF-acether increased pulmonary vascular and bronchial smooth muscle tone only when the perfusion medium contained both albumin and lipids. At this time, we cannot explain this observation. It is possible, however, that the link between the vascular site of action and the airway contraction is mediated by PAF-acether *per se* or by another product (possibly a lipid) which may also require the presence of albumin.

ACKNOWLEDGMENTS

Supported by NIH Grant HL 13315 and 07410. B. Arnoux is a Fellow of Institut National de la Sante et de la Recherche Medical (France); partially supported by Fondation de la Recherche Medical.

REFERENCES

Benveniste, J., Henson, P.M., and Cochrane, C.G. (1972). 'Leukocyte dependent histamine release from rabbit platelets: the role of IgE, basophils and a platelet-activating factor', *J. Exp. Med.*, **136**, 1356–1377.

Benveniste, J., Tence, M., Varenne, P., Bidault, J., Boullet, C., and Polonsky, J. (1979). 'Semi-synthese et structure proposée du facteur activant les plaquettes (PAF): PAF-acether, un alkyl-ether analogue de la lysophosphatidylcholine', *CR Acad. Sci.*, **289**, 1017–1021.

Benveniste, J., and Arnoux, B., (eds.) (1983). *Platelet-Activating Factor and Structurally Related Ether-lipids. INSERM Symposium no 23.* Elsevier Science Publishers B.V., Amsterdam.

Benveniste, J., Chignard, M., Le Couedic, J.P., and Vargaftig, B.B. (1983). 'Biosynthesis of platelet-activating factor (PAF-acether). II Involvement of phospholipase A_2 in the formation of PAF-acether and lyso PAF-acether from rabbit platelets', *Thromb. Res.*, **25**, 375–386.

Demopoulos, C.A., Pinckard, R.N., and Hanahan, D.J. (1979). 'Platelet-activating factor. Evidence for 1-0-alkyl-2-acetyl-*sn*-glyceryo-3-phosphorylcholine as the active component (a new class of lipid chemical mediators)', *J. Biol. Chem.*, **254**, 9355–9358.

Denjean, A., Arnoux, B., Masse, R., Lockhart, A., and Benveniste, J. (1983). 'Acute effects of intratracheal administration of platelet-activating factor in baboons', *J. Appl. Physiol.*, **55**, 799–804.

Gateau, O., Arnoux, B., Deriaz, H., and Benveniste, J. (1984). 'Acute effect of intratracheal administration of PAF-acether (platelet-activating factor) in Humans', *Am. Rev. resp. Dis.*, **129**, A283.

Godfroid, J.J., Heymans, F., Michel, E., Redeuilh, C., Steiner, E., and Benveniste, J. (1980). 'Platelet-activating factor (PAF-acether): total synthesis of 1-0-octadecyl-2-0-acetyl-*sn*-glycero-3-phosphorylcholine', *FEBS Letters.*, **116**, 161–164.

Hamasaki, Y., Mojarad, M., Saga, T., Tai, H., and Said, S. (1984). 'Platelet-activating factor raises airway and vascular pressures and induces edema in lungs perfused with platelet-free solution', *Am. Rev. resp. Dis.*, **120**, 742–746.

McManus, L.M., Hanahan, D.J., Demoupolous, C.A., and Pinckard, R.N. (1980). 'Pathobiology of the intravenous infusion of acetyl glyceryl ether phosphorylcholine (AGEPC), a synthetic platelet activating factor (PAF) in the rabbit', *J. Immunol.*, **124**, 2919–2929.

Mencia-Huerta, J.M., Razin, E., Ringel, E.W., Corey, E.J., Hoover, D., Austin, K.F., and Lewis, R.A. (1983). 'Immunologic and Ionophore-Induced generation of leukotriene B$_4$ from mouse bone marrow derived mast cell', *J. Immunol.*, **130**, **4**, 1885–1890.

Page, C.P., Paul, W., and Morley, J. (1984). 'Platelets and bronchospasm', *Int. Arch. Allergy appl. Immunol.*, **74**, 347–350.

Peter, S., McGlashan, D.W., Schulman, E.S. Schleimer, R.P., Hayes, E.C., Rokack, J., Adkinson, N.F., and Lichtenstein, L.M. (1984). 'Arachidonic acid metabolism in purified human lung mast cells', *J. Immunol.*, **132**, 1972–1979.

Roubin, R., Tence, M., Mencia-Huerta, J.M., Arnoux, B., Ninio, E., and Benveniste, J. (1983). 'A chemically defined monokine: macrophage-derived platelet-activating factor (PAF-acether)', In E. Pick (ed.) *Lymphokines*, Academic Press, New York, Vol.8. pp. 249–276.

Vargaftig, B.B., Lefort, J., Chignard, M., and Benveniste, J. (1980). 'Platelet-activating factor induces a platelet dependent bronchoconstriction unrelated to the formation of prostaglandin derivates', *Eur. J. Pharm.*, **255**, 10 256–10 260.

Vargaftig, B.B., Lefort, J., Wall, F., Chignard, M., and Medeinos, M.C. (1982). 'No steroidal antiinflammatory drugs if combined with antihistamine and anti-serotonin agents interfere with the bronchial and platelet effect of platelet-activating factor (PAF-acether)', *Eur. J. Pharm.*, **1982**, 121–130.

Role of Platelet Activating Factor in Human Disease

New Horizons in Platelet Activating Factor Research
Edited by C. M. Winslow and M. L. Lee
© 1987 John Wiley & Sons Ltd.

33

Studies of Platelet Activating Factor in Primates

Roy Patterson, Lewis J. Smith and Kathleen E. Harris

SUMMARY

The background of experience with the use of rhesus monkeys as a model of certain aspects of human asthma is reviewed. The comparative responses of rhesus monkeys to a variety of agonists including leukotriene D_4 (LTD_4). In rhesus monkeys PAF is as reactive as any agonist tested and induced airway hyperreactivity to subthreshold doses of LTD_4 or a second subthreshold dose of PAF. Cautious human challenges with PAF have been undertaken and are safe. Bronchial responses are rapid in onset, of short duration and no late reaction is evident. The major effect of PAF is on conductance rather than flow and PAF can induce hyperreactivity to methacholine in normal airways.

Table 1. Various Theories of the Etiology of Asthma

Psychosomatic
Allergic
Neurogenic
Result of bioactive mediators

(Aaronson and Rosenberg, 1985; Reed and Townley, 1983).

INTRODUCTION

Pharmacologic research related to prevention or reversal of asthma has been directed toward the major theories of the pathogenesis of asthma. These are listed in Table 1. It is currently recognized that asthma is neither psychosomatic nor entirely due to allergic exposure (although many cases of asthma are clearly exacerbated by allergen inhalation). The current major foci of research are directed toward an imbalance in neurologic control of airways or bioactive mediators which may induce acute reversible obstructive airway responses or hyperactive airways or both. The hyperactive airway is the basic abnormality of asthma and is of unknown etiology.

Primate Models of Asthma

Various presumptive models of human allergic disease have been developed. These include guinea pigs, rats, rabbits or other species in which the model is generated by parental immunization and may have some relevance to human asthma initiated by inhalation of allergens. The most appropriate model for study in the human asthmatic and the final evaluation of clinical effectiveness of therapeutic agents is by very carefully controlled clinical trials. Studies of human asthma are limited by factors of safety.

Table 2.   Characteristics of Rhesus Monkey Asthma

1.	Ascaris antigen and IgE antibody mediated (Weiszer *et al.*, 1968).
2.	Long duration: month to years (Patterson and Kelly, 1974; Patterson *et al.*, 1976).
3.	Airway response is reproducible in individual animal (Patterson and Kelly, 1974; Patterson *et al.*, 1976).
4.	Results from natural or experimental infection with ascaris species (Patterson *et al.*, 1983a).
5.	Asthmatic monkeys have hyper-reactive airways (Patterson *et al.*, 1976; Patterson and Talbot, 1969).

The model we have developed over the last two decades which most closely simulates human asthma is another primate model, rhesus monkey asthma. The characteristics of this model are summarized in Table 2.

Table 3.   Use of Rhesus Monkey Model of Asthma for Evaluation of Potential Mediators.

1.	Is acute airway response qualitatively similar to antigen?
2.	What is quantitative dose comparison with histamine, prostaglandins, leukotrienes, platelet activating factor?
3.	Does it induce airway hyper-reactivity?
4.	Can receptor antagonist activity against agonist be demonstrated?
5.	Can receptor antagonist activity against antigen induced asthma be demonstrated?

Evaluation of putative mediators of asthma

In considering the potential role of mediators as effectors of asthma it is assumed that the agonist is a natural biologic product of primates as compared with non-specific environmental organic or inorganic stimuli. For a presumptive mediator, the primate model may be used to evaluate the questions listed in Table 3.

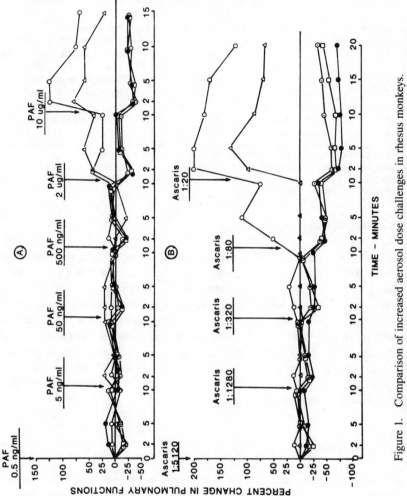

Figure 1. Comparison of increased aerosol dose challenges in rhesus monkeys.
A. PAF dose–response; B. *Ascaris* antigen dose–response in an *Ascaris*-reactive monkey.
Breathing frequency (○); pulmonary resistance (△); peak expiratory flow rate (☉); tidal
volume (□); dynamic compliance (●)

Table 4. Threshold Dose–Response Ranges of Agonists that Produce an Airway Response in Rhesus Monkeys

Rank of reactivity[1]	Agonist	Range of threshold concentration (μg ml^{-1})	Reference
1	PAF	0.05 – 100	Patterson and Harris 1983
2	LTD$_4$	30 – 500	Patterson et al., 1983b
3	PGI$_2$	100 – 1,000	[2] Patterson et al., 1980
4	PGF$_2\alpha$	600 – 2,000	Patterson et al., 1980
5	PGD$_2$	1,000	Patterson et al., 1980
6	Carbocholine	100 – 10,000	Miller and Patterson 1977
7	Histamine	1,000 – 20,000	Greenberger et al., 1979

[1] In order of the lowest to highest concentrations that give a positive response.
[2] Does not completely reproduce an antigen-induced type of airway response when aerosolized alone, but when PGD$_2$ and PGI$_2$ are aerosolized together an antigen type airway response occurs in the range of threshold concentration of 10–100 μg ml^{-1}

Platelet activating factor (PAF)

Synthetic PAF was evaluated in rhesus monkeys according to the questions which could be asked of the rhesus monkey model (Table 3). A qualitative response similar to antigen occurred (Figure 1). The quantitative comparison of the reactive dose of various agonists is shown in Table 4. These results show PAF is as reactive as any of the agonists tested and more clearly reactive than prostaglandins and histamine (Patterson and Harris, 1983). PAF induces airway hyper-reactivity to subthreshold doses of a second challenge with PAF or to leukotriene D$_4$ (Patterson et al., 1984). Finally, a receptor antagonist for PAF will partially inhibit PAF airway responses (Patterson et al., 1986). Studies of PAF receptor antagonism on antigen induced rhesus asthma have not yet been conducted.

Human studies with PAF

Because of various *in vitro* and *in vivo* studies suggesting prolonged or late or inflammatory reactions to PAF as recently reviewed (Morley *et al.*, 1984) bronchial challenges with PAF in humans were undertaken with caution. Only after extensive aerosol challenges in rhesus monkeys with hyperactive airways showed no prolonged, severe or systemic reactions were human studies initiated. After inceasing single dose aerosol challenges at two to three day intervals showed no severe or prolonged airway responses, graded dose bronchial challenges in humans were done in the standard time sequence (Smith *et al.*, 1985). The results will be reported in detail (Rubin *et al.*, 1986). The results are preliminarily summarized as follows. Cautious PAF bronchial challenges are safe in humans. Doses of PAF which produced a significant reduction in SGaw had lesser effect on flow. Responses were rapid and reversed rapidly in less than 1 h. No late responses under the conditions of the experiments were observed. PAF was a more potent agonist than methacholine and sensitized normal airways for methacholine (Rubin *et al.*, 1986).

ACKNOWLEDGMENTS

Supported by USPHS Grant AL 20060 and the Ernest S. Bazley Grant.

REFERENCES

Aaronson, D.W., and Rosenberg, M. (1985). 'Asthma: general concepts'. In: R. Patterson (ed.) *Allergic Diseases - Diagnosis and Management*, 3rd edn, J.B. Lippincott Co., Philadelphia, pp. 253–303.

Greenberger, P., Harris, K., and Patterson, R. (1979). 'The effect of histamine-1 and histamine-2 antagonists on airway responses to histamine in the rhesus monkey', *J. Allergy Clin. Immunol.*, **64**, 189.

Miller, M.M., and Patterson, R. (1977). 'Differential airway reactivity to carbachol and physostigmine sulfate in rhesus monkeys with and without reagin-mediated respiratory responses', *Int. Arch. Allergy Appl. Immunol.*, **53**, 349.

Morley, J., Sanjar, S., and Page, C.P. (1984). 'The platelet in asthma', *Lancet.*, **ii**, 1142, 1984.

Patterson, R., Bernstein, P.R., Harris, K.E., and Krell, R.D. (1984). 'Airway responses to sequential challenges with platelet-activating factor and leukotrine D$_4$ in rhesus monkeys', *J. Lab. Clin. Med*, **104**, 340.

Patterson, R., and Harris, K.E. (1983). 'The activity of aerosolized and intracutaneous synthetic platelet activating factor (AGEPC) in rhesus monkeys with IgE-mediated airway responses and normal monkeys', *J. Lab. Clin. Med.*, **102**, 933.

Patterson, R., Harris, K.E., and Greenberger, P.A. (1980). 'Effect of prostaglandin D$_2$ and I$_2$ on the airways of rhesus monkeys', *J. Allergy Clin. Immunol.*, **65**, 269.

Patterson, R., Harris, K.E., Lee, M.L., and Houlihan, W.J. (1986). 'Inhibition of rhesus monkey airway and cutaneous responses to platelet activating factor (PAF) (AGEPC) with the anti-PAF agent SRI 63-072', (submitted).

Patterson, R., Harris, K.E., and Pruzansky, J.J. (1983a). 'Induction of IgE-mediated cutaneous, cellular and airway reactivity in rhesus monkeys by *Ascaris suum* infection', *J. Lab. Clin. Med.*, **101**, 864–872.

Patterson, R., Harris, K.E., Smith, L.J., Greenberger, P.A., Shaughnessy, M.A., Bernstein, P.R., and Krell, R.D. (1983b). 'Airway response to leukotriene D$_4$ in rhesus monkeys', *Int. Arch. Allergy Appl. Immunol.*, **71**, 156.

Patterson, R., Harris, K.E., Suszko, I.M., and Roberts, M. (1976). 'Reagin mediated asthma in rhesus monkeys and relation to bronchial cell histamine release and airway reactivity to carbocholine', *J. Clin. Invest.*, **57**, 586.

Patterson, R., and Kelly, J.F. (1974). 'Animal models of the asthmatic state', *Ann. Rev. Med.*, **25**, 53.

Patterson, R., and Talbot, C.H. (1969). 'Respiratory responses in subhuman primates with immediate type hypersensitivity', *J. Lab. Clin. Med.*, **73**, 924.

Reed, C.E., and Townley, R.G. (1983). 'Asthma: Classification and pathogenesis'. In E. Middleton Jr., C.E. Reed, and E.F. Ellis, (eds.) *Allergy Principles and Practice*. 2nd edn, C.V. Mosby Co., St Louis, 1983, Vol. 2. pp. 811–831.

Rubin, A.E., Smith, L.J., Patterson, R. (1986). 'Effect of platelet activating factor (PAF) on normal human airways', *Am. Rev. Resp. Dis. (abstract)* (in press).

Smith, L.J., Greenberger, P.A., Patterson, R., Krell, R.D., Bernstein, P.R. (1985). 'The effect of inhaled leukotriene D_4 in humans', *Am. Rev. Resp. Dis.*, **131**, 368.

Weiszer, I.R., Patterson, R., and Pruzansky, J.J. (1968). '*Ascaris* hypersensitivity in the rhesus monkey. I. A model for the study of immediate type hypersensitivity in the primate', *J. Allergy.*, **41**, 14.

New Horizons in Platelet Activating Factor Research
Edited by C. M. Winslow and M. L. Lee
© 1987 John Wiley & Sons Ltd.

34

Inflammatory Features of Asthma

J. Morley, S. Sanjar and C.P. Page

In allergic asthma, inhalation of allergen commonly evokes an airway obstruction that has an acute onset (within minutes), but is transient (resolving within 1–2 h). Acute airway obstruction in response to allergen inhalation has been attributed to contraction of airway smooth muscle, partly because of spontaneous reversibility and partly because of the readiness with which this type of reaction can be suppressed, or reversed, by inhalation of β-adrenoceptor agonists. In a proportion of subjects, inhalation of allergen will also evoke a more protracted period of airway obstruction, with an onset that is delayed by 1–2 h following allergen inhalation. In such subjects, airway obstruction of delayed-onset is associated with exacerbation of airway reactivity. Delayed-onset airway obstruction that results from allergen inhalation is relatively resistant to inhibition or reversal by β-adrenoceptor agonists; on the other hand, it is susceptible to inhibition by glucocorticosteroids (Booij-Noord *et al.*, 1971). This pharmacological profile lends support to the clinical impression that delayed-onset responses to allergen are inflammatory reactions. Consequently, it might be inferred that airway obstruction in asthma is a reflection of inflammatory events within the lung that cause airway obstruction either directly, by obstruction of the lumen with mucus secretions and mucosal edema, or indirectly, by increasing the sensitivity of airway smooth muscle to diverse spasmogens.

Clinical observations favour the interpretation that asthma includes a major inflammatory component. Thus, visualization by bronchoscopy of the effect of a topical application of allergen upon the airways of asthma patients reveals an increased turgor that may be attributed to edema (Metzger *et al.*, 1985); additionally, it has been shown that application of allergen effects an acute retardation of mucociliary clearance in sensitive subjects (Mezey *et al.*, 1978). Both events might be categorized as manifestations of an inflammatory response to products released, or generated, as a consequence of interaction between cell-bound IgE and allergen, but the recruitment and activation of inflammatory cells may also contribute to these symptoms. For instance, there is an increased incidence of eosinophils within lavage fluid collected from asthma patients during the acute phase of a reaction to allergen inhalation (de Monchy *et al.*, 1985). These cells may be responding to allergen directly, for it is now recognized that macrophages, eosinophils and platelets can be activated by interaction between cell-bound IgE and allergen (Capron *et al.*, 1986) as can the mast cell, which hitherto has received greatest attention (Holgate *et al.*, 1986). It has long been recognized that eosinophils are prominent inflammatory populations within the lungs of asthma patients, but more recent studies have revealed that there can also be appreciable numbers of platelets within the lumen of asthmatic airways (A.D. Befus, personal communication) and that platelets within the lumen can be activated by exposure to allergen (Metzger *et al.*, 1985). Further evidence of cellular inflammation is provided by detection of mediators within lavage fluid (Tonnel *et al.*, 1982; Arnoux *et al.*, 1984) or sputum (Cromwell *et al.*, 1982; Grandel *et al.*, 1985).

Pathologists have envisaged asthma as an inflammatory disease in which there are abnormalities of mucus secretion and of mucociliary clearance, as well as persisting inflammatory cell populations in which eosinophils are prominent. This interpretation accords with the clinical pharmacology of the allergic response and might be anticipated from the properties of meditators that are known to be released during allergic or non-allergic inflammatory reactions, particularly since it has now been recognized that PAF is implicated in asthma.

INFLAMMATORY ACTIONS OF PLATELET ACTIVATING FACTOR (PAF)

PAF is able to mimic a number of facets of the sustained inflammatory reaction quite closely (Page *et al.*, 1984a); consequently, it has not proved difficult to establish that PAF has a profile of biological effects that is appropriate to a mediator of those events which characterize asthma. On intradermal injection into flank skin of experimental animals, PAF is a potent stimulus of increased vascular permeability (Morley *et al.*, 1983; Pirotzky *et al.*, 1984; Archer *et al.*, 1985). This effect of PAF is largely independent of platelet activation, since the response is not diminshed in animals that have been depleted of circulating platelets (Paul *et al.*, 1984). However, secretory products of platelets include materials which can induce increased vascular permeability (e.g. histamine, cationic proteins, serotonin) and it is apparent that both platelet-dependent and platelet-independent agencies contribute to plasma protein extravasation in lung tissue (Mojarad *et al.*, 1983; Voelkel *et al.*, 1982).

Impaired mucociliary clearance is evident in experimental animals during an acute response to topical allergen. Whether PAF can mimic this effect has yet to be established; however, it should be noted that this facet of the response to allergen is inhibited by cromoglycate (Allegra *et al.*, 1983), which in other circumstances inhibits inflammatory responses of pulmonary tissue to PAF (Page *et al.*, 1985). Consequently, the finding that relatively high concentrations of PAF affect mucous secretion (Hahn *et al.*, 1985) may yet prove to have significance *in vivo*.

The half-life of PAF *in vivo* has been reported as less than 1 min (Latrigue-Martei *et al.*, 1984), yet intratracheal instillation of PAF will effect an inflammatory reaction that persists for days or weeks (Camussi *et al.*, 1983). One of the earliest components of the inflammatory response to PAF is an intravascular accumulation and activation of both platelets and neutrophils (Dewar *et al.*, 1984). Such phenomena may be considered to be *in vivo* manifestations of the activation by PAF of platelets (Benveniste *et al.*, 1972; Kloprogge *et al.*, 1983) or neutrophils (Ford-Hutchinson, 1983; O'Flaherty *et al.*, 1981). It has also been observed that PAF is a stimulant of chemotaxis and activation of eosinophils *in vitro* (Lee *et al.*, 1984), hence the efflux of oesinophils into the airway lumen that follows application of PAF (Arnoux *et al.*, 1985; Lellouch-Tubiana *et al.*, 1985) can be regarded as a further example of concordance between *in vitro* and *in vivo* effects of PAF. In the baboon, a selective emigration of eosinophils into the airways is clearly evident by 1 h, as an increased incidence of this cell type within cell populations collected by lavage (Arnoux *et al.*, 1985). In skin sites, it was evident that mononuclear cells had been recruited into the injection site and that, by 24 h, a substantial proportion took the form of activated macrophages (Dewar *et al.*, 1984). In atopic subjects, there is a predominance of eosinophils amongst inflammatory cells (B.B. Vargaftig, personal communication). The capacity of eosinophils to generate PAF in substantial quantities (Snyder, 1985) and the sensitvity of eosinophils to activation by PAF may underlie the ability of a single application of PAF to effect cellular inflammation of long duration.

AIRWAY HYPER-REACTIVITY IN ASTHMA

A distinctive feature of asthma is the expression of non-selective airway hyper-reactivity (an enhanced sensitivity to diverse spasmogens or pulmonary irritants). The cellular basis for airway hyper-reactivity remains obscure but may be sought by investigation of the effect of agents which are known to exacerbate hyper-reactivity (i.e. reduce further the threshold to spasmogens). Foremost amongst these is the exposure to allergen, for in addition to eliciting an acute response (usually) and clinically evident late-onset obstruction (less frequently), there is also an increase of airway reactivity, whose intensity can be related to expression of a late-onset response (Cockcroft *et al.*, 1977). The association that exists between expression of a late-onset reponse and hyper-reactivity of the airways has led to a presumption that inflammatory events, that are first manifest during a late-onset response, serve as the determinants of airway hyper-reactivity and that hyper-reactivity is consequent upon release of an inflammatory mediator.

It is now known that hyper-reactivity can be evident prior to expression of the late-onset reaction (Durham *et al.*, 1986), which observation weakens this proposition and indicates that events during the acute allergic reaction may determine hyper-reactivity as implied by the protective effect of DSCG if administered prior to, but not subsequent to the acute response (Pepys, 1973). A range of materials are released or generated during inflammation, but the role of such materials as agencies of enhanced airway hyper-reactivity has usually been subjected to conjecture as opposed to experimental study. It must be re-emphasized that neither individual candidate compounds (histamine, kinins, leukotrienes and prostaglandins), nor cellular activation to yield combinations of such compounds (e.g. mast cell degranulation) have been shown to induce non-selective, long-lasting airway hyper-reactivity in either experimental animals or man (Morley et al., 1984).

PAF AND AIRWAY HYPER-REACTIVITY

PAF was initially considered as relevant to asthma as a consequence of the potency of this material as a spasmogen of airway smooth muscle in laboratory animals (Vargaftig et al., 1980). PAF was a novel spasmogen against which to evaluate anti-asthma drugs and aroused our interest, for it could be shown that therapeutic concentrations of ketotifen or theophylline would inhibit the increase of airway resistance that resulted from exposure of the guinea-pig to PAF (Morley et al., 1985a). This study was performed in spontaneously breathing animals, which are not well suited to drug evaluation, since these animals often respond to exposure to PAF by apnoea and may not survive repeated (>3−4) doses of PAF. Therefore, attempts were made to identify a preparation that might respond reproducibly to PAF over a longer period. The anesthetized, paralyzed guinea-pig ventilated by an air oxygen mixture provided such a preparation. Infusion of PAF into such animals over a period of 1 h elicited a substantial, sustained, non-selective hyper-reactivity (Mazzoni et al., 1985a).

Increased reactivity can be demonstrated conveniently by ascertaining the threshold dose of a spasmogen and by repeating this dose subsequent to a period of PAF infusion. Conversion from a threshold response to a maximal, or near-maximal, response is unequivocal evidence of hyper-reactivity. Modest increases of basal airway resistance do follow infusion of PAF, but in themselves are insufficient to account for more than a minor percentage of the increased response that is observed to follow injection of a spasmogen; neither is the increased reactivity dependent upon central reflex pathways, since section of the vagi does not diminish the increased airway responses that follow infusion of PAF (Mazzoni et al., 1985a). On the other hand, expression of airway hyper-reactivity in response to PAF is dependent upon platelet integrity, since increased reactivity is not evident in animals that have been depleted of platelets by use of a lytic anti-serum; yet, neutrophils which are also activated by PAF, do not appear to contribute to this phenomenon since lytic rabbit anti-guinea pig neutrophil antiserum is without noteworthy effect on the induction of hyper-reactivity by PAF.

It is evident from these studies that exposure to PAF can cause a change in sensitivity of airway smooth muscle and that platelet activation is an essential step in this process. The functional significance of platelet activation is enigmatic for it is evident that aggregation of platelets per se is insufficient to induce airway hyper-reactivity. One possibility is that the process of platelet activation in response to PAF may prove to have unique qualities that determine hyper-reactivity. The most obvious difference between responses to PAF and responses to other platelet stimuli is the coactivation of neutrophils; yet against this can be ranged our experience that substantial reduction of circulating neutrophils did not abrogate the induction of airway hyper-reactivity; moreover, neither LTB$_4$ nor anaphylotoxin (C5a) were able to induce increased hyper-reactivity, when infused in a similar manner to PAF.

When platelet aggregating agents are injected intravenously, there is a rapid accumulation of platelets within the lung (Page *et al.*, 1984b). Isotopic studies of platelet accumulation (Page *et al.*, 1983) indicate that retention of aggregates or microaggregates may be a passive process, since platelets rapidly return to the circulation following inactivation or removal of the aggregatory stimulus. The response to PAF can be so categorized, since intravenous injection of PAF induces an acute transient pulmonary entrapment of platelets; however, a minor proportion are retained within the lung for a longer period. It may be presumed that some of these platelets migrate into lung tissues, since exposure of the guinea-pig to PAF induces an emigration of platelets into pulmonary tissue (Lellouch-Tubiana *et al.*, 1985). Whether such platelets directly modify the function of airway smooth muscle remains a matter for conjecture; however, it does seem inherently unlikely that this effect will prove inconsequential, for already it has been shown that activation of platelets by PAF and the subsequent emigration of platelets so as to appose the surface of smooth muscle cells induces hypertrophy of arterial vascular smooth muscle (Handley *et al.*, 1983). Emigration of platelets into tissue remains the only effect of PAF that is known to induce a persisting charge of function in airway smooth muscle, other than measurement of airway hyper-reactivity *per se*. In the absence of evidence to the contrary increased airway reactivity and platelet-dependent changes of smooth muscle volume as a reaction to PAF should be presumed to be inter-related phenomena.

PROPHYLACTIC ANTI-ASTHMA DRUGS

The identification of prophylactic anti-asthma drugs has been an empirical process that has depended largely upon clinical observation and has not been the result of some scientific insight into the pathology that underlies asthma. The necessity of prophylactic therapy in asthma is often not clearly appreciated:

1. Since the perceived objective of reducing airway obstruction may be achieved more directly by drugs with bronchodilator or anti-inflammatory actions.
2. Since drugs which exhibit these properties and so give symptomatic relief can also have prophylactic activity as an additional, unrelated property.

That characteristic which differentiates prophylactic activity from bronchodilator or anti-inflammatory actions is an effect upon hyper-reactivity; consequently, it is not appropriate to refer to drugs which are prophylactic in asthma as anti-allergic; rather, these drugs should be termed prophylactic anti-asthma drugs, on the understanding that there exists clinical evidence that such an effect has been observed in asthma patients.

Clinical recognition of prophylactic anti-asthma drugs has been greatly hampered by an excessive attention to underlying mechanisms and a relative paucity of studies to ascertain the effects of anti-asthma drugs upon hyper-reactivity *per se*. Amongst chest physicians, there is some divergence of opinion as to optimization of tests for hyper-reactivity, but it can hardly be disputed that such measurements may be readily achieved without exotic equipment; hence, measurement of hyper-reactivity has been advocated as a routine clinical investigation in asthma (Hargreave and Woodcock, 1985). Measurement of airway reactivity has not yet been employed widely for investigation of drug effects. Presumably, there has been a reluctance amongst clinical pharmacologists to use sensitivity to constrictor stimuli as a response index in studies of drug effects in asthma, when simpler tests of lung function (FEV 1.0 or PEFR) are established indicators of severity in clinical circumstances. In the context of prophylaxis, it has been conventional to employ allergen provocation for drugs testing, with the result that prophylactic anti-asthma drugs are commonly termed anti-allergic drugs. It has been uncritically accepted that drug effects upon acute, or late-onset reactions to allergen are predictive of prophylactic efficacy, even though there is adequate evidence to show that neither assumption is valid (Morley *et al.*, 1985b, c).

Four drug categories can be classified as prophylactic in asthma: cromoglycate, ketotifen, theophylline and glucocorticosteroids. Selection in this order is appropriate, for the introduction of cromoglycate into asthma therapy (Altouyan, 1980) was the first anti-asthma drug to be included within this category. An uncertainty as to the mechanism of action of cromoglycate has promoted 20 years of research into the pharmacology of the mast cell, thereby detracting from the ability of this drug to abrogate exacerbation of airway hyper-reactivity, even though such a property was indicated by early trials of cromoglycate in allergen-sensitive asthmatics throughout the pollen season. In view of the extrapolations that have been made on the basis of the ability of cromoglycate to pre-empt acute and late-phase responses to allergen, it is noteworthy that an effect of cromoglycate on the intensification of airway hyper-reactivity that follows a delayed-onset response to allergen has only recently been reported (Cockcroft and Murdock, 1986).

Similar considerations hold to some extent for ketotifen, for this drug was also detected as an effective anti-asthma drug on the basis of clinical studies (Craps, 1980). Attempts were made to define the pharmacology of ketotifen by reference to laboratory tests that were considered relevant to cromoglycate at that time (Greenwood, 1982) and corresponding clinical studies of allergen inhalation have established that ketotifen can inhibit the acute and late-onset components of the reaction to allergen (Girard and Cuevas, 1977). For ketotifen, an inhibitory effect on airway hyper-reactivity has been observed (Dorow and Schiess, 1984) as would be anticipated from therapeutic efficacy in asthma (Craps, 1980).

Theophylline is not widely recognized as a prophylactic drug, and is usually categorized as a bronchodilator. The emphasis on bronchodilator activity accounts for the management of patients by reference to blood levels that are known to achieve bronchodilator responses in asthma. However, clinicians have long recognized that benefit may arise when plasma levels are maintained below 10.0 μg ml^{-1}. The basis of these non-bronchodilator benefits has not been established, but a prophylactic action due to abrogation of hyper-reactivity is favored for two reasons. Firstly, theophylline is able to suppress the development of late-onset reactions to allergen (Pauwels *et al.*, 1985) and whilst not definitive proof of an inhibitory effect on allergen-induced hyper-reactivity, such an observation is suggestive. Secondly, in a clinical comparison with cromoglycate, theophylline proved as effective as cromoglycate in asthma prophylaxis (Hambleton *et al.*, 1977).

Glucocorticosteroids exert diverse inhibitory effects upon inflammatory cell populations, so that asthma prophylaxis might be accepted *a priori* as a property of this drug category. Usage of glucocorticosteroids is often reserved for more severe asthma when substantial deficiencies in lung function are evident, due presumably to a sustained inflammatory response within the lung. Anti-inflammatory properties of glucocorticosteroids may therefore overshadow prophylactic benefit and only recently has inhibition of hyper-reactivity been demonstrated (Sotomayor *et al.*, 1984). This evidence of prophylactic efficacy receives support from the observation that steroid treatment not only reduces late-onset reactions to allergen, but also impairs the development of hyper-reactivity (Fabbri *et al.*, 1985) and it can be considered reasonable to classify these drugs as prophylactic anti-asthma agents.

PROPHYLACTIC ANTI-ASTHMA DRUGS AND PAF

Having ascertained the capacity of PAF to induce airway hyper-reactivity and having established a method for consistently eliciting such an effect (Mazzoni *et al.*, 1985a), it was logical to evaluate prophylactic anti-asthma drugs in such preparations (Mazzoni *et al.*, 1985b). Comparisons have been made using arbitrary doses, selected to ensure that each drug would be present in concentrations at least as great as those observed in therapy; hence, drugs have been administered intravenously as a 1 mg kg^{-1} bolus prior to PAF administration and as an infusion at 1 mg kg^{-1} thereafter. When inhibition was equivocal tests were repeated using a bolus dose of 10 mg kg^{-1} followed by an infusion at 10 mg kg^{-1}h^{-1}. β-adrenoceptor agonists were administered at a lower dose, as a bolus of 10 μg kg^{-1}and infusion of 10 μg kg^{-1}h^{-1}.

From our studies, it may be concluded that the hyper-reactivity that is evident upon termination of an infusion of PAF can be inhibited significantly by ketotifen, glucocorticosteroids, theophylline and cromoglycate; the selective PAF antagonists, kadsurenone and BN 52021 also inhibit this response. The efficacy of these drugs is in marked contrast with other drug categories such as histamine antagonists (mepyramine), histamine antagonist—mast cell stabilizing agents (oxatomide, azelastine), mast cell stabilizing drugs (lodoxamide, tranilast), the mast cell stabilizing—bronch-odilator drugs (isoprenaline and salbutamol), the cyclo-oxygenase inhibitor (indome-thacin) and a novel lipoxygenase inhibitor (QA 208-199).

Under the conditions of this test, drugs effected either dose-related inhibition of PAF-induced hyper-reactivity or were ineffective. Indomethacin and isoprenaline were exceptions, for these drugs intensify the expression of hyper-reactivity, even though these drugs inhibit the acute manifestations of PAF infusion. Whether the intensification of hyper-reactivity merely reflects an inherent capacity of the drug to elicit hyper-reactivity *per se*, as is indicated for indomethacin (Fish *et al.*, 1981) and as has recently been observed for isoprenaline (unpublished observations) has yet to be established.

IMPLICATIONS FOR PROPHYLAXIS

Current usage of anti-asthma drugs in prophylaxis is empirical and there is a marked divergence of opinion as to the utility of such drugs, particularly between different national groups. Prescribing patterns are determined by a range of factors, but it seems likely that uncertainty as to the basis of drug efficacy in asthma prophylaxis must be contributory. This problem is compounded by the failure to differentiate bet-ween spasmolytic effects of anti-asthma drugs and actions to pre-empt hyper-reactiv-ity. The association between an airway obstruction in which there are inflammatory and bronchoconstrictor elements on the one hand and hyper-reactivity that parallels these events yet persists after resolution of the acute inflammation and airway obstru-ction has been a major source of confusion. Until it is recognized that the three elements of an allergic response (acute bronchospasm, late-onset airway obstruction and enhanced airway reactivity) are linked, yet have distinctive pharmacology, conf-licting conclusions about drug effects in asthma will be inescapable. It has been widely advocated, and generally accepted, that an acute allergic reaction with persist-ing inflammation (typified by a late-onset reaction to allergen) and enhanced airway reactivity are linked causally and therefore must have paralleled pharmacology. This is invalid; thus, mast cell stabilizing agents, or β-adrenoceptor agonists can inhibit acute spasm of airway smooth muscle in response to allergen without affecting subse-quent hyper-reactivity whilst non-steroidal anti-inflammatory drugs (Fairfax *et al.*, 1983) and colchicine (S. Peters, personal communication) can inhibit late-onset reac-tions to allergen without affecting hyper-reactivity.

The virtue of the concept that PAF is central to asthma exacerbation is that not only does this provide an explanation for the symptoms of asthma, but it also provides a rationale for the unusual pharmacological profile which characterizes this disease. From the scheme presented (Figure 1), it is implied that bronchodilator drugs be utili-zed for acute symptomatic relief and that one of the four classes of established proph-ylactic anti-asthma drugs be employed routinely to pre-empt development of adverse events due to PAF which may only be detectable as altered hyper-reactivity. Clearly on the evidence presented, drug categories such as agents that inhibit mast cell activation, histamine antagonists, cyclo-oxygenase and lipoxygenase inhibitors and leukotriene antagonists would not be expcted to be useful as prophylactic drugs, a view point that is supported by clinical observation. Whether PAF antagonists fulfill the promise implied by the present studies will depend, in part, upon the consequences of non-selective PAF antagonism in other tissues, for a characteristic of both ketotifen and cromoglycate is an absence of toxic side effects, factors which limit the acceptability of glucocorticosteroids and theophylline. For maintenance therapy, novel prophylactic anti-asthma drugs must be non-toxic as well as effective, since they will have to be administered over lengthy periods (years) to both adults and children.

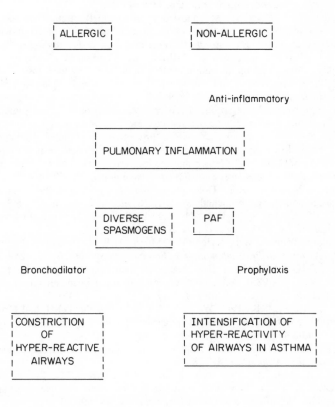

Figure 1.

REFERENCES

Allegra, L., Abraham, W.M., Chapman, G.A., and Wanner, A. (1983). 'Duration of mucociliary dysfunction following antigen challenge', *Journal of Applied Physiology.*, **55**, 726–730.

Altouyan, R.E.C. (1980). 'Review of clinical activity and mode of action of sodium cromoglycate', *Clinical Allergy.*, **10**, 481–489.

Archer, C.B., Page, C.P., Paul, W., Morley, J., and MacDonald, D.M. (1985). 'Inflammatory characteristics of PAF-acether in the skin of experimental animals and man', *International Journal of Tissue Reactions.*, **7**, 363–365.

Arnoux, B., Denjean, A., Page, C.P., Morley, J., and Benveniste J. (1985). 'Pulmonary effects of Platelet Activating Factor in a primate are inhibited by ketotifen', *American Review of Respiratory Diseases.*, **131**, A2.

Arnoux, B., Simoes-Caevoro, M.H., Landes, A., Mathieu, M., Duroux, P., and Benveniste, J. (1982). 'Alveolar macrophages from asthmatic release PAF-acether and lyso PAF-acether when stimulated with specific antigen', *American Review of Respiratory Diseases.*, **125**, 50.

Benveniste, J., Henson, P.M., and Cochrane C.G. (1972). 'Leucocyte dependent histamine release from rabbit platelets: The role of IgE, basophil and a platelet activating factor', *Journal of Experimental Medicine.*, **136**, 1356–1377.

Booij-Noord, H.J., Orie, N.G.M., and De Vries, K. (1971). 'Immediate and late bronchial obstructive reactions to inhalations of housedust and protective effects of disodium cromoglycate and prednisolone', *Journal of Allergy and Clinical Immunology.*, **48**, 344–354.

Camussi, G., Pawlowski, I., Tetta, C., Roffirello, C., Alberton, M., Brentjens, J., and Andres, G. (1983). 'Acute lung inflammation induced in the rabbit by local instillation of 1-0-octadecyl-2-acetyl-sn-glyceryl-3-phosphorylcholine or of a native platelet activating factor', *American Journal of Pathology.*, **115**, 78–88.

Capron, A., Dessaint, J.P., Capron, M., Joseph, M., Ameison, J.C., and Tonnel, A.B. (1986). 'From parasites to allergy: a second receptor for IgE', *Immunology Today.*, **7**, 15–18.

Cockcroft, D.W., and Murdock, K.Y. (1986). 'Protective effect of inhaled albuterol, cromolyn, beclomethasone and placebo on allergen-induced early asthmatic response (EAR), late asthmatic response (LAR) and allergen-induced increase in bronchial responsiveness to inhaled histamine', *Journal of Allergy and Clinical Immunology.*, **77**, 122 (Abs).

Cockcroft, D.W., Ruffin, R.E., Dolovich, J., and Hargreave, F.E. (1977). 'Allergen induced increase in non-allergic bronchial reactivity', *Clinical Allergy.*, **7**, 503–513.

Craps, L. (1980). 'The prophylaxis of bronchial asthma with ketotifen. Five years of clinical investigations', *Acta Therapeutica.*, **6**, 213–225.

Cromwell, O., Walport, M.J., Taylor, G.W., Morris, H.R., O'Driscol, B.R.C., and Kay, A.B. (1982). *Advances in Prostaglandin and Thrombosis Research.*, **9**, 251–259.

De Monchy, J.G.R., Kauffman, H.F., Venge, P., Koeter, G.H., Jansen, H.M., Sluiter, H.J., and De Vries, K. (1985). 'Broncho-alveolar eosinophilia during allergen-induced late asthmatic reactions', *American Review of Respiratory Diseases.*, **131**, 373–377.

Dewar, A., Archer, C.B., Paul, W., Page, C.P., MacDonald, D.M., and Morley J. (1984). 'Cutaneous and pulmonary histopathological responses to platelet activating factor (PAF-acether) in the guinea-pig', *Journal of Pathology.*, **144**, 24–34.

Dorow, P., and Schiess, W. (1984). 'Influence of ketotifen on airway responsiveness in asthmatics', *Journal of Asthma*, **21**, 81–88.

Durham, S.R., Lee, T.H., Cromwell, O., Shaw, R.J., Merrett, T.G., Merrett, J., Cooper, P., and Kay, A.B. (1984). 'Immunologic studies in allergen-induced late-phase asthmatic reactions', *Journal of Allergy and Clinical Immunology.*, **74**, 49–60.

Fabbri, L.M., Chiesura-Corona, P., Dal Vecchio, L., Di Giacomo, G.R., Zocca, E., De Marzo, N., Maestrelli, P., and Mapp, C.E. (1985). Prednisolone inhibits late asthmatic reactions and the associated increase in airway responsiveness induced by toluene diisocyanate in sensitized subjects. *American Review of Respiratory Diseases.*, **132**, 1010–1014.

Fairfax, A.J., Hanson, J.M., and Morley, J. (1983). 'The late reaction following bronchial provocation with house-dust mite allergen. Dependence on arachidonic acid metabolisms', *Clinical Experimental Immunology.*, **52**, 393−398.

Fish, J.E., Ankin, M.G., Adkinson, Jr., N.F., and Peterman, V.I. (1981). 'Indomethacin modification of immediate-type immunologic airway responses in allergic asthmatic and nonasthmatic subjects', *American Review of Respiratory Diseases.*, **123**, 609−614.

Ford-Hutchinson, A.W. (1983). 'Neutrophil aggregating properties of PAF-acether and leukotriene B4', *International Journal of Immunopharmacology.*, **5**, 17−21.

Girard, J.P., and Cuevas, M. (1977). 'Anti-asthmatic properties of a new peroral drug (HC 20-511)', *Acta Allergologica.*, **32**, 27.

Grandel, K.E., Wardlow, M.L., and Farr, R.S. (1985). 'Platelet activating factor in sputum of patients with asthma and COPD', *Federation Proceedings*, **44**, 184.

Greenwood, C. (1982). 'The pharmacology of ketotifen', *Chest*, **82** 45S−48S.

Hahn, H.L., Purnama, I., Lang, M., Sannwald, U., and Stenzel, H. (1985). 'Effects of platelet activating factor on release of mucous from tracheal sub-mucosal glands of the ferret', *American Review of Respiratory Diseases*, **131**, A27.

Hambleton, G., Weinberger, M., Taylor, J., Cavanaugh, M., Ginschansky, E., Godfrey, S., Tooley, M., Bell, T., and Greenburg S. (1977). 'Comparison of cromoglycate (cromolyn) theophylline in controlling symptoms of chronic asthma', *Lancet*, **i**, 381−385.

Handley, D.A., Lee, M.L., and Saunders R.N. (1983). 'Extravasation and aortic ultrastructural changes accompanying acute and sub-acute intraperitoneal administration of PAF', In J. Benveniste and B. Arnoux (eds.) *Platelet Activating Factor; INSERM symposium No. 23.* Elsevier Science Publishers, B.V. Amsterdam, pp. 245−250.

Hargreave, F.E., and Woolcock, A.J. (1985). *Airway responsiveness: Measurement and interpretation*, Astra Medical Publications.

Holgate, S.T., Hardy, C., Robinson, C. Agius, R.M., and Howarth, P.H. (1986). 'The mast cell as a primary effector cell in the pathogenesis of asthma', *Journal of Allergy and Clinical Immunology.*, **77**, 274−282.

Kloprogge, E., De Haas, G.H., Gorter, G., and Akkerman, H.W.N. (1983). 'Stimulus response coupling in human platelets. Evidence against a role of PAF-acether in the Third Pathway', *Thrombosis Research*, **30**, 107−112.

Latrigue-Martei, C., Godeneche, D., Chabard, J.L., and Berger, J.A. (1982). 'Pharmacokinetic study of PAF-acether: preliminary results after the intravenous administration of a 3H-labeled product to the rabbit', *Agents and Actions*, **12**, 703−704.

Lee, T.C., Lenihan, D.J., Malone, B., Roddy, L.L., and Wasserman, S.I. (1984). 'Increased biosynthesis of platelet activating factor in activated human eosinophils', *Journal of Biological Chemistry.*, **259**, 5526−5530.

Lellouch-Tubiana, A., Lefort, J., Pirotzky, E., Vargaftig, B.B., and Pfister, A. (1985). 'Ultrastructural evidence for extravascular platelet recruitment in the lung upon intravenous injection of platelet activating factor (PAF-acether) to guinea-pigs', *British Journal of Experimental Pathology.*, **66**, 345−356.

Mazzoni, L., Morley, J., Page, C.P., and Sanjar, S. (1985a). 'Prophylactic anti-asthma drugs impair the airway hyperreactivity that follows exposure to platelet activating factor (PAF)', *British Journal of Pharmacology.*, **86**, 571P.

Mazzoni, L., Morley, J., Page, C.P., and Sanjar, S. (1985b). 'Induction of hyperreactivity by platelet activating factor in the guinea-pig', *Journal of Physiology.*, **365**, 107P.

Metzger, W.J., Hunninghake, G.W., and Richerson, H.B. (1985). 'Late asthmatics responses: inquiry into mechanisms and significance'. *Clinical Allergy.*, **3**, 145−165.

Mezey, R.J., Cohen, M.A., Fernandez, R.J., Januszkiewicz, A.J., and Wanner, A. (1978). 'Mucociliary transport in allergic patients with antigen-induced bronchospasm', *American Review of Respiratory Diseases.*, **118**, 677−684.

Mojarad, M., Hamasaki, Y., and Said, S.I. (1983). 'Platelet activating factor increases pulmonary microvascular permeability and induces pulmonary oedema', *Bulletin Européen de Physiopathologie Respiratoire.*, **19**, 253–257.

Morley, J., Hanson, J.M., and Page, C.P. (1984). 'Mediator characterisation and asthma', *Lancet.*, **i**, 162.

Morley, J., Page, C.P., Mazzoni, L., and Sanjar, S. (1985a). 'Anti-allergic drugs in asthma', *Triangle.*, **24**, 59–70.

Morley, J., Page, C.P., and Paul, W. (1983). 'Inflammatory actions of platelet activating factor (PAF-acether) in guinea-pig skin', *British Journal of Pharmacology.*, **80**, 503–509.

Morley, J., Page, C.P., and Sanjar, S. (1985b). 'PAF and airway hyperreactivity', *Lancet.*, **ii**, 451.

Morley, J., Page, C.P., and Sanjar, S. (1985c). 'Pharmacology of the late response to allergen and its relevance to asthma prophylaxis', *International Archives of Allergy and Applied Immunology.*, **77**, 73–78.

O'Flaherty, J.T., Wykle, R.L., Miller, C.H., Lewis, J.C., Waite, M., Bass, D.A., McCall, C.E., and De Chatelet, L.R. (1981). '1-0-alkyl-2-acetyl-*sn*-glyceryl-3-phosphorylcholines: A novel class of neutrophil stimulants', *American Journal of Pathology*, **103**, 70–90.

Page, C.P., Archer, C.B., Paul, W., and Morley, J. (1984a). 'PAF-acether: a mediator of inflammation and asthma', *Trends in Pharmacological Science.*, **5**, 239–241.

Page, C.P., Guerreiro, D., Sanjar, S. and Morley, J. (1985). 'Platelet activating factor (PAF-acether) may account for late-onset reactions to allergen inhalation', *Agents and Actions.*, **16**, 30–33.

Page, C.P., Paul, W., and Morley, J. (1983). 'In-vivo aggregation of guinea-pig platelets in response to synthetic platelet activating factor (PAF-acether)', *Agents and Actions.*, **13**, 506–507.

Page, C.P., Paul, W., and Morley, J. (1984b). 'Platelets and bronchospasm', *International Archives of Allergy and Applied Immunology.*, **74**, 347–350.

Paul, W., Page, C.P., Cunningham, F.M., and Morley, J. (1984). 'The plasma protein extravasation response to PAF-acether is independent of platelet accumulation', *Agents and Actions.*, **15**, 80–82.

Pauwels, R., Van Renterghem, D., Van Der Straeten, M., Johannesson, N., and Persson, C.G.A. (1985). 'The effect of theophylline and enprophylline on allergen induced bronchocontrictions', *Journal of Allergy and Clinical Immunology*, **76**, 583–590.

Pepys, J. (1973). 'Immunopathology of allergic lung disease', *Clinical Allergy*, **3**, 1-22.

Pirotzky, E., Page, C.P., Roubin, R., Pfifster, A., Paul, W., Bonnet, J., and Benveniste, J. (1984). 'PAF-acether-induced plasma exudation in rat skin is independant of platelets and neutrophils', *Microcirc. Endothel. Lymphatic.*, **1**, 107-122.

Snyder, F. (1985). 'Chemical and biochemical aspects of platelet activating factor: A novel class of acetylated ether-linked choline phospholipids', *Medical Research Review.*, **5**, 107–140.

Sotomayor, H., Badier, M., Vervloet, D., and Orehek, J. (1984). 'Seasonal increase of carbachol airway responsiveness in patients allergic to grass pollen: reversal by corticosteroids', *American Review Respiratory Diseases.*, **130**, 56–58.

Tonnel, A.B., Joseph, M., Gosset, P., Fournier, E., and Capron, A. (1982). 'Stimulation of alveolar macrophages in asthmatic patients after local provocation tests', *Lancet.*, **i**, 1406–1408.

Vargaftig, B.B., Lefort, J. Chingard, M., and Benveniste, J. (1980). 'Platelet-activating factor induces a platelet dependent bronchoconstriction unrelated to the formation of prostaglandin derivatives', *European Journal of Pharmacology.*, **65**, 185–192.

Voelkel, N.F., Worthen, S., Reeves, J.T., Henson, P.M., and Murphy, R.C. (1982). 'Nonimmunological production of leukotrienes induced by platelet activating factor', *Science.*, **218**, 286–288.

New Horizons in Platelet Activating Factor Research
Edited by C. M. Winslow and M. L. Lee
© 1987 John Wiley & Sons Ltd.

35

Kadsurenone Differentially Affects Platelet Activating Factor and Peptide Stimulated Prostaglandin Release in Unilateral Ureteral Obstruction

Steven M. Weisman, Robert M. Freund, Diane Felsen and E. Darracott Vaughan, Jr

Platelet activating factor (PAF) is an endogenous biologically active phospholipid with a number of sites of synthesis and activity. In addition to its production by inflammatory cells, PAF synthesis and release has recently been demonstrated from the kidney (Pirotsky *et al.*, 1984). Many of PAF's pro-inflammatory actions may be mediated through interactions with arachidonic acid (AA) metabolism, suggesting a role for such an interaction in the tissue response to injury.

Unilateral ureteral obstruction (UUO) results in renal parenchymal injury as well as profound aberrations in hemodynamic parameters (Vaughan *et al.*, 1971). Alterations in endogenous and exogenous renal AA metabolism in the resulting hydronephrotic kidney (HNK), which include an enhancement of prostaglandin (PG) synthesis and an unmasking of thromboxane (TxA_2) synthesis, may be responsible for the hemodynamic defects associated with this condition (Morrison *et al.*, 1977).

Our previous findings have shown that PAF is a potent stimulus for PG release from the isolated perfused HNK (Weisman *et al.*, 1985). In the present experiment, the effect of three structurally distinct specific PAF-receptor antagonists—kadsurenone (Shen *et al.*, 1985), triazolam (Kornecki *et al.*, 1984) and CV-3988 (Terashita *et al.*, 1983)—on renal PG release was studied. Both PGE_2 and TxB_2 release were quantified to confirm that PAF-stimulated PG release represents a receptor mediated phenomenon, and to determine whether PAF-receptor antagonism might differentially affect their release. In addition, the effect of these agents on peptide stimulated PG release from the HNK was examined.

MATERIALS AND METHODS

New Zealand white male rabbits weighing between 2.3 and 3.0 kg were used in these experiments. The left ureter was aseptically ligated as previously described (Weisman et al., 1985).

Seventy-two hours after obstruction, the animals were anesthetized and a laparotomy performed to expose the renal vessels. Both the renal artery and renal vein were cannulated with PE-90 tubing and the kidneys flushed through the renal artery cannula with 10 ml of heparinized saline.

After flushing, the kidneys were transferred to a water jacket chamber (37 °C) and were perfused with oxygenated (95 percent O_2 – 5 percent CO_2) Krebs-Henseleit media containing 0.25 percent bovine serum albumin (BSA) at 10 ml min^{-1}. After a 3 hour equilibration period, aliquots of the renal effluent were collected over 5 min periods for radioimmunoassay (RIA) of prostaglandin E_2 (PGE$_2$) and TxB$_2$ before (basal) and after agonist stimulation (stimulated) as previously described (Weisman et al., 1985). All agonists were introduced as a 100 ng bolus (100 μl) into the renal artery cannula and flushed with 500 μl of the perfusion buffer. After this control period, antagonists were added to the perfusion media and infused through the renal artery cannulae for 15 min. With antagonist infusion continuing agonists were tested again. The appropriate vehicle was added to the perfusion media during both the control and experimental periods to control for any effects of the vehicle on agonist stimulated PG release. The recovery period consisted of a 30 min washout of antagonist followed by repeating the agonist stimulation.

The following agonists and antagonists were used and were prepared as described:

PAF (1-0-alkyl-2-acetyl-sn-glyceryl-3-phosphorylcholine) prepared from bovine heart lecithin (Sigma, St Louis). 100 μg ml^{-1} ethanol stock diluted in Krebs buffer to a concentration of 1 μg ml^{-1}.

Angiotensin II (AII) and bradykinin (BK) (Sigma, St Louis) prepared as 1 mg ml^{-1} aqueous stock diluted to 1 μg ml^{-1} in Krebs buffer.

PAF Receptor Antagonists

Kadsurenone (kindly supplied By T. Shen, Merck and Co). 1 mg ml^{-1} solution in DMSO. Diluted in Krebs–BSA to a final concentration of 1 μg ml^{-1} and a vehicle concentration of 0.1 percent DMSO.

CV-3988 (kindly supplied by Takeda Chemical Corp) 12.4 mg ml^{-1} in saline. Diluted in Krebs–BSA to a final concentration of 12.4 μg ml^{-1} (20 μM) and a vehicle concentration of 0.1 percent saline.

Triazolam (kindly supplied by the Upjohn Corp) 1.72 mg ml^{-1} solution in ethanol. Diluted in Krebs–BSA to a final concentration of 1.72 μg ml^{-1} (5 μM) and a vehicle concentration of 0.1 percent ethanol.

Table 1. Percent Inhibition of PGE$_2$ and TxB$_2$ Release by PAF Receptor Antagonists

Agonist		Kadsurenone 3 μM $n = 6$	Drug Triazolam 5 μM $n = 6$	CV−3988 20 μM $n = 6$
PAF	(100 ng)			
	PGE$_2$	28.2%[1]	0%	92.0%[1]
	TxB$_2$	62.5%[1]	35.0%[1]	95.0%[1]
BK	(100 ng)			
	PGE$_2$	0%	0%	37.0%[1]
	TxB$_2$	35.0%[1]	12.7%[1]	64.0%[1]
AII	(100 ng)			
	PGE$_2$	0%	0%	54.1%
	TxB$_2$	31.9%[1]	N.D.	70.0%[1]

[1] $p < 0.05$
Krebs perfused HNKs were stimulated with a bolus injection of each agonist prior to, and following a 15 min period in which antagonists were added to the perfusion media. PG release was measured by RIA ($n = 6$) for each agonist and antagonist and the percent inhibition calculated

RESULTS

In these experiments, three different PAF-receptor antagonists were found to have inhibitory actions on stimulated PG release from the isolated perfused HNK (Table 1). All three of the antagonists studied exhibited an inhibitory effect on PAF−stimulated Tx release. At the doses used, CV-3988 was the most efficacious, decreasing TxB$_2$ release from 52.9 ng to 4.5 ng, representing a 95.0 percent inhibition. Kadsurenone also diminished PAF-stimulated Tx release as did triazolam by 62.5 percent and 35.0 percent, respectively. PGE$_2$ release stimulated by PAF was also affected by these drugs. CV-3988 inhibited PGE$_2$ synthesis by 92.0 percent while kadsurenone decreased PGE$_2$ release by 28.2 percent. Triazolam was unique, in that it significantly inhibited PAF-stimulated TxB$_2$ release without inhibiting PGE$_2$ release.

In addition to their effect on PAF-stimulated PG release, the PAF-receptor antagonists had an effect on peptide stimulated PG release in the HNK. Both the BK- and AII- stimulated Tx release was affected by the receptor antagonists, although to a lesser extent than was PAF-stimulated release. CV-3988 decreased BK- and AII-stimulated TxB$_2$ release by 64.0 percent and 70.0 percent respectively. Kadsurenone had a similar action and inhibited BK-stimulated release by 35.0 percent and AII-stimulated release by 31.9 percent. Triazolam inhibited BK-stimulated TxB$_2$ release by 12.7 percent.

PGE$_2$ release stimulated by BK and AII was not as greatly affected by the three antagonists. In fact, kadsurenone and triazolam had no effect on the stimulated release of PGE$_2$ by these agonists. CV-3988, on the other hand, diminished BK- and AII-stimulated PGE$_2$ release by 37.0 percent and 54.0 percent respectively.

In summary, all three of the PAF antagonists examined had a greater inhibitory effect on TxB$_2$ release than PGE$_2$ regardless of the agonist employed. While each of the drugs affected BK- or AII-stimulated PG release, their greatest activity was against PAF-stimulated release.

DISCUSSION

A myriad of interactions exists between the renin–angiotensin, prostaglandin and kinin systems in the kidney. In UUO, stimulation of the HNK by the effector molecules of the renin-angiotensin (AII) and kinin systems (BK) results in an exaggerated PG release. In addition, we have previously shown that PAF, which may also be released intrarenally, is a potent stimulus for renal PG release from the HNK (Weisman *et al.*, 1985). The finding that three structurally distinct PAF-receptor antagonists significantly inhibit PAF-stimulated PG release from the HNK is further evidence in support of this release being receptor mediated. Of particular interest is our finding that these drugs, at the doses administered, have a greater effect on Tx release than PGE$_2$ release stimulated by PAF, suggesting the possibility of a differential site for PGE$_2$ and Tx synthesis within the HNK. This finding is consistent with our previous observation of differential agonist-stimulated PGE$_2$ and TxB$_2$ release. Equivalent bolus doses of AII and PAF release equivalent amounts of PGE$_2$, whereas PAF is more potent than AII in stimulating TxB$_2$ release from the HNK. Thus by using both agonists and antagonists, it is possible to dissociate TxB$_2$ and PGE$_2$ release. This may indicate the existence of differential sites of synthesis or coupling of receptors to synthetic enzymes which may differ in their accessibility to both the agonists and antagonists (Weisman *et al.*, 1985). The possibility also exists, that these agents may alter the activity of thromboxane synthetase in addition to their PAF-antagonistic properties, thus preferentially inhibiting Tx release. To study this possibility further, we examined the effects of these drugs, at the concentration used in the perfusion studies, on renal microsomal arachidonic acid metabolism, assessed by conversion of ^{14}C-AA to radiolabelled metabolites. These studies along with platelet aggregation studies using AA as the agonist, in the presence of the PAF-receptor antagonists, confirm that these drugs have no significant inhibitory action on PGE$_2$ or TxB$_2$ synthesis in these systems (unpublished findings).

The observation that kadsurenone, triazolam, and CV-3988 significantly alter AII- and BK-stimulated PG release, with TxB$_2$ release being inhibited preferentially, suggests that these peptides may stimulate intrarenal PAF release.This may be secondary to phospholipase activation by AII and BK which may be important in the synthesis and release of PAF from the renal medulla. While this hypothesis is attractive, it is conceivable that such findings represent non-specific effects of these antagonists, and it requires measurement of PAF release from these kidneys for confirmation.

The findings presented here are intriguing in that they suggest that part of the bioactivity of vasoactive peptides in the kidney may be mediated by PAF. This may be of greater significance in UUO in which intrarenal PAF levels may be elevated as a result of the functional and biochemical aberrations associated with this condition.

REFERENCES

Blank, M.L., Snyder, F., Byer, L.W., Broods, B., and Muirhead, E.E. (1979). 'Antihypertensive activity of an alkyl ether analog of phosphatidyl-choline', *Biochem. Biophys. Res. Commun.*, **90**, 1194–1202.

Fitzpatrick, F.A. (1982).'A radioimmunoassay for thromboxane B_2'. In W.E.M. Lands and W.L. Smith (eds.) *Methods in Enzymology*, Academic Press, New York, Vol. 86, pp. 286–297.

Kornecki, E., Ehrlich, Y., and Lenox, R. (1984). 'Platelet-activating factor-induced aggregation of human platelets specifically inhibited by triazolobenzodiazepines', *Science.*, **226**, 1454–1456.

Morrison, A.R., Nishikawa, K., and Needleman, P. (1977). 'Unmasking of Thromboxane A_2 synthesis by ureteral obstruction in the rabbit kidney', *Nature (London).*, **267**, 259–260.

Okegawa, T., Jonas, P.E., De Schryver, K., Kawasaki, A., and Needleman, P. (1983). 'Metabolic and cellular alterations underlying the exaggerated renal prostaglandin and thromboxane synthesis in ureter obstruction in rabbits', *J. Clin. Invest.*, **71**, 81–90.

Pirotsky, E., Bidault, J., Burtin, C., Gubler, M.C., and Benveniste, J. (1984). 'Release of platelet activating factor, slow-reacting substance, and vasoactive amines from isolated rat kidneys', *Kid. Int.*, **25**, 404–410.

Shen, T.Y., Hwang, S-B., Chang, M.N., Doebber, T.W., Lam, M.T., Wu, M.S., Wang, X., Han, G.Q., and Li, R.Z. (1985). 'Characterization of platelet-activating factor receptor antagonist isolated from haifenteng (*Piper futokadsura*): Specific inhibition of *in vitro*, and *in vivo* platelet-activating factor-induced effects', *Proc. Natl. Acad. Sci. USA.*, **82**, 672–676.

Terashita, Z., Tsushima, S., Yoshioka, Y., Nomura, H., Inada, Y., and Nishikawa, K. (1983). 'CV-3988—A specific antagonist of platelet activating factor (PAF)', *Life Sciences.*, **32**, 1975–1982.

Vargaftig, B.B., Chignard, J., Benveniste, J., Lefore, J., and Wall, F. (1981). 'Background and present status of research on platelet-activating factor (PAF-aether)', *Ann. N.Y. Acad. Sci.*, **370**, 119.

Vaughan, E.D., Jr., Gillenwater, J.Y., and Shenasky, J. H., II. (1971). 'Mechanisms of acute hemodynamic response to ureteral occlusion', *Invest. Urol.*, **9**, 109–118.

Weisman, S., Felsen, D., and Vaughan, E.D., Jr. (1985). 'Platelet-activating factor is a potent stimulus for renal prostaglandin synthesis: Possible significance in unilateral ureteral obstruction', *J. Pharm. Exp. Ther.*, **235**, 10–15.

New Horizons in Platelet Activating Factor Research
Edited by C. M. Winslow and M. L. Lee
© 1987 John Wiley & Sons Ltd.

36

Cebus apella Primate Responses to Platelet Activating Factor and Inhibition by Platelet Activating Factor Antagonist SRI 63–072

*Dean A. Handley, Ronald G. Van Valen, Mark L. Lee
and Robert N. Saunders*

ABSTRACT

We have evaluated the effects of intravenous injection of synthetic PAF in the non-human primate *Cebus apella*. Measurements conducted were hemoconcentration (HC; monitored by changes in hematocrit), bronchoconstriction (BC; increased airway resistance to fixed airway ventilation) and *in vivo* clearance of [^{3}H]PAF. Animals exhibited reproducible but varying sensitivities to PAF-induced HC, where 3.5–30 μg kg^{-1} PAF was required to produce 28–32 percent HC for the colony. There was no evidence of BC following PAF injection. Labeled PAF was rapidly cleared from the plasma, with a t$_{1/2}$ = 30–40 s. Prior injection of the PAF receptor antagonist SRI 63-072 at 3 mg kg^{-1} inhibited cebus HC responses to 3.5 μg kg^{-1} PAF by 96 percent (ED$_{50}$ = 0.85 mg kg^{-1} i.v.). These results show that the *Cebus* exhibits a reproducible HC effect to PAF which can be inhibited by a PAF receptor antagonist.

INTRODUCTION

A major vascular response to PAF involves increased endothelial permeability (Wedmore and Williams, 1981), leading to extravasation of protein rich plasma and hemoconcentration (McManus *et al.*, 1981). While the vascular effects of PAF have been extensively studied in guinea-pigs, rats, rabbits and dogs, relatively few investigations in primates have been performed (Denjean *et al.*, 1983; McManus *et al.*, 1981; Patterson and Harris, 1983). We have examined the hematocrit and pulmonary effects of PAF in the *Cebus apella* and describe the inhibitory effects of the PAF receptor antagonist SRI 63–072.

MATERIALS AND METHODS

The C_{18}-PAF used in this study was synthesized by literature procedures and evaluated for biological activity and chemical purity (Handley *et al.*, 1985). Labeled PAF (9′, 10^{L3}H) with a specific activity of 50 Ci mM^{-1} was mixed with cold PAF (total dosage: 3.5 μg kg^{-1}) and injected according to HC studies. Blood samples were taken at 0.5–1.0 min time intervals, centrifuged and the radioactivity measured in the plasma and packed cell volume. Male *Cebus* (3.0–4.5 kg) were anesthetized with ketamine (10–15 mg kg^{-1} i.m.) for HC studies. All animals were given 3.5 μg kg^{-1} PAF i.v. in tris-Tyrode's (TT) containing 2 percent ethanol and blood samples were taken before PAF to determine starting hematocrit and then at 2 min intervals starting 1 min after PAF injection. The HC was expressed as percent change from starting values. With these responses determined, the PAF dose was increased for less sensitive animals to obtain a 28–32 percent HC for the colony. Animals were then tested at one week intervals until four to seven PAF-induced control HC values were obtained for each animal. SRI 63–072 (> 98 percent pure) was solubilized in tris-Tyrode's (TT, pH 7.4) and given 5 min before PAF. After inhibitor testing, animals were subsequently tested the following week with PAF alone at their respective PAF dose to confirm HC responses. In this type of cross-over design, the entire colony of cebus were evaluated with the PAF antagonist. The ED$_{50}$ for 63-072 was only from animals at the 3.5 μg kg^{-1} sensitivity dose (n = 5).

For pulmonary studies, *Cebus* were partially anesthetized with ketamine for capture, given flaxedil (0.1 mg kg^{-1} i.m.), intubated with an endotracheal catheter (Magill 10200, Fr. 12) and artificially respirated (7.5 ml kg^{-1}, 60 breaths min^{-1}) using a Harvard respirator. Pulmonary resistance to fixed airway ventilation using a Statham–Gould P231D transducer and physiograph was monitored following 3.5 μg kg^{-1} PAF (HC was also measured).

RESULTS

The HC of individual animals challenged with 3.5 μg kg^{-1} PAF occurs by 10 min after PAF administration (Figure 1) and the hematocrit returned to starting values within 12–18 h (not shown). The initial phase of clearance of radioactivity was rapid, with a t$_{1/2}$ = 30–40 s (Figure 2). The second phase of radioactivity clearance was slower with an approximate t$_{1/2}$ of 10–15 min. As only 5–10 percent of injected radioactivity was recovered in the packed cell volume, circulating blood cells are not participating in the removal of PAF from the plasma compartment. The individual doses of PAF required to produce 28–32 percent HC for the *Cebus* colony ranged from 3.5–30 μg kg^{-1} (Figure 3). Once these individual PAF doses were established, the weekly HC profiles were highly reproducible.

Administration of SRI 63-072 5 min before PAF inhibited the expected HC profiles of all animals in the *Cebus* colony; the extent of inhibition was related to the

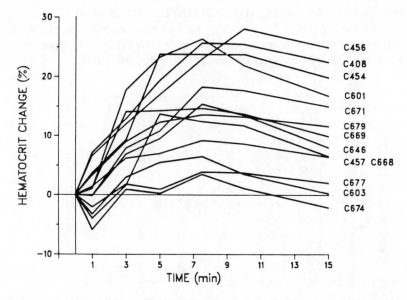

Figure 1.   Individual HC profiles for *Cebus* challenged with 3.5 μg kg⁻¹ PAF i.v. The starting hematocrit values of the animals have been normalized to zero. *Reproduced from Handley* et al., Immunopharmacology, *1986, by permission* of *Elsevier Science Publishers B.V.*

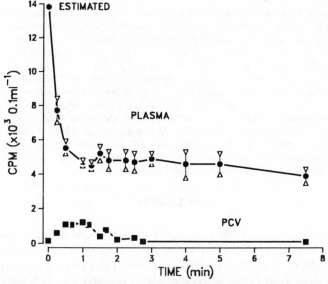

Figure 2.   Time course of [³H]PAF clearance (50 Ci mM⁻¹ sp. act.) where total PAF dose was 3.5 μg kg⁻¹ ($n = 3$). Shown are radioactivity from plasma (upper panel) and packed cell volume (PCV) (lower panel). Evidence suggests a rapid clearance phase ($t_{1/2} = 0.5–1.0$) followed by a slower distribution phase ($t_{1/2} = 10–15$ min).

individual animal sensivity to PAF (Figure 3). The ED_{50} for SRI 63-072 (against 3.5 μg kg^{-1} PAF) was 0.85 mg kg^{-1}. At 3.5 μg kg^{-1} PAF, no increases in pulmonary resistance pressure to fixed airway ventilation were observed (Figure 4, upper panel). However, normal HC profiles were observed (Figure 4, lower panel).

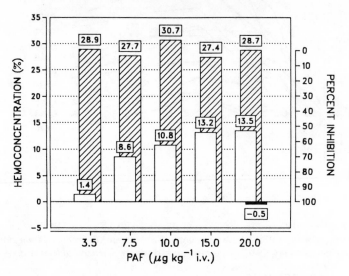

Figure 3. Doses of PAF needed to produce 28−32 percent HC for the *Cebus* colony range from 3.5 μg kg^{-1} to 20.0 μg kg^{-1}. Individual responses varied less than 10 percent of mean when tested at weekly intervals. The average HC increase for each group of animals tested at the indicated PAF dose (2−5 animals per group) are shown in the lined bars, with the actual percent value enclosed above each bar. Inhibition by SRI 63−072 of PAF-induced HC in the *Cebus* (open bars) was seen at 3.0 kg^{-1} i.v. 1−5 min before PAF (actual percent value enclosed above each bar). The percent inhibition is indicated in the right ordinate. Doubling the dose of SRI 63−072 to 6 mg kg^{-1} doubled the inhibition in the 20 mg kg^{-1} group from 55 percent to 100 percent. *Reproduced from Handley* et al., Immunopharmacology, *1986 by permission of Elsevier Science Publishers B.V.*

DISCUSSION

Injection of PAF to *Cebus* reveals marked individual differences in sensitivity in terms of hematocrit changes. All PAF-induced HC responses were inhibited by prior injection of SRI 63-072 in a dose-dependent manner. The inhibition of the PAF antagonist was proportional to the individual animal sensitivity to PAF-induced HC, where the most sensitive animals expressed >95 percent inhibition. In these animals, [^{3}H]-PAF was rapidly cleared with an initial $t_{1/2}$ = 30−40 s, evident as a rapid distribution in the plasma followed by slow elimination ($t_{1/2}$ = 10−15 min).

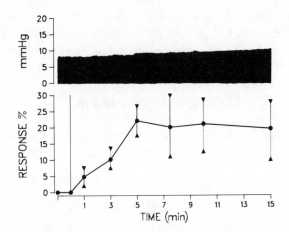

Figure 4.   Representative physiograph tracing of increased resistance to fixed airway ventilation (upper panel) and HC profiles (mean ± S.D., *n* = 4, lower panel) as a function of time after 3.5 μg kg⁻¹ PAF injection. There was no evidence of bronchoconstriction following PAF, although the animals exhibited the expected HC responses. *Reproduced from Handley* et al., Immunopharmacology, *1986, by permission of Elsevier Science Publishers, B.V.*

The rate of [³H]-PAF disappearance from plasma is similar to that observed in rats (Blank *et al.*, 1981) but slightly faster than that observed in rabbits (Lartrigue-Mattei *et al.*, 1984). The presence of only a small portion of the radioactivity in the packed cell volume in the *Cebus* suggest that PAF binding and uptake by blood cells in this species is minimal. The injected PAF may be anticipated to react with cellular receptors, be incorporated into membrane lipid bilayers and complex with albumin (Yamashita *et al.*, 1983).

There was no evidence of *Cebus* bronchial reactivity to PAF. The unresponsiveness of *Cebus* platelets to PAF has been previously reported (Cargill *et al.*, 1983). The lack of bronchial response in *Cebus* supports the concept of platelet-dependent bronchoconstriction by PAF (Vargaftig *et al.*, 1980). That baboons and rhesus exhibit bronchoconstriction following intratracheal PAF (Denjean *et al.*, 1983; Patterson and Harris, 1983) may reflect differences in platelet sensitivity (Namm *et al.*, 1982) or route of administration.

The hemoconcentration responses of the *Cebus* are similar to those reported in the baboon in terms of dose of PAF used and time frame for hematocrit changes (McManus *et al.*, 1981). Pretreatment with SRI 63-072 inhibits the PAF-induced HC, where individual animal sensitivities to PAF (in terms of HC) parallel the effectiveness of the drug (in terms of inhibition). Thus, while SRI 63-072 is 96 percent inhibitory against HC in the most sensitive *Cebus* (3.5 μg kg⁻¹ PAF), only 50 percent inhibition was seen in less sensitive animals that required 20 μg kg^{-1} PAF. Although vascular receptors for PAF have not been defined to date, the involvement of the vascular endothelium in PAF-induced hemoconcentration (Humphrey *et al.*, 1984) and hypotension (Kasuga *et al.*, 1984) is known. It is possible that endothelial receptor expression may be related to animal sensitivity of PAF vascular effects.

ACKNOWLEDGMENTS

We recognize careful manuscript revisions by Mr J. Borovian, the research assistance of Mr R. Deacon and Ms C. Farley and the excellent manuscript preparation by Ms Rosalie Piegario.

REFERENCES

Blank, M.L., Cress, E.A., Whittle, T., and Snyder, F. (1981). '*In vivo* metabolism of a new class of biologically active phospholipids: 1-alkyl-2-acetyl-*sn*-glycero-3-phosphocholine, a platelet activating-hypotensive phospholipid', *Life Sciences.*, **29**, 769−775.

Cargill, D.I., Cohen, D.S., Van Valen, R.G., Klimek, J.J., and Levin, R.P. (1983). 'Aggregation release and desensitization induced in platelets from five species by platelet activating factor (PAF)', *Thromb. Haemost.*, **49**, 204−209.

Denjean, A., Arnoux, B., Masse, R., Lockhart, A., and Benveniste, J. (1983). 'Acute effects of intratracheal administration of platelet-activating factor in baboons', *J. Appl. Physiol.*, **55**, 799−804.

Handley, D.A., Lee, M.L., and Saunders, R.N. (1985). 'Evidence for a direct effect on vascular permeability of platelet-activating factor induced hemoconcentration in the guinea pig', *Thromb. Haemost.*, **54**, 232−235.

Humphrey, D.M., McManus, L.M., Hanahan, D.J., and Pinckard, R.N. (1984). 'Morphological basis of increased vascular permeability induced by acetyl glyceryl ether phosphorylcholine', *Lab. Invest.*, **50**, 416−425.

Kasuga, Y., Masuda, Y., and Shigenobu, K. (1984). 'Possible role of endothelium in the vasodilator response of the rat thoracic aorta to platelet activating factor (PAF)', *J. Pharma. Dyn.*, **7**, 138−149.

Lartigue-Mattei, C., Godeneche, D., Chabard, J.L., Petit, J., and Berger, J.A. (1984). 'Pharmacokinetic study of ^{3}H-labeled PAF-acether. II Comparison with ^{3}H-labeled lyso-PAF-acether after intravenous administration in the rabbit and protein binding', *Agents Actions.*, **15**, 643−646.

McManus, L.M., Pinckard, R.N., Fitzpatrick, F.A., O'Rourke, R.A., Crawford, M.H., and Hanahan, D.J. (1981). 'Acetyl glyceryl ether phosphorylcholine. Intravascular alterations following intravenous infusion into the baboon', *Lab. Invest.*, **45**, 303−308.

Namm, D.H., Tadepulli, A.S., and High, J.A. (1982). 'Species specificity of the platelet responses to 1-0-alkyl-2-acetyl-*sn*-glycero-3-phosphocholine', *Thromb. Res.*, **25**, 341−248.

Patterson, R., and Harris, K.E. (1983). 'The activity of aerosolized and intracutaneous synthetic platelet-activating factor (AGEPC) in rhesus monkeys with IgE-mediated airway responses and normal monkeys', *J. Lab. Clin. Med.*, **102**, 933−942.

Vargaftig, B.B., Lefort, J., Chignard, M., and Benveniste, J. (1980). 'Platelet-activating factor induces platelet-dependent bronchoconstriction unrelated to the formation of prostaglandin derivatives', *Eur. J. Pharmacol..*, **65**, 185−192.

Wedmore, C.V., and Williams, T.J. (1981). 'Platelet-activating factor (PAF), a secretory product of polymorphonuclear leukocytes, increases vascular permeability in rabbit skin', *Br. J. Pharmacol.*, **74**, 916–919.

Yamashita, M., Homma, H., Inoue, K., and Nojima, S. (1983). 'The metabolism of platelet activating factor in platelets and plasma of various animals', *J. Toxicol. Sci.*, **8**, 177–181.

New Horizons in Platelet Activating Factor Research
Edited by C. M. Winslow and M. L. Lee
© 1987 John Wiley & Sons Ltd.

37

Synergistic Effect of a Platelet Activating Factor Antagonist with Azathioprine and Cyclosporin A in Allograft Survival

Marie L. Foegh, Bijan S. Khirabadi, John R. Rowles and Peter W. Ramwell

The involvement of platelet activating factor (PAF) in cell-mediated rejection is a novel idea. There are a number of reasons for such a proposal. Firstly, Camussi and collaborators (1981), in a rabbit model of hyperacute rejection, showed increased PAF in plasma. This type of rejection occurs shortly following perfusion of the transplanted organ and is due to preformed humoral antibodies against the allograft. A unique feature of hyperacute rejection is platelet thrombi formation causing cessation of blood flow through the allograft. Thus, with the major involvement of platelets in this rabbit model it is not difficult to accept the idea that PAF might be released.

In contrast to hyperacute rejection, cell-mediated rejection takes place within the first week following transplantation and is characterized by lymphocyte activation in response to the foreign antigens of the allograft. The foreign antigens are then processed and presented to the lymphocytes by monocytes and macrophages. Platelets are not generally thought to play a major role in cell mediated rejection; however, the platelets are deposited in the allograft during rejection and are released back into the circulation by infusion of prostacyclin (Leithner *et al.*, 1981). PAF is released from platelets and macrophages upon stimulation (Camussi *et al.*, 1981) and a lymphocyte cell-line has also been shown to release PAF (Bussolono *et al.*, 1984), but not human peripheral blood lymphocytes (Jouvin-Marche *et al.*, 1984). Increased vascular permeability is a consistent feature of rejection and is a characteristic of PAF. PAF stimulates the formation of the arachidonate metabolites, which are known to modulate immune responses (Foegh *et al.*, 1984) including allograft rejection (Foegh *et al.*, 1985). Thus, we have also investigated the effect of a potent, naturally occurring PAF antagonist (BN 52021) (9H-1, 7a-(epoxymethano)-1H,-6aH-cyclopenta [c]furo[2,3-b]-

343

furo-[3',2'-:3,4]cyclopentyl[1,2-d]-furan-5,9,-1-2-(4H)-trione, 3-tert-butylhexahydro-4,-7b,-11,hydroxy-8-methyl, Beaufour Institut, Le Plessis-Robinson, France, 10 mg kg^{-1} day^{-1} i.m. in two divided doses) on rat cardiac allograft survival.

An intra-abdominally heterotopic cardiac allograft model is used where Lewis rats are recipients and Lexis x Brown-Norway F_1 hybrids serve as donors. The aorta is anastomosed end-to-side to the abdominal aorta and the pulmonary artery is anastomosed to the vena cava. Thus the allograft is a perfused beating heart. The allograft is monitored every day by palpation of cardiac beats through the abdominal wall. Rejection is defined as cessation of heart beats. In this histo-incompatible model, rejection occurs at day 8 ± 0.4 days. The experiments are conducted with low doses of the conventional immunosuppressive drugs with the object of determining whether a PAF antagonist potentiates their effect in prolonging allograft survival. We have compared the effect of daily treatment with the PAF antagonist BN 52021 either by itself or in combination with azathioprine 5 mg kg^{-1} day^{-1} i.p.) or cyclosporin A (0.5 mg kg^{-1} day^{-1} i.m.).

The low doses of azathioprine and cyclosporin A do not prolong allograft survival compared to untreated controls, nor does the PAF antagonist, BN 52021, prolong allograft survival significantly (12.2 ± 1.5 days). In contrast, the combination of the PAF antagonist BN 52021 with either low-dose azathioprine or cyclosporin A improve cardiac allograft survival significantly. The prolongation of allograft survival time was from 11.3 ± 0.5 and 10.3 ± 0.4 days to 14.8 ± 0.6 and 14.0 ± 0.5 days, respectively (Foegh et al., 1986a,b). The improved allograft survival obtained by combining BN 52021 with low-dose azathioprine or cyclosporine A implies that PAF may be involved in cell-mediated rejection. There is no difference in the histological appearance at the time of rejection between the different treatment modalities; they all showed severe mononuclear cell infiltration and myocytolysis and some degree of myocardial hemorrhage. The prolongation of graft survival in this model is of particular interest since rat platelets are insensitive to PAF which is in accordance with the reported absence of PAF receptors on rat platelets (Inarrea et al., 1985). A likely mechanism for the protective effect may be due to BN 52021 attenuation of either the macrophage–lymphocyte interaction or of lymphokine or monokine secretion. These putative mechanisms need, however, to be tested in vitro.

The prolonged allograft survival might also have been obtained through more vascular mechanisms such as blocking of PAF induced coronary artery spasms (Feuerstein et al., 1985) which would improve graft perfusion and possibly graft survival. A further mechanism might be attenuation of PAF induced vascular permeability which would lead to slowing of cell migration into the allograft. However, we did not find BN 52021 and azathioprine to affect lymphocyte recruitment more than azathioprine treatment by itself in this rat cardiac allograft model (Khirabadi et al., 1986).

The prolongation in cardiac allograft survival with BN 52021 may not appear prominent. However, it is of the same magnitude as that obtained with prednisolone in combination with either azathioprine (Foegh et al., 1985) or cyclosporin A (Rowles et al.,1986). This model does not permit accurate prediction of the situation in transplant patients. Nevertheless, the data suggest that the PAF antagonist BN 52021 might be a suitable candidate for allowing the use of a lower dose of cyclosporin A.

ACKNOWLEDGMENTS

This work was supported by a grant from American Heart Association 84-1147 and grants from National Institute of Health, HL32319 and HL37241.

REFERENCES

Bussolino, F., Foa, R., Malavi, F., Ferrando, M.L., and Camussi, G. (1984). 'Release of platelet-activating factor (PAF)-like material from human lymphoid cell lines', *Exp. Hematol.*, **12**, 688−693.

Camussi, G., Aglietto, M., Coda, R., Bussolini, F., Piacibelli, W., and Tetta, C. (1981). 'Release of platelet-activating factor (PAF) and histamine II. The cellular origin of human PAF: monocytes, polymorphonuclear neutrophils and basophils', *Immunology.*, **42**, 191−199.

Foegh, M.L., Alijani, M.R., Helfrich, G.B., and Ramwell, P.W. (1984). 'Icosanoids and organ transplantation.' *Ann. Clin. Res.*, **16**, 318−323.

Foegh, M.L., Khirabadi, B.S., and Ramwell, P.W. (1985). 'Prolongation of experimental cardiac allograft survival with thromboxane related drugs', *Transplation.*, **40**, 124−125.

Foegh, M.L., Khirabadi, B.S., Rowles, J.R., Braquet, P., and Ramwell, P.W. (1986a). 'Prolongation of cardiac allograft survival with BN 52021 a specific antagonist of platelet activating factor', *Transplantation.*, **42**, 86−88.

Foegh, M.L., Khirabadi, B.S., Rowles, J.R., Braquet, P., and Ramwell, P.W. (1986b). 'Inhibition of PAF and leukotriene expression in acute cardiac allograft rejection in rats', *Pharmacol. Res. Comm.*, (in press).

Inarrea, P., Gomez-Cambronero, J., Nieto, M., and Sanchez Crespo, M. (1985). 'Characteristics of the binding of platelet-activating factor to platelets of different animal species', *Europ. J. Pharmacol.*, **105**, 309−315.

Ito, S., Camussi, G., Tetta, C., Milgrove, F., and Andres, G. (1984). 'Hyperacute allograft rejection in the rabbit', *Lab. Invest.*, **51**, 148-161.

Jouvin-Marche, E., Ninio, E., Beaurain, G., Tence, M., Niaudet, P., and Benveniste, J. (1984). 'Biosynthesis of PAF-acether (platelet-activating factor) VII. Precursors of PAF-acether and acetyl-transferase activity in human leukocytes', *J. Immunol.*, **133**, 892−898.

Leithner, C., Sinzinger, H., and Schwarz, M. (1981). 'Treatment of chronic transplant rejection with prostacyclin—reduction of platelet deposition in the transplant, prolongation of platelet survival and improvement of transplant function', *Prostaglandin.*, **22**, 783−788.

Khirabadi, B.S., Foegh, M.L., Goldstein, H.A., and Ramwell, P.W. (1986). 'The effect of prednisolone , thromboxane antagonist and platelet activating factor antagonist on lymphocyte and platelet migration in experimental cardiac transplantation', (submitted).

Rowles, J.R., Foegh, M.L., Khirabadi, B.S., and Ramwell, P.W. (1986). 'The synergistic effect of cyclosporin A and iloprost on survival of rat cardiac allografts', *Transplantation.*, **42**, 94−96.

New Horizons in Platelet Activating Factor Research
Edited by C. M. Winslow and M. L. Lee
© 1987 John Wiley & Sons Ltd.

38

Platelet Activating Factor—Induced Ischemic Bowel Necrosis: Its Prevention by PAF Antagonists

Wei Hsueh, F. Gonzalez-Crussi, Josepha L. Arroyave,
Robert C. Anderson, Mark L. Lee and William J. Houlihan

Ischemic bowel necrosis is a serious clinicopathological condition that carries a high mortality rate and grave sequelae. In infants, bowel necrosis, or 'neonatal necrotizing enterocolitis', occurs predominantly in premature infants who often also have respiratory distress syndrome. In adults, bowel necrosis is often a serious complication of shock, sepsis and disseminated intravascular coagulation (DIC). In either case, the cause is probably multifactorial and the pathogenesis is complex. Although the etiology probably varies depending on the clinical context, the morphologic findings point to a common pathogenesis, i.e. hypoperfusion of the bowel. Thus, common mediators, likely to be potent vasoconstrictors, are involved in both conditions. We have produced a model of ischemic bowel necrosis in the rat (Gonzalez-Crussi and Hsueh, 1983), by injecting 2 μg of synthetic platelet activating factor (PAF) (1-0-alkyl-2-acetyl-*sn*-glyceryl-3-phosphorylcholine) into the aorta immediately above the renal arteries, of adult male Sprague–Dawley rats (body weight 250–300 g). The dose of PAF could be reduced to half and still result in similar lesions, if the rat was pretreated with 20 μg of bacterial endotoxin (LPS). This model is of interest because PAF is a naturally occurring substance formed by many cells (Camussi *et al.*, 1981, 1983; Mencia-Huerta and Benveniste, 1981), and the lesions produced (Figure 1) were morphologically identical to those of human patients with necrotizing enterocolitis although in human patients most surgically resected bowel specimens belong to the late, severe lesions. The mechanism of actions of PAF is unclear, but the development of necrosis is probably independent of platelet activation, since rat platelets are relatively unresponsive to PAF (Sanchez Crespo *et al.*, 1981; Gonzalez-Crussi and Hsueh, 1983). Thus the hypoperfusion is not due to occlusion of the vessel lumen by thromboemboli, but probaby a result of vasoconstriction of the microvasculature as shown by Evans blue injection (see 'Results' below). We have previously reported release

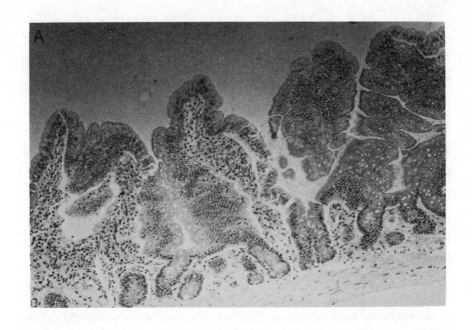

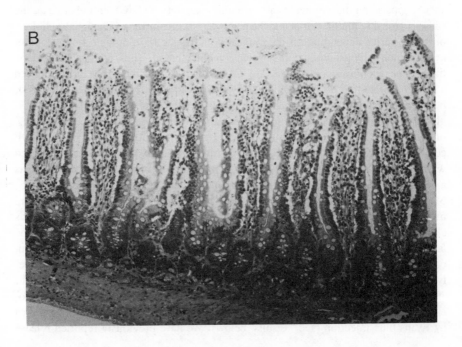

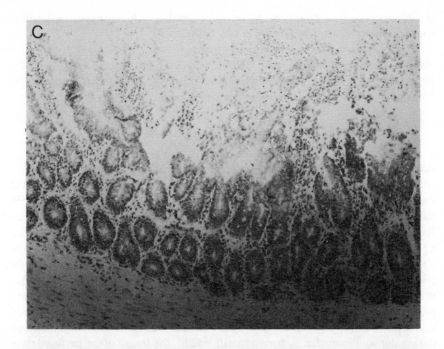

Figure 1. PAF-induced bowel necrosis. A. Normal control. B. Mild lesion with superficial mucosal necrosis. C. Moderate lesion involving entire thickness of mucosa. D. Severe, transmural necrosis

of sulfidopeptide leukotrienes as the secondary mediators for vasoconstriction of the intestinal microvasculature (Hsueh *et al.*, 1986).

In the present study, three different PAF antagonists, i.e. SRI 63-072, SRI 63-119 (Sandoz Research Institute), and ONO-6240 (ONO Pharmaceutical Co., Osaka, Japan) (Miyamoto *et al.*, 1984), were investigated for their ability to prevent the development of PAF-induced ischemic bowel necrosis.

METHODS

Adult male Sprague–Dawley rats (body weight 280 ± 20 g) were anesthetized with Nembutal, the carotid artery was cannulated to record the blood pressure and the jugular vein was cannulated for drug injection and collection of blood. The PAF antagonists were injected slowly into the jugular vein 10 min before administration of PAF. The abdomen was incised along the midline and 2 μg PAF (approximately 7 μg kg^{-1}, or 20 μg LPS immediately followed by 1 μg of PAF were injected into the abdominal aorta above the level of the renal arteries as previously described (Gonzalez-Crussi and Hsueh, 1983). The intestines were exposed and examined periodically with a stereomicroscope. Hematocrit (Hct) and WBC count were determined before injection of PAF and at 30, 60 and 120 min following PAF injection. To assess the extent of bowel perfusion, 5 ml of Evans blue (2 g dl^{-1}) was injected into the jugular vein immediately before sacrifice (2 h), the length of the perfused (blue) small bowel was measured and expressed as a percent of the entire small bowel length. Sections were taken from the poorly perfused areas for histological examination as previously described (Gonzalez-Crussi and Hsueh, 1983). If no grossly abnormal lesion was seen, 20–30 random blocks were taken for microscopic examination.

RESULTS

Immediately following PAF injection, there was a profound and sustained hypotension accompanied by hemoconcentration (increased Hct) and leukopenia (Figures 2-5). Injection of 2 μg of PAF invariably resulted in segmental necrosis of the small bowel. (Table 1). Examination by stereomicroscope showed an immediate vasoconstriction of the mesenteric vascular bed, followed by a discoloration of the bowel after various periods of time. Evans blue injection showed that it was mainly the microvasculature of the bowel, rather than the large mensenteric vessels, which were affected. The hypoperfused areas generally correlated with grossly discolored areas. Microscopic examination of the bowel showed a good correlation of the gross and microscopic lesions of moderate (transmucosal) or severe (transmural) degree. However, mild (superficial mucosal) microscopic lesions often escaped detection by unaided eye or by stereomicroscopy. Combined administration of LPS (20 μg) had effects similar to those of 2 μg of PAF alone (Table 1).

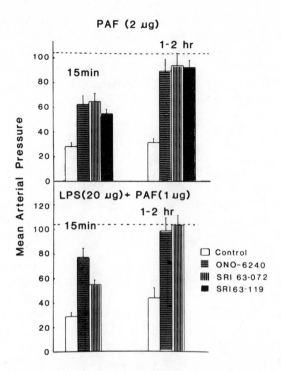

Figure 2. Effects of PAF antagonists on PAF-induced bowel necrosis: Changes in mean systemic blood pressure (mmHg). The inducing agent used was either PAF (2 μg) alone (upper panel) or LPS (20 μg) + PAF (1 μg) (lower panel). The left panel shows initial change in B.P., the right panel shows the median value of blood pressure between 1 and 2 h (mean ± S.E.M.). Control: only inducing agent(s) were given. Other groups also received inducing agent(s), but were pretreated with ONO-6240, SRI 63-072 and SRI 63-119 (3 mg kg^{-1}). See Table 1 for numbers of animals in each group. Mean arterial pressure before PAF administration was 104 (dotted line) ± 4

As shown in Figure 2, SRI 63-072 (3 mg kg^{-1}), SRI 63-119 (3 mg kg^{-1}) and ONO-6240 (2 mg kg^{-1}) significantly improved the initial hypotension and totally reversed the sustained hypotension. These drugs also prevented the hemoconcentration and improved the leukopenia caused by PAF, although not correcting it entirely (Figures 3 and 4). The hypoperfusion and gross necrotic lesions of the bowel caused by PAF injection were totally prevented by pretreatment of these three antagonists (Figure 5). However, microscopic examination still revealed focal mild lesions (loss of superficial lining). At a much lower dose, 0.3 mg kg^{-1}, only SRI 63-072 was effective in some of the animals treated, although bowel necrosis still developed in four out of six animals treated (Table 1). None of these drugs affected blood pressure or Hct when used alone.

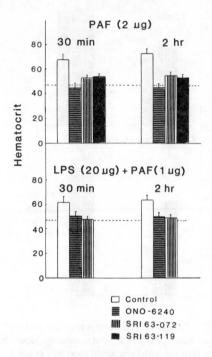

Figure 3. Effects of drugs on PAF-induced bowel necrosis: Changes in hematocrit (mean ± S.E.M.). See Figure 1 legend for symbols. Normal Hct in 70 rats was 47.3 (dotted line) ± 1.7

DISCUSSION

Ischemic bowel necrosis of the adult or necrotizing enterocolitis of the neonate is a serious clinical condition which carries a grave prognosis. The pathogenesis of this disease is unknown, exept that shock and DIC are frequently associated with ischemic bowel necrosis and decreased platelet count was often oserved in necrotizing enterocolitis. Since PAF produced profound, sustained shock (Halonen *et al.*, 1980) and caused platelet aggregation in man and rabbits (McManus *et al.*, 1981; Vargaftig *et al.*, 1981), it is possible that PAF is involved in the development of ischemic bowel necrosis clinically. Thus our rat model of ischemic bowel necrosis produced by PAF or combined LPS and PAF may be of clinical relevance. In the present study we have shown that pretreatment of the animals with PAF antagonists completely prevented the development of bowel necrosis and reversed the hypotension caused by PAF and PAF with LPS. The potential clinical application of these drugs deserves further study.

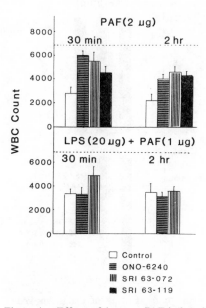

Figure 4. Effects of drugs on PAF-induced bowel necrosis: changes in peripheral WBC count (mean ± S.E.M.). See Figure 1 legend for symbols. WBC count before PAF administration in 50 rats was 6875 (dotted line) ± 230

ACKNOWLEDGMENT

This work was supported by NIH grant AM 34574 and a grant from Children's Memorial Hospital Research Foundation.

REFERENCES

Camussi, G., Aglietta, M., Coda, R., Bussolino, F., Piacibello, W., and Tetta, C. (1981). 'Release of platelet-activating factor (PAF) and histamine. II. The cellular origin of human PAF: monocytes, polymorphonuclear neutrophils and basophils', *Immunol.*, **42**, 191–199.

Camussi, G., Aglietta, M., Malavasi, F., Tetta, C., Piacibello, W., Sanavio, F., and Bussolino, F. (1983). 'The release of platelet activating factor from human endothelial cells in culture, *J. Immunol.*, **131**, 2397–2402.

Gonzalez-Crussi, F., and Hsueh, W., (1983). 'Experimental model of ischemic bowel necrosis. The role of platelet activating factor and endotoxin', *Am. J. Pathol.*, **112**, 127–135.

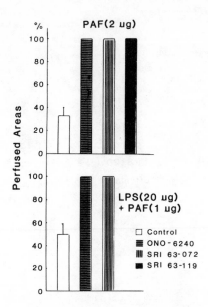

Figure 5. Effects of drugs on PAF-induced bowel necrosis: Perfused areas as a percent of total length of small intestine, determined by Evans blue injection at 2 h, mean ± S.E.M.

Hsueh, W., Gonzalez-Crussi, F., and Arroyave, J.L. (1986). 'Platelet activating factor induced ischemic bowel necrosis. An investigation of secondary mediators in its pathogenesis', *Am. J. Pathol.*, **122**, 231–239.

Halonen, M., Palmer, J.D., Lohman, I.C., McManus, L.M., and Pinckard, R.N. (1980). 'Respiratory and circulatory alterations induced by acetyl glyceryl ether phosphorylcholine, a mediator of IgG anaphylaxis in the rabbit', *Amer. Rev. Resp. Dis.*, **122**, 915–924.

McManus, L.M., Hanahan, R.J., and Pinckard, R.N. (1981). 'Human platelet stimulation by acetyl glyceryl ether phosphorylcholine', *J. Clin. Invest.*, **67**,903–906.

Mencia-Huerta, J.M., and Benveniste, J. (1981). 'Platelet activating factor (PAF-acether) and macrophages. II. Phagocytosis associated release of PAF-acether from rat peritoneal macrophages', *Cell Immunol.*, **57**, 281–292.

Miyamoto, T., Ohno, H., Yano, T., Okada, T., Hamanaka, N., and Kawasaki, A. (1984). 'A new potent antagonist of platelet activating factor', *Kyoto conference on Prostaglandins.*, Nov. 25–28, 1984, Kyoto, Japan (Abstract S13-9).

Sanchez-Crespo, M., Alonso, F., Inarrea, P., and Egido, J. (1981). 'Nonplatelet-mediated vascular actions of 1-*O*-alkyl-2-acetyl-*sn*-3-glyceryl-phosphorylcholine (a synthetic PAF)'. In F. Russo-Marie, B. Vargaftig, and J. Benveniste (eds.) *Pharmacologie de l'inflammation et l'allergie: Lipids et cellules* INSERM Paris, p. 473–478.

Table 1. Preventive effect of PAF antagonist on the bowel necrosis induced by PAF

PAF Antagonist	Dose of PAF (μg)	Dose of LPS (μg)	No. of Experiments	No of animals with lesions		Severity of microscopic lesions
				Gross	Micro	
None	2	0	7	7	7	moderate (2) to severe (5)
SRI 63−072 (3 mg kg^{-1})	2	0	8	0	3	mild
SRI 63−119 (3 mg kg^{-1})	2	0	8	0	2	mild
ONO−6240 (2 mg kg^{-1})	2	0	6	0	2	mild
SRI 63−072 (0.3 mg kg^{-1})	2	0	6	4	6	mild (2) to moderate (4)
SRI 63−119 (0.3 mg kg^{-1})	2	0	3	3	3	moderate (2) severe (1)
ONO−6240 (0.3 mg kg^{-1})	2	0	3	3	3	mild (1) to moderate (2)
None	1	20	11	11	11	mild (2), moderate (5) severe (4)
SRI 63−072 (3 mg kg^{-1})	1	20	5	0	1	mild
ONO−6240 (2 mg kg^{-1})	1	20	5	0	2	mild

Vargaftig, B.B., Chignard, M., Benveniste, J., Lefort, J., and Wal, F. (1981). 'Background and present status of research on platelet-activating factor (PAF-acether)', *Ann. N. Y. Acad. Sci.*, **370**, 119−137.

New Horizons in Platelet Activating Factor Research
Edited by C. M. Winslow and M. L. Lee
© 1987 John Wiley & Sons Ltd.

39

Alveolar Macrophage Production of Platelet Activating Factor after Exposure to Cotton Dust

Lena Beijer and Ragnar Rylander

INTRODUCTION

Persons exposed to organic dusts may experience a gradual onset of airflow limitation over the working day. A hallmark of the reaction induced by cotton dust is that it is more pronounced on the first day of the working week, Monday disease (Weill, 1981). Many organic dusts, particularly cotton dust, are contaminated with gram-negative bacteria which contain endotoxins on their outer cell wall. A series of reports has demonstrated a close relationship between the Monday decrease in FEV_1 and the amount of bacterial endotoxin in cotton dust (Castellan *et al.*, 1984; Rylander *et al.*, 1985). It has previously been shown that exposure to endotoxin causes an accumulation of platelets in the pulmonary capillaries (Hinton *et al.*, 1983) and that it induces alveolar macrophages (AM) to produce platelet activating factor (PAF-acether) (Rylander and Beijer, 1986).

In view of this, experiments were undertaken to investigate whether exposure to cotton dust could induce the production of PAF-acether in free lung cells.

MATERIALS AND METHODS

A standard cotton dust, obtained from Cotton Inc., USA was used. It was placed in a groove on a disc passing under a suction tube. The dust aerosol was led through a continuous flow exposure chamber. The amount of airborne dust was measured by pulling chamber air through Millipore filters which were weighed. The level of airborne dust in the cage was between 15 and 30 mg m^{-3}.

Guinea pigs were exposed once for 40 min in the exposure chamber. Certain animals were exposed a second time at 24, 48, 72 and 96 h after the first exposure. Control animals were exposed to laboratory air. At various times after the exposure, the animals were sacrificed and free lung cells were harvested by lung lavage with saline. Neutrophils and alveolar macrophages (AM) were separated on a continuous density gradient and the cells were disintegrated in distilled water containing serum albumin.

The cell lysates were tested for their ability to induce release of serotonin from platelets, according to the method described by Henson (1976). Rabbit platelets were loaded with tritium-marked serotonin. The platelets were mixed with the cell lysate and incubated for 10 min. After centrifugation the serotonin released by the platelets into the medium was measured in a liquid scintillator. The results were expressed as percent of the release obtained by a PAF-acether standard which was either synthetic PAF-acether (10^{-8} M) or supernatant from human neutrophils stimulated with zymosan.

In one part of the cell lysate, the proteins were precipitated with ethanol and removed after centrifugation. The ethanol was evaporated and the remainings dissolved in buffer containing phospholipase A_2. Finally some of the samples were analyzed with HPLC (kindly performed by Dr J. Benveniste, Paris).

RESULTS

Differential counts of free lung cells obtained by lung lavage showed that exposure to the cotton dust caused a small increase in the number of neutrophils in the airways 4 h after exposure. No PAF-acether activity could be detected in those cells.

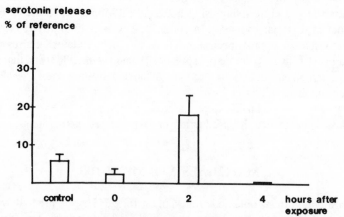

Figure 1.   Serotonin release from AM at different times after exposure to 25−30 mg m^{-3} cotton dust. Mean from ten animals; bars indicate S.E.M.

Figure 1 shows the release of serotonin by disintegrated AM harvested at different time intervals after the exposure to cotton dust.

In control animals exposed to room air, a small activity was seen, (5 percent of the reference). Similar values were obtained from cells harvested immediately after the cessation of the cotton dust exposure. AM obtained from animals 2 h after the exposure caused a significantly larger amount of serotonin to be released (18 percent of the reference, $p < 0.1$). At 4 h, no activity could be detected.

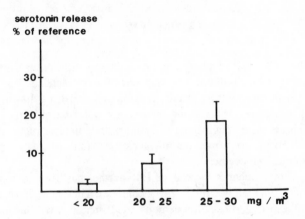

Figure 2.   Serotonin release from AM 2 h after the exposure to different amounts of cotton dust. Mean from 9, 8 and 13 animals; bars indicate S.E.M.

Figure 2 demonstrates that a dose–response relationship was present between serotonin release activity in the AM and the dust concentration in the exposure chamber.

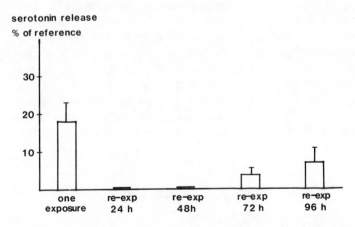

Figure 3.   Serotonin release 2 h after exposures to 25–35 mg m³ of cotton dust. Mean from 3, 8, 3, 7 and 6 animals; bars indicate S.E.M.

The results from animals exposed a second time to cotton dust showed that no activity was detected in the groups receiving a repeated exposure at 24 and 48 h (Figure 3). In animals re-exposed 72 h after the initial exposure, the activity was 3 percent and in those re-exposed after 96 h 6 percent.

COMMENTS

The results demonstrate that inhalation of cotton dust in guinea-pigs caused AM to produce a substance which induced serotonin release from platelets. The substance was recoverable in the ethanol fraction after precipitating and discarding the proteins, distinguishing it from enzymes, and the activity was not detectable after treatment with phospholiphase A_2, distinguishing it from arachidonic acid metabolites. Also the analyses with HPLC confirmed that the substance studied is, or resembles, the glycerophospholipid PAF-acether.

The capacity of macrophages to produce PAF-acether has been demonstrated by several researchers, but mainly with *in vitro* techniques. This is the first time that the PAF-acether synthesis in AM has been demonstrated after an *in vivo* inhalation by an agent related to lung disease in humans.

The symptoms in humans after exposure to cotton dust are most pronounced on Mondays after an exposure free weekend and less pronounced after the repeated exposure on Tuesday. In the experiments we found AM PAF-acether production after the first exposure to cotton dust but not after repeated exposures.

In the experiments with repeated exposures, there was a relationship between an increased number of neutrophils in the lung lavage and the lack of capacity of AM to form PAF-acether. Also, after a single exposure to cotton dust, the formation of PAF-acether in the AM decreased at the time when the neutrophils migrate into the airways. Whether these phenomena are causally related is not known at present.

The exact mechanism whereby PAF-acether could be involved in the development of lung reactions following cotton dust exposure in man has yet to be ascertained. Possible pathways, supported by data from different animal models, are a direct constricting activity on smooth muscle in bronchi or parenchyma (Stimler, 1981) or the modulation of release of inflammatory and constricting mediators (Hamasaki *et al.*, 1984; Voelkel *et al.*, 1983) from platelets or other inflammatory cells present in the lung.

ACKNOWLEDGMENT

This study was supported by funds from Ellen, Walter and Lennart Hesselman's Foundation and Cotton Inc. (agreement 77/342).

REFERENCES

Castellan, R.M., Olenchock, S.S., Hankinson, J.L., Millner, P.D., Cocke, J.B., Bragg, C.K., Perkins, H.H., and Jacobs, R.R. (1984). 'Acute bronchoconstriction induced by cotton dust: dose-related response to endotoxin and other dust factors', *Ann. Occup. Med.*, **101**, 157–163.

Hamasaki, Y., Mojarad, M., Saga, T., Tai, H-H., and Said, S.I. (1984). 'Platelet-activating factor raises airway and vascular pressures and induces edema in lungs perfused with platelet-free solution', *Am. Rev. Resp. Dis.*, **129**, 742–746.

Henson, P.M. (1976). 'Activation and desensitization of platelets by platelet-activating factor (PAF) derived from IgE-sensitized basophils. I. Characteristics of the secretory response', *J. Exp. Med.*, **143**, 937–952.

Hinton, D.E., Lantz, R.C., Birch, K., and Burrell, R. (1983). 'Quantitative morphologie studies of the lung following inhalation of bacterial endotoxin'. In P.J. Wakelyn and R.R. Jacobs (eds.). *Proceedings from Seventh Cotton Dust Research Conference*, National Cotton Council, pp. 39–44.

Rylander, R., and Beijer, L. (1986). 'PAF-acether induction in alveolar macrophages by bacterial endotoxin', *Am. Rev. Resp. Dis.*, (submitted).

Rylander, R, Haglind, P., and Lundholm, M. (1985). 'Endotoxin in cotton dust and respiratory function decrement among cotton workers in an experimental cardroom', *Am. Rev. Resp. Dis.*, **131**, 209–213.

Stimler, N.P., Bloor, C.M., Hugli, T.E., Wylke, R.L., McCall, C.E., and O'Flaherty, J.T. (1981). 'Anaphylactic actions of platelet-activating factor', *Am. J. Pathol.*, **105**, 64–69.

Voelkel, N.F., Simpson, J., Worthen, S., Reeves, J.T., Henson, P.M., and Murphy, R.C. (1983). 'Platelet-activating factor causes pulmonary vasoconstriction and edema via platelet-independent leukotriene formation', *Adv. Prostaglandin Thromboxane Leukotriene Res.*, **12**, 179–183.

Weill H. (1981). 'International Conference on byssinosis', *Chest.*, **suppl 79**, 1S–139S.

New Horizons in Platelet Activating Factor Research
Edited by C. M. Winslow and M. L. Lee
© 1987 John Wiley & Sons Ltd.

40

Is Platelet Activating Factor in Peritoneal Fluid of Female Patients with Endometriosis the Cause of Infertility?

Santosh Nigam and Sandor Sipka

INTRODUCTION

Endometriosis (EM) is regarded as a chronic intraperitoneal inflammatory process strongly correlated with infertility. Its histogenesis is postulated as a proliferation of endometrial tissue outside the cavity of the uterus. Among several pathophysiological processes proposed for EM (Muse and Wilson 1982), much attention has been paid to the link between EM, altered prostanoid secretion and tubo-ovarian endocrine dysfunction (Ylikorkala and Mäkilä, 1985).

One common alteration in all patients with EM is the increased volume of peritoneal fluid (Drake, *et al.*, 1980). The enhanced number of macrophages (MΦ)found in the peritoneal fluid (PF) of women with EM (Haney *et al.*, 1981) raises the possibility that the MΦ may act as anti-fertility effector in the microenvironment in which fertilization occurs.

With increasing recognition that ectopic implantation of endometriotic tissue plays a part in inflammation, its interaction with the classic inflammatory cell, the MΦ, gains significance. In this study we have found that MΦ isolated from the PF of female patients with and without EM release a lipid material that strongly affects platelets and is similar, if not identical, to synthetic platelet activating factor (PAF).

PATIENTS AND METHODS

Fourteen patients with mild and severe EM and eleven patients without EM were investigated in this study. All except four of the fourteen patients with EM were infertile. Ten patients recruited for tubal ligation served as controls. The mean age ± standard deviation (S.D.) of the patients was 34.5 ± 3.9 years, 36.0 ± 4.5 years and 36.7 ± 3.6 years in the respective groups. The first group of fourteen patients was found to have EM at the time of diagnostic laparoscopy. In this group, ten had mild and four severe EM according to a classification of the American Fertility Society (American Fertility Society, 1979). All patients fulfilled the following criteria: they were married, had been unable to conceive for at least one year or more and had histologically diagnosed EM. In all cases, a male infertility factor could be excluded. None of these patients were on medication at the time of laparoscopy.

PF was aspirated during laparoscopy under general anesthesia from the anterior uterovesical space and posterior cul-de-sac via a hollow cannula under direct vision with the patient in a 15° Trendelenburg position and was collected in polypropylene tubes containing heparinized saline (5 units ml^{-1}). The sample was discarded if the hematocrit was greater than 5 percent. MΦ were isolated from the PF by adherence to Sephadex G10 that had been pretreated with a tissue culture medium RPMI 1640 containing bicarbonate and HEPES (30 mM) supplemented with 10 percent fetal bovine serum (FBS). The cell suspension was allowed to adhere for 90 min at 37 °C. Non-adherent cells were then washed out with 20 ml of warm tissue culture medium. The effluent was collected and centrifuged at 150 g for 10 min at 4 °C to concentrate the cells. The MΦ (approx. 1 million ml^{-1}) were either challenged with Ionophore A 23187 (1 μg ml^{-1}) in phosphate buffer or left unstimulated (resting MΦ) for 1 h at 37 °C. Supernatants were collected, centrifuged and stored at −20 °C until further processing. For the extraction of PAF-like activity (PAF-LA), supernatants were treated as described by Chilton *et al.*, 1984. PAF-LA was further separated by normal phase high-pressure liquid chromatography (Figure 1) using an Ultrasphere-Si (5 μm) Altex column, elution being achieved with isopropanol and *n*-hexane as described by Blank and Snyder, 1983. The eluate containing PAF-LA was collected according to its predetermined retention time with a synthetic standard of PAF.

PAF-LA was determined by aggregation of washed rabbit platelets pretreated for 20 min with 0.1 mM acetylsalicylic acid in Tyrode's buffer containing an ADP scavenger complex (Roubin *et al.*, 1982). The results are given in pmol using a calibration curve with synthetic standard. PAF-LA was also characterized by inducing chemiluminescense in human neutrophils (Nigam and Brühahn unpublished results). The statistical analysis was done by the Kruskal-Wallis non-parametric procedure.

RESULTS

The isolated MΦ from PF of patients with and without EM were investigated for their ability to release PAF-LA expressed in pmol (Figure 2).

When stimulated with Ionophore A 23187 (Io), the MΦ from PF of patients with EM released more than three times the PAF-LA found in patients without EM, 19.0 ± 9.3 v 6.2 ± 2.9 (mean ± S.D.), and almost seven times that in patients for tubal ligation, 19.0 ± 9.3 v 2.9 ± 1.0, who served as controls. The PAF-LA released by the resting MΦ (without stimulating agent Io) from the PF of patients with EM was also significantly higher, (approx. four times) than in patients without EM. No release occurred in patients for tubal ligation in the absence of Io.

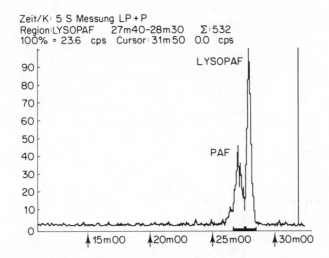

Figure 1. High pressure liquid chromatographic separation of radioactive PAF and lyso-PAF on a normal phase Ultrasphere-Si (5μm) Altex column

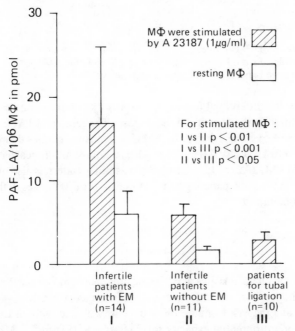

Figure 2. PAF-LA (mean ± S.D.) released by 1 million MΦ isolated from PF of patients with and without EM. Number of patients are indicated in parenthesis

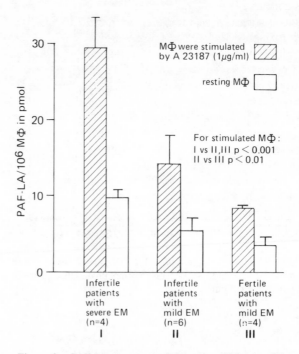

Figure 3.   PAF-LA (mean ± S.D.) released by 1 million
MΦ isolated from PF of patients with severe and mild EM.
Number of patients are indicated in parenthesis

Figure 3 illustrates the differential release of PAF-LA by MΦ from the PF of patients with EM in relation to the severity of the disease. The release of PAF-LA after Io stimulation in infertile patients with severe EM is more than two times that in infertile patients with mild EM, 29.2 ± 4.0 v 14.1 ± 3.8, and almost four times that in fertile patients with mild EM, 29.2 ± 4.0 v 8.5 ± 0.4. A similar pattern is also observed with the resting MΦ in the same patient groups. However, the differences in the three groups are not so pronounced.

DISCUSSION

One of the most striking characteristics of EM is the presence of MΦ in the PF (Haney *et al.*, 1981) revealing a chronic intraperitoneal inflammatory process. We have shown in our study that the MΦ from the PF of patients with and without EM have, if stimulated with Io, a differential capacity for PAF release (Figure 2). Moreover, this effect is more pronounced in patients with severe EM (Figure 3). It can thus be speculated that the ectopic endometrium implants may release certain stimuli—the role of LTB$_4$ is under study—which would not only increase the number of MΦ in the area but could also activate the MΦ to release PAF-LA. Increased acid phosphatase and myeloperoxidase activities, indicators of MΦ activation, have been reported in patients with EM (Halme *et al.*, 1982). The possibility that MΦ from PF of patients with severe EM possess a recognition unit for particulate activation of the complement pathway, which could be involved in release of prostanoids (Drake *et al.*, 1981), cannot be ruled out. Such a recognition unit has been suggested for mouse peritoneal MΦ (Rouzer *et al.*, 1980). It is still unclear whether or not activated MΦ in patients with EM incorporate more of these recognition units, which may be induced by stimuli released from ectopic endometrial implants, or whether MΦ from PF of patients without EM have lost such recognition units.

The data presented here are indicative of the increased synthesis of PAF-LA by MΦ in a local environment in which fertilization occurs, thus further substantiating the implication of MΦ in the inflammatory process. Since PAF-LA may cause vascular changes (permeability, blood pressure) and/or smooth muscle contraction, any alteration in the PAF content of PF, which is in contact with the tubal microenvironment, during the various stages of the inflammatory process, might adversely influence reproduction.

ACKNOWLEDGMENT

We are grateful to the Association for International Cancer Research (AICR), UK, for partly supporting this work. We thankfully acknowledge the assistance of Sonja Nemesh, Christine Brühahn and Barbara Steiger.

REFERENCES

American Fertility Society (1979). 'Classification of endometriosis', *Fertility and Sterility*, **32**, 633–634.

Blank, M.L., and Snyder, F. (1983). 'Improved high performance liquid chromatographic method for isolation of platelet activating factor from the phospholipids', *J. Chromatogr.*, **273**, 415–420.

Chilton, F.H., Ellis, J.M., Olson, S.C., and Wykle, R.L. (1984). '1-*O*-Alkyl-2 arachidonoyl-*sn*-glycero-3-phosphocholine—a common source of platelet activating factor and arachidonate in human polymorphonuclear leukocytes', *J. Biol. Chem.*, **259**, 12 014–12 019.

Drake, T.S., Metz, S.A., Grunert, G.M., and O'Brien, W.F. (1980). 'Peritoneal fluid volume in endometriosis', *Fertility and Sterility*, **34**, 280–281.

Drake, T.S., O'Brien, W.F., Ramwell, P.W., and Metz, S.A. (1981). 'Peritoneal fluid thromboxane B2 and 6-ketoprostaglandin Flα in endometriosis', *Am. J. Obstet. Gynecol.*, **140**, 401–404.

Halme, J., Becker, S., Hammond, M., and Raj, M. (1982). 'Increased activation of peritoneal macrophages in infertile women with endometriosis', *Society for Gynecologic Investigation*, **1982**, Abstract 316.

Haney, A.F., Muscato, J.J., and Weinberg, J.B. (1981). 'Peritoneal fluid cell population in infertility patients', *Fertility and Sterility*, **35**, 696–698.

Muse, K.N., and Wilson, E.A. (1982). 'How does mild endometriosis cause infertility?', *Fertility and Sterility*, **38**, 145–152.

Nigam, S., and Brühahn, C. 'Decreased activity of macrophages in peritoneal exudate of patients with breast cancer', (in preparation).

Roubin, R., Mencia-Huerta, J.M., and Benveniste, J. (1982). 'Release of platelet activating factor (PAF-acether) and leukotrienes C and D from inflammatory macrophages', *Eur. J. Immunol.*, **12**, 141–146.

Rouzer, C.A., Scott, W.A., Kempe, J., and Cohn, Z.A. (1980). 'Prostaglandin synthesis by macrophages requires a specific receptor-ligand interaction', *Proc. Natl. Acad. Sci. USA*, **77**, 4279–4284.

Ylikorkala, O., and Mäkilä, U.M. (1985). 'Prostacyclin and thromboxane in gynecology and obstetrics', *Am. J. Obstet. Gynecol.*, **152**, 318–329.

Index

Vasodilation, 211
Ventricular contractility, 357
Ventricular hypertension, 238

Verapamil, 217

Washed rabbit platelets, 364